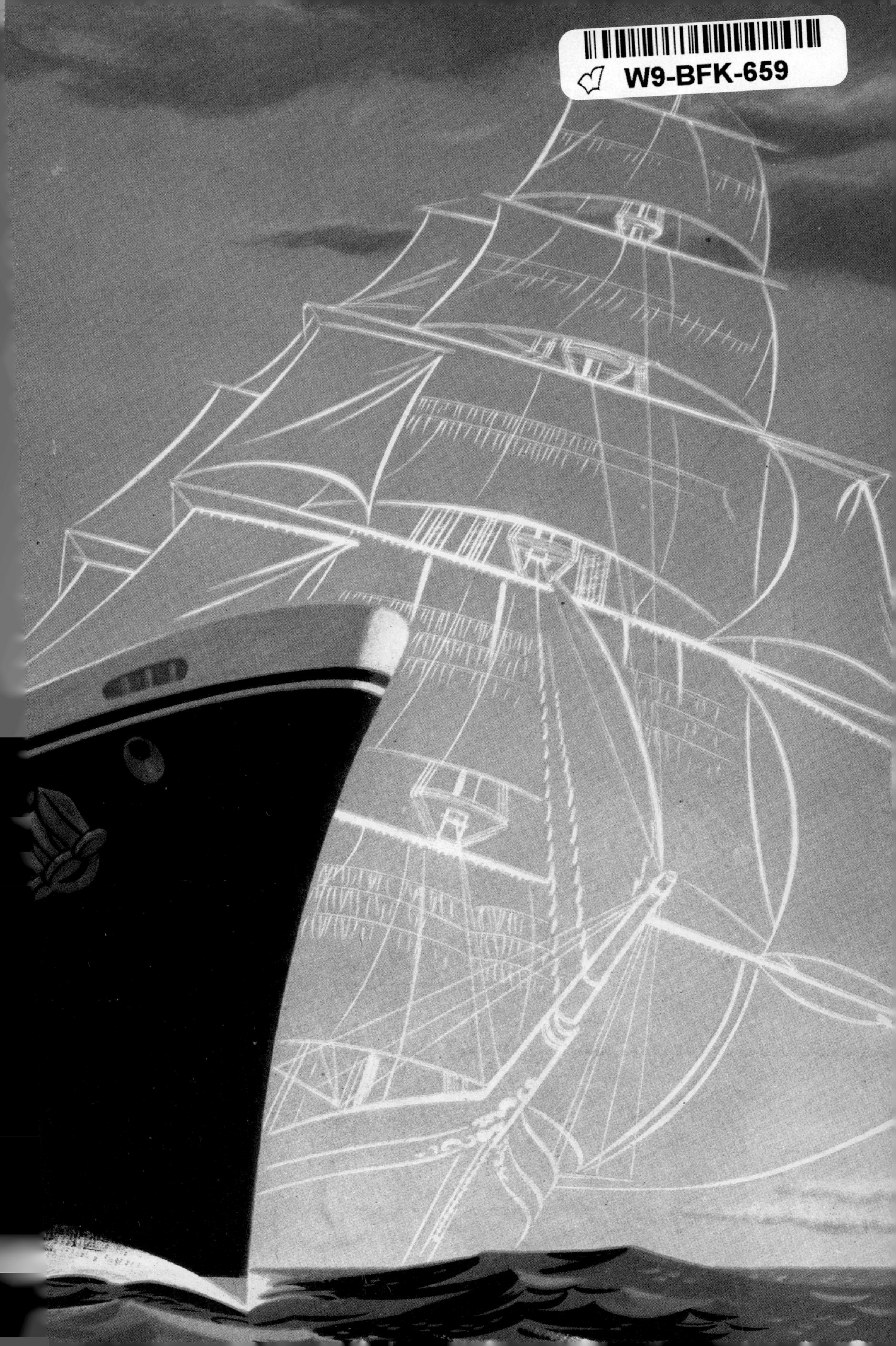

# THE MODERN
# WONDER BOOK OF SHIPS

# *The Modern* WONDER BOOK OF SHIPS

NORMAN CARLISLE
and
EUGENE NELSON

THE JOHN C. WINSTON COMPANY
PHILADELPHIA
TORONTO

FIRST EDITION

MADE IN THE UNITED STATES OF AMERICA

# CONTENTS

# ACKNOWLEDGMENTS

*The publishers wish to express their appreciation to Captain R. T. Merrill, USCGR, who read the proof and offered valuable suggestions. The publishers are also grateful to the following sources for the use of the photographs in this book:*

Acme Photo: Pages 101, 103, 104, 106, 107, 109, 110, 111.

British Information Service: Pages 41, 242, 251, 272.

British Official Photograph: Pages 46, 238, 249, 250.

Caterpillar Tractor Co.: Pages 189, 235, 279, 281, 282.

Costa, Joe, New York *Daily News:* Pages 145, 243, 269.

Cunard White Star Ltd.: Pages 30, 33, 273.

Fairchild Aërial Surveys: Page 225.

French Press and Information Service: Pages 25, 191, 237.

Hakanson, R. C.: Page 222.

Hill and Knowlton: Pages 220, 221, 223, 224, 226, 227, 228, 230, 231.

Levick, Edwin, Inc.: Page 247.

Nautical Photo Agency: Page 34.

Netherlands Information Bureau: Pages 2, 4, 13, 16, 37, 244.

Press Association: Pages 186, 205.

*Ships Magazine:* Pages 209, 213, 216, 233.

Sperry Gyroscope Co.: Pages 253, 258, 262.

Standard Oil Company of New Jersey: Pages 139, 271, 274, 284.

Three Lions: Page 245.

Todd Shipyards Corporation: Pages 208, 215.

Travel and Industrial Development Association of Great Britain and Ireland: Page 42.

United Fruit Company: Pages 240, 259, 280.

United States Coast and Geodetic Survey: Page 287.

United States Coast Guard: Pages 14, 113, 127, 131, 132, 133, 134, 135, 136, 138, 140, 141, 142, 147, 149, 150, 153, 154, 156, 159, 161, 162, 163, 164, 166, 167, 169, 170, 171, 172, 255.

United States Lines: Pages 137, 144, 260.

United States Marine Corps: Page 177.

United States Maritime Commission: Pages 1, 19, 22, 23, 29, 36, 178, 179, 207, 236, 239, 246, 254, 256, 257, 266, 267, 275, 276.

United States Navy: Pages 39, 40, 44, 45, 47, 49, 51, 52, 53, 55, 56, 57, 58, 59, 60, 61, 62, 63, 64, 65, 67, 68, 71, 73, 74, 77, 78, 82, 175, 176, 180, 181, 182, 183, 184, 185, 190, 192, 193, 195, 196, 199, 200, 203, 204, 206, 210, 278, 283.

United States Steel Corporation: Pages 229, 232.

Warner Brothers Pictures Inc.: Pages 85, 86, 87, 88, 91, 93, 97, 98.

War Shipping Administration: Pages 241, 263, 264.

White, Jeffery, Studio: Page 219

CHAPTER 1

# THE STORY OF SAILING SHIPS

*Built in America, the* Three Brothers *was the largest sailing vessel in the world.*

FIVE thousand years ago the hot Egyptian sun beamed down on the sluggish Nile River and turned the stream's curdled brownness to molten gold. The sun sparkled, too, on the golden throne that was carefully placed under an awning of peacock feathers erected on the afterdeck of the galley.

The Pharaoh Khufu, who sat on the throne, turned his lean, vigorous face to an official standing beside him. "Well, well! Where is this miracle ship of yours? I see naught on the bosom of Father Nile except a few clumsy bumboats!"

The official to whom the Pharaoh spoke pointed. "Yonder she comes, my lord," he replied, bowing. Then his shipbuilder's pride got the better of his court manners. He cried out excitedly: "And see how she runs before the wind! Ah, see how my beauty dances!"

Swiftly the long, trim ship they were watching came dancing up the river. Her high linen sail was aloft and drawing well. She was indeed worthy of the plaudits that came involuntarily from the lips of those

*Unfurling her sails to the wind, this boat heads for sea with a "bone" in her teeth.*

high dignitaries of ancient Egypt. The approaching craft was long and narrow, with an enormous overhang of bow and prow. Her straight, high sides had thirty oars apiece. There was a lofty "bipod" mast to catch the higher currents of the wind. Different, indeed, was this high-stepping craft from the slow-moving broad-beamed ships with their heavy sterns and bows and low-slung sails that the Egyptians had been building for fully two thousand years without variation or improvement.

As the new ship drew closer to the royal galley, the cries of wonder increased. Pharaoh turned to the shipbuilder. "How now, man, art afraid your craft will fall asunder that you must needs *tie* it together?"

"Aye, my lord," replied the craftsman seriously. He gestured to his new creation as it drew alongside. Now everyone could plainly see that an enormous cable or truss made out of lengths of hide twisted together ran the full length of the ship. This huge truss ran from a great forward bollard, where the individual thongs were stoutly tied, to a similar bollard in the ship's stern. It was held up and taut by two massive forked beams that put enough strain on the hide rope to withstand thousands of pounds of pressure.

"You see, lord," went on the shipbuilder, now the center of all eyes. "When you commissioned me to construct a boat that would carry huge blocks of granite from the quarries without sinking, as our old-fashioned ships were doing, I knew I would have to alter seriously the plan of our craft. Those old ships were meant to carry light cargoes like corn and slaves, not lumps of stone that weigh heavily and take up little room.

"So I built the ship long and narrow for speed and quick handling. Yet she is so roomy that she can carry a large cargo of granite blocks for your pyramid. To bow and stern I gave a great overhang so she could make landings without smashing up as our old, squat craft have done. But to keep the weight of the bow and stern from buckling the ship, I had to use that huge rope you see to keep the ship from falling apart, even as your majesty in your all-seeing wisdom has remarked!" And the triumphant shipbuilder bowed low.

Thus we can picture the way in which one of the great improvements in shipbuilding occurred, for Egypt was a land of adventurous traders and the Nile was its great waterway. Thousands of years before the Christian era, these daring people were carrying on a thriving commerce in corn, slaves, and cattle along the Nile River and even through the Red Sea.

Even as early as 6000 B.C., the Egyptians were using sailing boats that were a vast improvement over the simple log raft which had been the cave man's method of navigating small rivers and lakes. The Egyptian boats of 6000 B.C. were an improvement, too, over the dug-out canoes equipped with a square, leather sail that many native peoples used until quite late in history. The earliest Egyptian sailing boats of which we have accurate knowledge had a distinct shape to the body of the vessel, copied from the underbody of a duck or a swan.

From 6000 B.C. until Pharaoh Khufu's time, about 3000 B.C., Egyptian boats had a mast and a square sail set well forward in the bow. A small passenger cabin perched aft. Paddlers, as many as twenty of them to a side, were used until some genius discovered that rowing gives more power than paddling. For steering, a huge oar was mounted on a forked post in the center of the stern and was worked by means of a leathern thong. After the time of Khufu, Egyptian boats became so large that eventually they needed four and even five steering oars.

Great voyages were made in these ships, although the largest of them seldom exceeded sixty-five feet in length and could carry no more than fifty seamen and passengers. First they went on the calm surface of Father Nile, then out onto the blue Mediterranean and the hot Red Sea, farther and farther afield as the centuries passed. With their tiny craft and their primitive navigation instruments, those early Egyptian seamen were as bold and hardy as any sailors the world has ever known.

At first, all distant voyages were carried out by fleets of only two or three ships sailing together. About 1600 B.C., however, an Egyptian queen, Hatsheput by name, planned the most ambitious voyage the world had ever seen. There was a rich, fair country known as "Punt" somewhere to the south of Egypt. Thither the queen sent a large fleet of Egypt's finest sailing ships to bring back whatever treasures they could find in Punt.

The fleet was absent from Egypt for three years. They sailed down

*Dutch racing yachts skim the water off the coast of Friesland, Holland.*

the Nile and through a canal that led into the Red Sea. From there they journeyed south, but no one knows exactly where their destination lay, for the land of Punt remains a mystery to modern historians. When finally the ships sailed back to their queen-commander, they brought home cargoes undreamed of by the Egyptians. There were live monkeys, piles of leopard skins, elephant tusks, ebony, frankincense, many varieties of precious woods, and heaps of incense.

This daring voyage seems to have satisfied the Egyptians, for after it they settled back to enjoy the reputation they had made. As usual, when a country ceases to go forward and make progress, some other country soon takes the lead.

More daring than the Egyptians were the Phœnicians, a race of fierce, hardy, and utterly fearless men who were certainly "born to the sea." They not only far surpassed the Egyptians as builders and navigators but even dared to leave the comparative safety of the Mediterranean Sea and sail to England. They eventually circumnavigated Africa! Originally they lived on the coast of Asia Minor, just north of Palestine. They were the first of a long line of sailor-princes and merchants.

The Phœnicians were apparently too busy trading and fighting, building and sailing, to leave any good pictorial representations of their ships for us to study. However, some good likenesses (dating from about 700 B.C.) have been found carved on the stone palace walls of the Assyrians, the conquerors of the Phœnicians. It appears that the Phœnician ships were definitely better than those of the Egyptians. The great, up-curving prow of the ships of Pharaoh Khufu's time had now become a ram, capable of dealing a mortal wound to an enemy ship.

The ships themselves were now larger. In fact, it seems that the Phœnicians invented not only the bireme, a vessel with two rows of oars, one above the other, but also the trireme, with three banks of oars similarly arranged. Thus the Phœnician sailors were able to gain an increase in speed and power without lengthening their ships in order to accommodate more rowers sitting in two single rows. Because of this feature, the Phœnicians were able to take longer voyages than the earlier sailors. Since the rowers had to sit one above the other on ledges or platforms in the biremes and triremes, the ships also increased in height. In addition, they were long, narrow, straight, and had flat bottoms.

In such ships as these, at least one party of Phœnicians, some six centuries before Christ, sailed down the length of the Red Sea and on around Africa. They returned through the Straits of Gibraltar. It took three years for this trip, the same length of time as for that earlier Egyptian cruise. Each spring the Phœnician seamen had landed, planted crops, cultivated them, harvested them, then loaded their new supply of food into their ships and continued on their way!

In time, however, the Phœnicians bowed to another champion of the waves, the Greeks. If we were to believe the songs and poems of the ancient Greeks, we would have to believe that they invented boats. The truth is that at first they openly copied the ships of the Phœnicians, and later improved on them. The Greeks were the first to give us detailed descriptions of their warships in Homer's poems and other writings.

The Greek warship was long and narrow, a trireme. There were between one hundred and one hundred and fifty rowers in such a vessel. The men took turns at rowing, for rowing a warship was not considered a disgrace to a Greek man-at-arms. Rowing a merchant ship was something else! The ships were now equipped with stout metal beaks so that they could ram enemy vessels.

As time passed and Greek power increased, some of the warships had four and even five banks of oars. The men on the lowest bench used the shortest oars; the rowers sat in tiers, one man to an oar; and the rowing benches extended from the sides of the hull to timbers built between the decks. The Greek warships were the first vessels to have a castle-like wooden structure built on their decks from which the warriors could hurl javelins and shoot arrows. This was the origin of the forecastle.

Some students of the Mediterranean oar-propelled vessels believe that this arrangement of oars was a physical impossibility and hold the theory that the multiple grouping of oars was on the same horizontal plane rather than on different ones.

There was a vast difference between the Greek warships and their commercial vessels. The latter were broad and slow-moving, meant to carry large cargoes. They were double-ended and flat-bottomed, and their bow and stern posts were usually gaily ornamented. These vessels depended more upon their large, square sails than they did upon oars.

Greek power faded, too, about 300 B.C. Rome and Carthage took up the battle for world supremacy; Rome with her army, Carthage with her fleet. When Rome had developed to the point where she needed supplies from foreign lands, she ventured out onto the sea. There, however, she was thwarted at every turn by the sea power of Carthage, which by this time had grown into a great city of sea traders. That meant war, but up until then Rome had had practically no experience in shipbuilding.

Fortunately for the great city of the Latins, a five-banked Carthaginian ship was wrecked on the Italian shore at this period in Rome's development. The Romans, a very practical people, salvaged the ship. They measured her in detail and so learned how to build a galley. Then the Romans started to construct a fleet of their own.

The Romans built and launched that fleet in just sixty days from the felling of the first trees. With only dry-land practice, they boldly sailed against Carthage. Lack of practice was just as disastrous in battle then as now. The Romans were beaten, their fleet destroyed.

Undaunted, the Romans built an even larger fleet. Some inventive-minded Roman perfected a sort of drawbridge affair called a corvus. This was really a gangway carried on the prow of a Roman ship, fastened so that it could be let down with a crash onto the deck of an enemy ship. A spike in its end attached this drawbridge firmly to the deck upon which it fell. The Roman infantry could swarm over this bridge onto the enemy decks and slay all who opposed them, for at hand-to-hand fighting the Roman legionnaires had no superiors. By means of this drawbridge, which turned a sea fight which the Romans did not understand into a land battle at which they were masters, the Romans defeated Carthage in 260 B.C. and so won the supremacy of the Mediterranean.

The Romans, who thought far more about war than they did about trade, rapidly improved on their first warships. They constructed towers both fore and aft. When Julius Cæsar fought the Veneti tribesmen off the coast of France, his ships were armed with great spars to which were attached keen, curved steel blades like sickles. These "maritime reaping hooks" slashed through the rigging and brought the sails of the Veneti ships tumbling down onto the decks, thus immobilizing the tribesmen and rendering them easy prey for Cæsar's hard-thrusting swordsmen.

As Rome's power and wealth increased, her ships became larger and more beautiful. We have a written account of one of Rome's famous "corn" ships, which carried grain from the fertile Nile Valley to Rome's hungry millions. The ship was 130 feet long; 29 feet deep; and 30 feet wide. Her stern was shaped like a gooseneck and was gilded; the foresail was dyed a brilliant flame color. She had two masts, and the forward one slanted at a sharp angle. It was probably the ancestor of the familiar bowsprit. Some of the larger Roman corn ships measured 200 feet in length and had three masts.

*The sixteenth-century galley relied more on its oars than on its sails.*

The Romans also developed large passenger ships. Kings and wealthy citizens had their private vessels with luxurious deck houses, bronze baths, marbled rooms, and well-filled libraries. The sails were often of silk, delicately colored; and sometimes parts of the upper works were jewel-encrusted.

Viking ships of those days were faster and probably better built and more seaworthy than were the Spanish ships of the 1500's. They were designed to weather the roughest seas and so were long, low, and rakish, with curving bow and stern and a great breadth of sail. They were usually "clinker built," that is, they had overlapping wooden plates, like shingles on a modern roof. The keel of the Viking ship was of stout oak beams. The boards that formed the sides were held securely in place by heavy iron rivets. Some of the larger dragon ships had thirty rowers to a side, the men adding their power to the sail, which was of bright colors bearing strange, weird designs. The dragon ships had the gilded head of a dragon at the prow and a high gilded dragon's tail at the stern. Rows of shining, painted shields hung over the gunwales added to the splendid spectacle and also protected the rowers from arrows in a battle. The average length of a dragon was about seventy-five feet. Smaller Viking ships, of slightly different design, were called serpents and cranes.

On a voyage, the Vikings took turns rowing when the wind failed. At night they erected a huge tent over the deck and slept in leather sleeping bags. With great stores of salted meat and fish and ale on board, they made lengthy voyages and, although they sorely harassed the people of France, England, and Ireland, the Vikings actually took with them improvements in shipbuilding.

Since the type of ship the Vikings perfected proved to be more seaworthy than the galleys of the Mediterranean, it came in time to be the leading type of vessel for sailing on the open sea. Alfred the Great, who established the foundations of the British navy, used the Viking dragon as a model, although he improved on it in various ways. With the ships he built, Alfred chased the Norsemen out of England, thus making the country safe for the Saxons for a while. Later William the Conqueror used the Viking ships as a pattern for the vessels that carried his army to England, where he defeated the Saxons and took their country.

The Viking serpent was constructed with a raised deck fore and aft. These were the not-so-ancient ancestors of the forecastle and the quarterdeck of modern ships. Amidships of the serpent was the lower maindeck, or "waist." Here were the oarsmen and the crew who handled the sail;

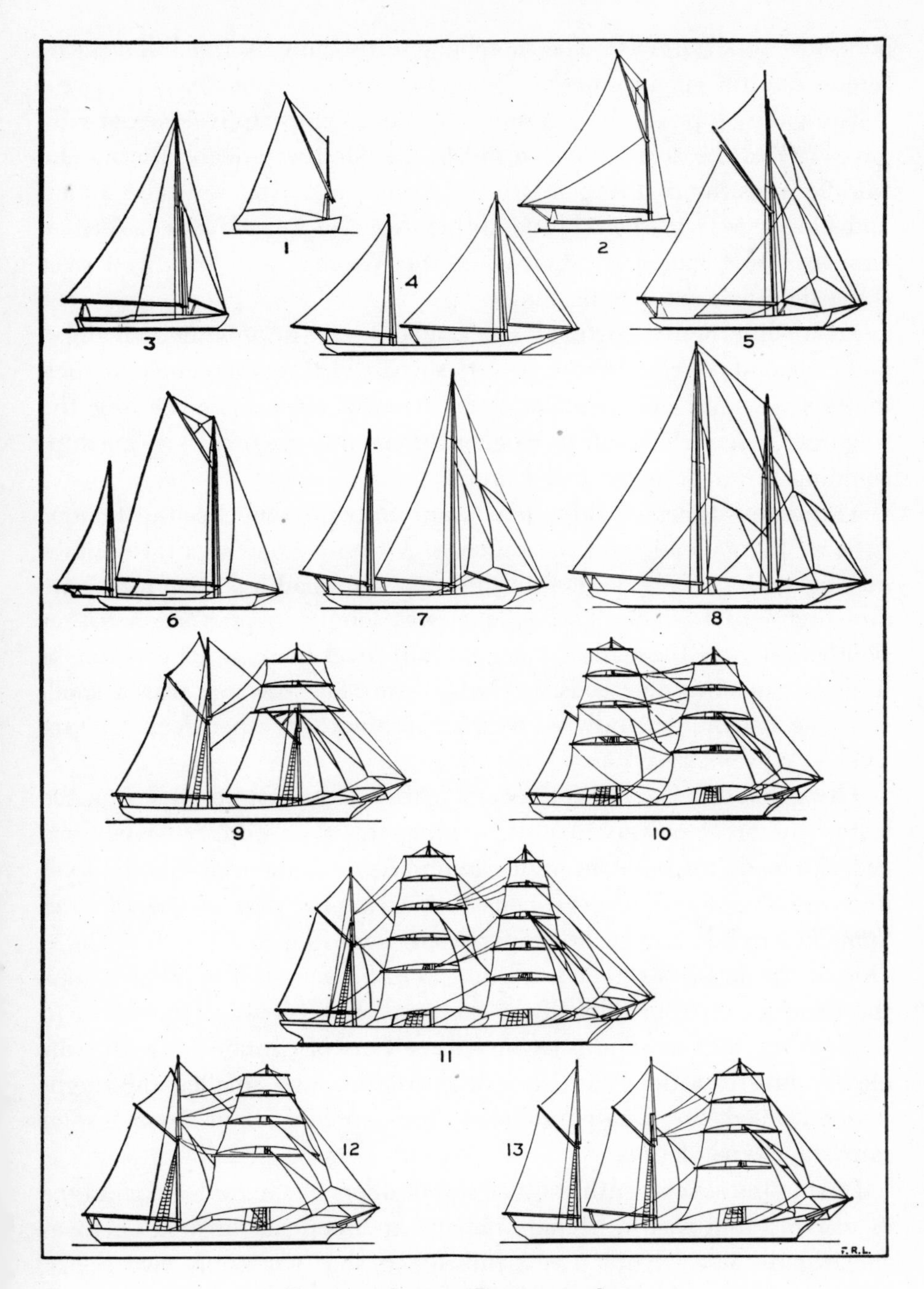


TYPES OF SAILING BOATS AND SHIPS

*1, sailing dinghy; 2, catboat; 3, knockabout; 4, Chesapeake Bay bugeye; 5, sloop; 6, yawl; 7, ketch; 8, schooner; 9, topsail schooner; 10, brig; 11, bark; 12, hermaphrodite brig; 13, barkentine.*

here, too, was the mast. The merchant ships built by the Vikings differed from the warships only in being broader in the beam.

The galley type of ship, manned by slaves and captives, eventually gave way to the true sailing vessel in the Mediterranean. During the Middle Ages the two Italian cities of Venice and Genoa waged a long and bloody war to see who would control the inland waters. Venice won and was hailed as "Queen of the Waters" and had well over three thousand ships in her navy.

Meanwhile, Spain, Portugal, and England were improving their ships. Soon the craft of these three powers surpassed those of Venice in such matters as more decks, masts, cabins, and better lines. During the reign of Queen Elizabeth in England there was great activity in shipbuilding throughout most of Europe.

Three new types of ships now came into prominence—the famous galleon, the galleass, and the pinnace. A true galleon was three times as long as she was wide, low in the waist, and had a square forecastle and high quarterdeck. The galleass was longer in proportion to her width than was the galleon, usually had level decks, and was not so high in the sides and ends as the galleon. The pinnace was a small ship like a sloop, generally without a continuous weather deck. Columbus' *Nina* was classed as a pinnace.

The galleon is usually connected with Spain. This country was the last of the great powers to start building this type ship, but when she did, she made the galleons higher and of heavier material than had yet been used. Some of the galleons that formed a part of the ill-fated Spanish Armada had main timbers that were four and five feet thick. One of the Armada's galleons, the *St. Philip,* was so huge that it took the wind away from the sails of the small English ships that tried to engage her. The *St. Philip* carried three tiers of cannon on each side, eleven guns to a tier. The English ships, although smaller, outfought and outsailed the clumsy galleons, thus spelling their doom as an important type of ship.

During the seventeenth century shipbuilders began to develop a type of warship that was to become famous in American history. This was the frigate. The frigate was a full-rigged ship with only two decks, whereas a "ship-of-the-line" type of warship had three decks on which were frequently mounted about one hundred cannon. A ship-of-the-line was more a floating platform for artillery than it was a sailing ship and was hard to handle and very slow. The frigates, on the other

*Ships of this type were used in the days of Christopher Columbus.*

hand, were especially designed for speed and ease of working so that they could prey on enemy merchantmen. Frigates were as a rule very fast sailers and carried between thirty-four and thirty-eight guns. They were regularly employed as scouts, cruisers, armed convoys for merchantmen, and other such duties. In fact, the modern cruiser bears much the same relationship to a battleship as the frigate did to the ship-of-the-line.

American frigates reached the peak of their development between the end of the Revolution and the War of 1812. Best known is the *Constitution,* or *Old Ironsides* as she was proudly called, since her sailors claimed that enemy cannon balls bounced off her hard wooden planks! American frigates gave an excellent account of themselves in the War of 1812, both in sailing and fighting. The *Essex,* another celebrated frigate of that period, drove British whalers and merchant vessels from the Pacific practically singlehanded.

After the War of 1812 there began a great race between England and

America for the control of trade. Naturally, such a race would be won by the nation with the fastest ships. For this business the Atlantic packets were developed. These ships were full-bodied, with able hulls and very stout spars, sails, and rigging. The decks were flush, and there was a galley between the foremast and the mainmast. In the longboat, which was lashed amidships, there was kept an assortment of pigs, sheep, and chickens to provide fresh meat for the ship's company. A cow to give milk was generally kept in a small house on the main hatch. There were fairly comfortable cabins aft for the passengers.

The packet ships carried passengers, mail, bars of precious metals, and quantities of general merchandise. They were mostly American owned and built. Their captains were Americans too, but few Americans shipped in them as sailors. Instead, these ships were usually worked by a rough, ready-fisted class of Englishmen who were proud of their nickname of "packet rats."

These vessels plowed back and forth across the North Atlantic with all the speed their able captains and mates could crack on. They averaged twelve knots, carrying plenty of sail, and often raced each other from America to England and back again for considerable wagers. On several occasions the trip to England was made in sixteen days.

The packets were well built and comparatively dry, something unusual up until that time. They were smart-looking vessels too. The hulls were black and the ports were rimmed with white. In the earlier ships the interior woodwork was green. In the later ships it was yellow, gray, and red.

The great flood of immigration that flowed from Europe to our country between the War of 1812 and the Civil War was carried in packets. These hard-working, efficient ships finally yielded to the pressure of the steamships about the time of the Civil War. After that struggle was finished, packets were no longer seen on the ocean.

The packets took the Atlantic trade away from England. It remained for an entirely new type of ship—the clipper ship—to make it possible for America to take much of the Oriental trade away from England too.

The clippers were born out of the desire of American merchants for greater and greater speed. Our merchants were doing fairly well with the packets, but they were not satisfied. To meet this need, John W. Griffiths, a New York designer, drew up plans for a ship the like of which had never before been seen. The first ship to be constructed to

Griffiths' specifications was the *Rainbow,* which was launched at New York in 1845.

Many shipbuilders claimed that the *Rainbow* was a freak, for the ship was very long for her breadth and had her greatest beam well aft of the bow. The bow itself was narrow and concave, so that it could knife through the seas. Heretofore, ships' bows had been broadly rounded so that they could smash through the waves. But the *Rainbow* neither capsized nor sank when the wind became rough, as many of her critics prophesied she would. After the *Rainbow's* second trip out and back from Canton, China, the whole world realized that here was the fastest ship afloat and that an entirely new type of sailing ship had been produced.

Soon other clippers were coursing the seven seas. One of the first was the *Sea Witch,* built in 1846, whose speed was far greater than that of any steamship then afloat.

Greatest builder of clipper ships was Donald McKay, a Nova Scotian who made his home in Boston. His first clipper ship, the *Staghound,* still holds the record of thirteen days for a sailing ship from Boston Light to the equator. The *Staghound* was followed by a much larger clipper, the *Flying Cloud,* said to be the fastest sailing ship on long

*Despite its four sails, this shallow-water boat uses only one mast.*

*United States Coast Guard trains its cadets on the* Eagle, *a three-masted bark.*

voyages ever to fly the American flag. The *Flying Cloud* was a vision of great, billowing sails of finely woven, high-grade cotton cloth unmatched for quality and strength by the sails of any other nation. Her figurehead was a winged angel blowing a trumpet. On her first voyage the *Flying Cloud* ran from New York to San Francisco in eighty-nine days, going around Cape Horn. From there she crossed to China for a load of tea and covered the two thousand miles from Canton to Java Head in six days.

Any of McKay's clippers could outsail the fastest racing yacht today. His greatest achievement was his *Lightning*, built in 1854. On her maiden voyage to Liverpool she established herself as the world's fastest ship by making the trip in less than fourteen days. She also made a run of 436 miles in twenty-four hours, the greatest day's run ever made by any sailing ship and one that was unequaled by a steamship for many years. The record is not surpassed very often, even in these days, by our transatlantic liners. The *Lightning* is said to have been the perfect clipper ship, the "sharpest" ship afloat. Her length was 250 feet and her beam only 50 feet. Yet her mainmast was 164 feet high and she carried a spread of 13,000 running yards of canvas!

What would have been McKay's greatest achievement met with a tragic end. She was the magnificent *Great Republic,* one of the largest sailing ships ever built. Unquestionably, she holds the world's record for the amount of sail she could carry. Her mainmast was 131 feet long and 44 inches in diameter. Above this were the topmast, which was 76 feet long, the topgallantmast, 28 feet long, the royalmast, 22 feet long, the skysailmast 19 feet long. Atop all this was a 12-foot pole, so the mainmast, with all these added structures, rose a towering 200 feet above the deck.

As she lay at her dock in New York, a warehouse near by caught fire and sparks flew into the rigging. Soon she was a great roaring pyre of flame that could be seen for miles. Members of the crew daringly went aboard and cut down the masts in the hope of saving the ship, but the flames set fire to her decks and soon the entire ship was ablaze. There was nothing to do but to open the sea cocks and let water in to sink her. Later she was raised, but the masts were never restored. Some idea of what kind of speed she might have shown had she ever put to sea with her full press of sail can be gained from the fact that even with a much smaller mast she made the run from Sandy Hook to Land's End in only thirteen days.

Only the finest material and craftsmanship went into the building of these "dream ships." Every man who worked on one took pride in doing his utmost to make that clipper a champion. The finest oak and Southern pine were used. The ships were copper fastened, and the hulls were sheathed in sheet metal so that they would slide through the water with the least possible amount of friction. Stanchions, rails, and cabins were of mahogany and rosewood. Most of the clippers were painted black with a crimson or gold band around the hull. The lower masts were white to the tops, but yards and bowsprit were black. With her flashing speed and towering spread of canvas, the clipper was a creation of breath-taking beauty. It was almost a living expression of the genius of our Yankee shipbuilders.

Wonderfully designed and built though they were, much of the success which the clippers attained was due to the men who sailed them. The famous clippers were handled by marvelous captains, men who dared to carry such a spread of sail as no captain of an ordinary ship would have dreamed of carrying for fear the strain would "yank the sticks" out of his craft. The skippers drove around Cape Horn and across to China with rackings on the topsail halyards and locks on the mainsheets so that no timid seaman could take in sail against the skipper's

*The modern yacht of this type with a small sail abaft the rudder is called a yawl.*

orders. Thus the clipper ships cut in two the time required for voyages to China and Australia and this gave to America the lion's share of world trade.

The English were not left behind in the race to build fast ships. The principles of design that made the clippers such brilliantly capable ships were studied, and English shipbuilders succeeded in producing vessels that were in some ways superior. The first English clipper, the *Challenge,* raced an American clipper of the same name from China to London and beat the American craft by a narrow margin. With this performance as a stimulus, many English clippers were laid down, among them the first of the famous Aberdeen clippers, the *Stornoway.*

The race from China to England was more than a sporting event, although it had all the qualities of a sporting contest. After the tea crop in the Orient matured, the first ships to get their cargoes back to England would receive much higher prices than those coming in later. The first British ship to succeed in breaking the Yankee clipper record was the *Lord of the Isles,* which reached England first in the season of 1856. One of the greatest races was that between the English clipper, *Crest of the Waves* and the American clipper, the *Sea Serpent.* These two ships sailed at the same hour from Shanghai, and the captains of both of them vowed that they would come first to London. A prize of $7.50 a ton had been offered to the ship that arrived first with her cargo, and captains and crews were determined to win this bonus. Neck and neck they raced each other around the world, frequently catching sight of each other's sails. They arrived off the Isle of Wight at the same hour, with the *Crest of the Waves* slightly in the lead. However, the Yankee captain was not yet defeated. He rushed ashore in the pilot's boat, took a train to London, hurried to the custom house and registered his ship as having arrived, although she had not really reached the Thames.

The greatest race of all was a competition between five British tea clippers, the *Ariel, Taeping, Fiery Cross, Taitsing,* and *Serica.* They left Foochow, China, at intervals on May 29, 30, and 31, 1865, bound for London. Forty-six days later the first of the ships, the *Fiery Cross,* rounded the Cape of Good Hope, followed a short time later on the same day by the *Ariel.* Within six days all the ships had rounded the Cape and were racing up the African coast. On the morning of September 5, the *Ariel* and the *Taeping* raced side by side up the English Channel and into the Thames. They had left Foochow just twenty minutes apart, and the *Taeping* won by less than that. A few minutes after they had landed, the *Serica* appeared. The other two ships docked on September 7 and 8. The sailing times of all the ships had been nearly identical, probably the most astonishing record of its kind in all the history of sailing ships. When one considers that these ships had traversed sixteen thousand miles, subject to the differences in winds and in the seamanship of the respective captains, such a record seems almost incredible.

One of the most remarkable ships built by English shipbuilders was the *Sir Lancelot,* constructed by Steele of Greenock. Built in 1865, she was one of the last of the great sailing ships. She was built for speed, and no pains were spared to make her the fastest ship afloat. She could carry forty-six thousand square feet of canvas. This vast spread enabled her to make the journey from China to England in eighty-nine days. At one time, in crossing the Indian Ocean, she maintained a speed of three hundred miles a day for a solid week. One of her most astonishing features was her ability to beat into a direct head wind.

For a few years the clipper ships ruled the sailing world, and people watched their performances with breathless eagerness to see what speed record would be shattered next. Then, about the time of the Civil War, the iron ships powered by steam engines began to be a common sight on the sea lanes. The clippers, which were expensive to build and maintain, could not compete against the combination of the iron ships' speed and economy. Last of the famous clippers was the *Cutty Sark*, launched in 1869. For a few years the clippers held on as ocean tramps, picking up a stray cargo here and there, but their day was definitely done. Soon there were no more of these flashing white-winged dream ships plying the seven seas. But they have left a memory of fast sailing and beauty that will never grow dim so long as men make ships and sail them.

CHAPTER 2

# THE STORY OF STEAMSHIPS

*A cargo ship of special design, the* Robin Locksley, *was built for the United States Merchant Marine.*

FAR AWAY on the horizon the lookout of the fast sailing packet, the *Contract,* sighted a rising plume of black smoke. In the year 1819, that sight could mean only one thing. There in the mid-Atlantic a ship was on fire. The lookout shouted the information down to the captain, who promptly ordered the ship's course to be altered. He well knew what a terrible danger was presented by a fire at sea and did not hesitate to rush to the rescue.

The wind was good, and the alteration in course gave the *Contract* a chance to take full advantage of it. To the captain's astonishment, the column of smoke seemed to remain the same distance away. He ordered more sails, and slowly the *Contract* began to gain on the ship she had set out to rescue. Passengers and members of the crew crowded the rail, expressing their anxiety as they saw the tremendous volume of smoke pouring out of the vessel, which, by this time, they could see clearly. The captain studied the ship through his binoculars, and to his astonishment saw that there was no sign of unusual activity aboard her. Members of her crew moved around her decks in a leisurely fashion, and she gave no evidences of distress. Then the captain's gaze took in the black pipe that thrust itself up amidships. He saw that the smoke was coming from this pipe.

With an air of excitement the captain turned to announce to his passengers and crew that they were undoubtedly looking upon one of the wonders of the age, for the craft that they had come to rescue was not on fire at all, but must be the new steam packet of which there had been much talk.

The steamboat that was such a rarity in 1819 was actually not such a new invention. Looking back, it now seems very strange that it took so long for the invention to reach a stage where ships propelled by steam could go to sea.

The story of man's knowledge of steam itself goes far back into antiquity to Hero of Alexandria. In 130 B.C. he developed a curious piece of apparatus that might be called the first steam engine. He mounted a hollow sphere between two supports, one of which was hollow. Through it came steam from a closed vessel that was supported over a fire. Into the sphere he placed two pipes with ejecting nozzles. When steam escaped, the whole sphere revolved. After Hero there are a few evidences that much was done to harness the powerful force represented by steam. In the first half of the seventeenth century one Salomon de Caus was able to demonstrate that steam given off by boiling water could be used for such purposes as lifting water, and at about the same time Giovanni Branca created the idea of the modern turbine. In 1663 Edward Somerset, the second Marquis of Worcester, published a description of "An Admirable and Most Forcible Way to Drive Up Water by Fire."

These men were among those who thought about, and experimented with, the possibilities of steam, but the first real marker on the road to applying it to propelling boats is the work of a Frenchman, Denis Papin. In 1690 Papin published his first ideas about building steam engines. In 1703 he presented his original and brilliant idea for applying it to water craft. He announced his intention to build a boat that would carry about two tons. He believed that it could be operated by two men by means of a wheel he had perfected. Papin went about his work thoroughly. He studied the resistance that water would offer to the hull of the boat and found what he believed to be the correct line on which his ship should be built. He worked out a simple way for condensing steam in a cylinder made of thin metal. The expanding steam raised a piston and rod on which was a latch. When the water had heated enough the piston moved upward and was kept there by means of the latch. Then the fire was taken away, the latch loosed, and the piston dropped back into its former position. A rope and a pulley attached to the rod furnished the motive power.

After many years of patient work and many difficulties, Papin actually did succeed in building a boat that carried out some of these ideas. He boldly set out to sail his craft down the Fulda River near Hannover, Germany. Miraculously, his craft worked, and thousands of people gathered on the shores to watch this fantastic experiment. Papin was overjoyed. He had given a small demonstration of what his steamboat could do; now he would really show the world. He proposed to steam down the river, and out to sea, where he would cross to London. It

*The steamship* Great Eastern *was famous as a luxury liner in 1857.*

was a bold plan, and Papin set out full of hope. He did not know it, but he was risking his life, for there were angry mutterings among all the rivermen, who thought that this new craft would provide a serious challenge to their crude sail- and oar-propelled boats.

"We'll stop this upstart Frenchman," they vowed.

Triumphantly Papin sailed down the river, his steamboat puffing proudly. At Munden he looked ahead and saw that the river was blocked, for the boatmen had thrown a solid cordon of boats across the river. As the steamboat drew near the men stood up grimly, armed with clubs. A roar of rage went up from hundreds of throats as they saw the steam monster. Papin's steamboat came closer and closer, and when he was within hailing distance he asked them to permit his boat to pass. The answer came swiftly and cruelly. Boats shot forward, and in a moment men were swarming aboard Papin's craft. Heavy clubs smashed the machinery, blows rained on poor Papin, who managed to flee ashore. His steamship was a total wreck.

*The first and largest ship built by the United States Maritime Commission—the* S.S. America.

In 1730 an Englishman, Dr. John Allen, came forward with a very different idea, which he announced in his book bearing the lengthy title "Brief Narrative of Several New Inventions and Experiments, Particularly the Navigating of a Ship in a Calm." What Dr. Allen proposed was nothing less than jet propulsion—and the year was only 1730!

Allen's idea was to propel a ship by forcing water, or some other fluid, through the stern by means of an engine. Dr. Allen experimented with a tin boat of minute size. He placed this little boat in calm water and loaded it until it sank in the water to a depth of a little over three inches. Into the boat he also placed a cylindrical-shaped object six inches high and about three inches in diameter and filled it with water. At the bottom of the cylinder was a small pipe, a quarter-inch square; this led through the stern of the craft at a distance of an inch and a half below the surface of the water in which the boat was floating. As soon as Allen removed his finger from the outlet pipe in the stern, the water ran out of the cylinder; this action caused the boat to travel at about one-fifth of a mile per hour. Although nothing came of Dr. Allen's experiments at the time, adaptions of his ideas are being used successfully today.

Another Englishman, Jonathan Hulls, began some exciting experiments about the same time. His idea was to apply the principle of steam propulsion to a small tugboat, a subject on which he issued a booklet entitled: "A Description and Draught of a New-Invented Machine for Carrying Vessels or Ships out of or into Any Harbour, Port or River, Against Wind and Tide or in a Calm." He thought that ships would welcome the existence of such a towboat. In obtaining his patent, he explained: "In some convenient part of the towboat there is placed a vessel about two-thirds full of water, with the top close shut. This vessel being kept boiling, rarifies the water into a steam; this steam being conveyed through a large pipe into a cylindrical vessel, and there condensed, makes a vacuum, which causes the weight of the atmosphere to press on this vessel and so presses down a piston that is fitted into this cylindrical vessel in the same manner as is Mr. Newcomen's engine by which he raises water by fire."

Meanwhile progress had been made in the stationary steam engine. Thomas Newcomen developed something like Papin's atmospheric engine. Young James Watt, experimenting with Newcomen's engine, which relied on atmospheric pressure to drive the piston into a vacuum, saw there were several things wrong with it and set out to correct them. When he tried to repair a Newcomen engine in 1764, he saw that this engine was extremely wasteful of steam, and therefore produced little power. He decided that the secret of improved power lay in

*The Cunard steamship* Lucania *had the typical high smoke stacks of World War I.*

finding some way to avoid condensing the steam in the cylinder itself. To accomplish this he developed a separate condenser into which a stream of water would spray. From this condenser he used an air pump to draw off the injected water, the condensed steam, and the air that had succeeded in getting in. With this and other improvements he was able to keep the steam at a much higher temperature and obtain far more power. Watt also developed an ingenious method of gearing that translated the up-and-down movement of the steam engine's piston into rotary movement for applying the power. His engine provided the basis for propelling boats, although apparently Watt himself did not think of such a use for his invention.

Many experimenters went to work with the idea of using a Watt engine on a boat. One of them was a Frenchman named François Dorothée who built a sizable craft about one hundred and fifty feet long. On July 15, 1783 at least ten thousand people gathered at Lyon to watch Dorothée's steamboat attempt its maiden voyage. The experiment was a huge success, because the boat moved against the current, puffing furiously, and reached the Isle of Barbe, turned around and came back again. This exploit was repeated several times, amid the roars of the crowd.

American inventors were busy too, among them John Fitch, a skilful Revolutionary War gunsmith. To him goes the honor of having created the first paddle steamboat that worked. His first boat was nothing more than a skiff, equipped with paddles located at the side and revolved by cranks attached to a steam engine. Although the steam engine was much like other Watt engines being used in Europe, the ingenious Fitch had made an engine with a big horizontal cylinder in which the steam worked with equal force at each end. This cylinder turned a shaft to which were attached twelve paddles, six on each side of the boat. In 1788 Fitch built another boat that was sixty feet long and powered by a steam engine with a twelve-inch cylinder. This vessel actually made the trip from Philadelphia to Burlington, a distance of twenty miles. The next year Fitch built another boat that was even more pretentious and that was a remarkable success. It achieved a speed of eight miles an hour and made regular passenger runs on the Delaware during the summer of 1790, piling up a mileage of nearly three thousand miles. Poor Fitch was not to enjoy the benefits of his great success, however, for his faint-hearted backers withdrew their financial support and Fitch committed suicide.

Many people think of Robert Fulton as the inventor of the steamboat, but as we have seen by the stories of these early experimenters, numerous successful steamboats had been built and operated long before Fulton thought of turning his talents to developing an improved water craft. Fulton was a painter who went to England to study under Sir Benjamin West, the famous English artist. After that Fulton went to France; there he met Robert R. Livingston, the United States Minister to France. Livingston was filled with many inventive ideas, among them the dream of a steamboat to open up the rivers of New York State. He was a very practical man and had already gone to the legislature of the State of New York and persuaded it to give him the exclusive rights to navigating all kinds of boats that were propelled by the force of fire or steam on the waters within the jurisdiction of the state. Livingston had tried to build a steamboat, but it had not been very successful.

Livingston soon realized that Fulton had much inventive skill and started to talk to him about steamboats. Before long they had agreed on a partnership that had the goal of producing a successful steamboat that would enable Livingston to take advantage of the grant he had received in New York. Wisely, Fulton went to work with model boats to try to create the best possible design. Should they use paddles, sculls, endless chains, or water wheels? They sought the answer to these and many other questions in models that were propelled by clockwork.

At last they were ready to construct a full-sized steamboat. It was seventy French feet long and had an eight-horse-power engine that is generally believed to have been a Watt engine. After a year's work the boat was finally ready for her first voyage, and Fulton and Livingston were waiting impatiently for the day of the experiment. A few days before the planned voyage, young Fulton

*Ready to slide down the ways of a French shipyard at St. Nazaire, this freighter will enter France's Merchant Marine.*

*The* Clermont, *designed by Robert Fulton, was the first successful American steamboat.*

was eating his breakfast when an excited messenger burst into the room.

"Please, sir—" he shouted.

"Well, speak up," Fulton demanded, knowing by the look on the man's face that something was terribly wrong.

"Please, sir, the boat has broken in two and gone to the bottom!"

Fulton rushed down to the Seine and found that the messenger had indeed spoken the truth. There was no sign of the boat that had lain there so proudly.

"We've got to raise it!" Fulton cried. He gave furious orders, assembled a crew of workmen, and he himself plunged into the icy waters of the river. His friends argued with him, trying to make him at least stop to eat, but he refused. For twenty hours, without food or sleep, he stayed there, directing the work of the men. He was determined that he would not lose the boat on which he had worked so hard. At last it was raised, and Fulton could look grimly at the shattered hull and the battered wreckage of the engine.

"We're lucky it happened now," was Fulton's comment, for he knew that he had made a mistake in not making the hull much stronger than he had. As it was, no lives had been lost, and few people knew of this abrupt end to the first Fulton steamboat. Fulton set out desperately to correct his mistakes and build another boat. On August 9, 1803 he was ready with another boat and with it steamed triumphantly up the Seine at a speed of three and a quarter miles an hour. This low speed was a terrible disappointment to Fulton, who had predicted that a steamboat could move at a speed of sixteen to twenty-four miles per hour. He made the sad discovery that most of the power was lost in the effort of the paddles to grip the water. He revised his estimate to an opinion that perhaps the steamboat could not be expected to travel faster than five or six miles an hour.

Although his steamboat met with no favor in France, Fulton felt that he was ready to go back to his native America, to attempt there the creation of a steamboat that would be his crowning achievement. He ordered a huge engine from Watt in England. Although he had to wait two years for it, at length it arrived in America. Meanwhile Fulton had constructed a remarkable craft which he named the *Clermont*. It is true that there was hardly a single original invention in the boat, but Fulton had been very skilful in combining the inventions of other men.

There was great excitement in New York City and all along the Hudson when the day arrived on which Fulton was to try out his steamboat. Actually, Fulton had tested her out on August 9, 1807, but not many people had seen this experiment. The official test was to come on August 17. Fulton invited a number of guests, and some forty of them appeared on the appointed day. A number of others expressed their unwillingness to venture on the water in such a dangerous contraption. There was a widespread opinion that the *Clermont* would blow up before she had gone far, but the pessimists were proved wrong when, with a mighty sound of roaring steam, she set off up the Hudson, her machinery creaking and the whole craft throbbing. Hour after hour she beat her way against the current, but her engine kept on pounding faithfully. Fulton restlessly paced the deck, now examining the machinery, now talking to the passengers to answer their questions, now exhorting the fireman to stoke the boilers more vigorously. After thirty-two hours the *Clermont* puffed proudly into Albany, having traversed the one hundred and fifty miles at an average of nearly five miles per hour. All the way up the river Fulton had the great satisfaction of passing sloops and schooners that were barely making headway against the unfavorable breeze, which did not bother the *Clermont* at all.

Sailing boat captains resolved that this new menace to their trade should not be allowed to sail safely up and down the river; so in the months that followed they made every effort to ram the new steamboat. Although her paddles were smashed on more than one occasion, the *Clermont* continued to make her regular trips, eventually reducing the time to Albany to only thirty hours, which was eighteen hours less than the best sailing packet time.

The steamboat had definitely come to stay, and Fulton was the unchallenged master of the river. He did not stop with the *Clermont*, but continued to build one steamboat after another, building about seventeen in the next eight years. No two were alike and each one showed some improvement over its predecessor. Steamboat travel came to be accepted as a commonplace, and within a few years steamboats were plying up and down many rivers.

Fulton was content to keep his steamboats busy on the Hudson River, but other enterprising men were dreaming of the possibilities of seagoing steamships, although many years went by before the *Savannah*, the first steam-equipped ocean-going vessel, put out to sea. She was not truly a steamship, for she started her career as a sailing packet. Her first trip under steam was hardly a success, for when she was fourteen days out of Savannah, bound for Liverpool, she ran short of fuel. Knowing that the arrival of the *Savannah* was expected and would be looked on as a test of the effectiveness of steam, her captain ordered the ship to proceed under sail so that the small amount of fuel could be saved. He used it to good advantage by starting up the engines as the craft neared Liverpool and then steamed triumphantly into the harbor amid the rousing cheers of the crowds assembled to greet the arrival of the steamship. Her triumph was short-lived, for her owners, exasperated at the difficulties of operating a steamboat, ordered her engines removed; so she ended her days, as she had begun them, as a sailing packet.

Various other sailing vessels were fitted up with steam engines, but not until 1838 did a ship cross the Atlantic entirely under steam power. The craft that earned that honor was a ship called the *Sirius*, which had originally been fitted up as a brigantine. She was quite small, being only 178 feet long and 25 feet wide, with a weight of 703 tons. She had never been intended for ocean crossings. The *Sirius* left London with ninety-four passengers aboard. With a stop to take on coal at Queenstown, she set out across the Atlantic, her engines pounding furiously. When the crew learned that her captain proposed to cross the entire ocean without the use of sails, they threatened to mutiny. The very idea of crossing the ocean in such a craft was bad enough, but to do it with steam seemed the height of folly. However, the mutiny was put down, and the men grudgingly agreed to try the passage. As the *Sirius* neared New York seventeen days later, she had burned all the coal in her bunkers. The captain gave orders to tear down her spars and burn them, and on the strength of this fuel, the *Sirius* steamed into New York Harbor, the first craft to be driven across the Atlantic by steam.

The *Sirius* won this honor by a narrow margin, for three days later New Yorkers saw another craft steam into the harbor. And a very different craft she was. Here was a ship that was no mere sailing ship with engines thrust into her; this was a ship really designed as an ocean steamer. The proud *Great Western* had made the crossing in just fifteen days. When she reached New York she had faced no such desperate shortage of fuel, for one-fourth of her coal still remained unused in the bunkers. She was big for her time, this 1,320-ton craft, and designed to stand the worst punishment of the sea.

*Completing its voyage on May 22, 1819, the S.S.* Savannah *was the first steamship to cross the Atlantic.*

*An early Cunarder, the* Britannia, *made many Atlantic voyages in 1840.*

Steam was beginning its rule of the sea, a rule that would be only briefly challenged by the swift and beautiful Yankee clippers. From this point on, the history of the steamboat becomes a story of larger and larger ships, with constant improvements in the steam engines that drove them. A sailing man named Samuel Cunard, who had made a fortune in carrying the mails between Halifax, Newfoundland, Boston, and Bermuda, conceived the idea of regular steamship passenger service of a much faster and more reliable kind than had yet been offered. He visualized a regular transatlantic express line of mail steamships that would displace the uncertain services of government brigs that operated at the whim of wind and weather. He got his chance in 1838, when the British Government sent out circulars inviting bids for a faster and more reliable means of transit for mail by steam vessels. One of these circulars reached Cunard, and he immediately set out to seize the opportunity. He turned in the lowest bid and was awarded a contract.

To carry it out, he constructed four steamers, the *Britannia, Acadia, Columbia,* and *Caledonia,* which were launched in 1840 They were paddle wheelers, built of wood, each ship being 207 feet long and 34 feet wide, with a tonnage of 1,154 tons. Each had an indicated horse power of 740, a cargo capacity of 225 tons, and accommodations for

115 cabin passengers. On July 4, 1840 the *Britannia* sailed from England for America on a regular set schedule, the first steamship to proceed on an announced schedule. She carried 64 passengers and made the journey from Liverpool to Boston in 14 days and 8 hours, including a stop-over at Halifax. Samuel Cunard, who made the voyage on the *Britannia,* became the hero of the day.

For a time the paddle-wheel steamers continued to be used. In 1859 there came out the *Great Eastern,* which was equipped with both paddle wheel and screw propeller. Eventually the screw propeller alone was used as a means of propulsion. After repeated experiments, there appeared in 1862 the *China,* which used a screw propeller. Her performance settled the controversy about the merits of the two types of propulsion. By 1874 the world had steamers the size of the *Bothnia* and the *Scythia.* These sister ships were 420 feet in length and registered at about 4,500 tons. They could carry over 1,400 passengers each. They also embodied two innovations that eventually came to be standard on all liners: steam steering equipment and water-tight compartments. In the thirty-five years that separated the launching of the *Britannia* from that of the *Bothnia,* the steamship had indeed made vast progress. The latter ship was four times as large, carried four times as many cabin passengers, and fourteen times as much freight. In addition, the *Bothnia* carried 1,100 extra steerage passengers. The *Bothnia* with this vastly greater load maintained a speed nearly twice as fast as that of the *Britannia,* with the same consumption of coal.

A ship that created great interest was the *Servia,* which appeared in 1881. She was built of steel and was equipped with the very recent invention, electric lights. She had a speed of seventeen knots, which was remarkably fast compared with the speed of previous ships. She soon had competitors in the form of the *Umbria* and the *Etruria* and other ships. The *Umbria* was capable of the astonishing speed of nineteen and one-half knots, with an emergency capacity of twenty-one.

From this point on liners grew steadily in size and speed, until in recent years there appeared such tremendous giants as the superliner *Queen Elizabeth,* which, converted into a troopship during the war, did not make her maiden passenger voyage until October 16, 1946. Two hundred passengers sailed on the *Britannia;* about 2,300 find comfortable accommodations on the *Queen Elizabeth,* and in her troopship days she sometimes carried as many as 15,000 men. Her tremendous length makes her one of the longest man-made objects in the world, her

1,031 feet being topped only by the "length" of the Empire State Building, which is 1,248 feet high. Weighing 83,673 tons she carries, on her 14 decks, 21,000 pieces of furniture, 10 miles of carpeting and 35 public rooms, including lounges, bars, ballrooms, and smoking rooms, not to mention two movie theaters and two swimming pools. At night 2,000 portholes blaze over the ocean, and in daylight her black hull, white superstructure, and black and red funnels rise unbelievably high above the water.

Perhaps modern science, which has created the miracle of atomic power, will find a way to apply this vast new force to moving ships. Meantime, steam will continue to power water craft. The great liners of today owe their swift progress to the work of many men—the men who helped make the steamboat possible.

The building of these ships is one of the miracles of modern engineering. The experimental days are gone when steamship builders risked their lives and fortunes in building ships that might not even work. Science has taken the guesswork out of shipbuilding.

Ships designed for cargo and passengers take shape first in the minds of officials of the steamship lines, who will transmit their ideas to the naval architects employed by the shipbuilding companies. Once the general idea has been conceived, the engineers make a drawing that shows what the ship will look like. This first drawing is only a general scheme of things, like an architect's sketch of a proposed house.

After that come models. The first model ship may be about twenty feet long. It is made of soft pine, cut and whittled to the exact contour of the underwater part of the ship. This model is taken to a towing basin, where it is tested. Calculations made by the engineers at the towing basins are so precise that they even consider the curvature of the earth in arriving at their performance figures. A second model, self-propelled and powered by a tiny electric motor, may be made in order to make further tests of hull with rudder and propeller. Then a third wood model three or four feet long is needed as a guide for the men who will draw the detailed design of the ship. Its purpose is to give them a three-dimensional view of the hull. This model is lined off to indicate just how formation of steel plates will be determined on the actual ship. The scale is so exact that the model is used in determining the size of individual steel plates.

It is from this beginning that the detailed drawings emerge, to give a plan, broken down into sections, for every square foot of the ship's structure. These plans are incredibly complicated. They show every rivet, every sheet of metal, in the proper dimensions.

Even this is only a beginning, for the hull and superstructure of a ship are merely its external parts, like the walls of a house. Inside this hull must go an entire power plant—the plant that propels the ship, heats and lights it, delivers fresh and salt water to thousands of taps, maintains the communications system; in short, the heart that makes the ship a living thing.

When you build a house, you can connect it to the public services systems that are brought from far-away power plants through the streets. A ship must have similar plants, but more inclusive and vital, installed right in its body.

All these things, too, must be planned and drawn. Every pipe, every joint and turn and valve, must be designed, every cable and wire must be indicated. Hence, after detailed drawings for the hull proper are made, separate sets of plans are created for all these installations.

How exact these must be can be understood by a reference to plumbing. When a plumber installs the drains in a house, for instance, he has a relatively simple job, because he knows that *down* will always stay *down* and that drainage will run off in that direction, barring some accidental stoppage or a change in the law of gravity.

There can never be such assurance in regard to drain pipes on a ship. The ship, in mountainous seas, will toss and turn; pipes originally designed to slope down may suddenly find themselves going uphill, and a steep hill at that. Consequently, this piping system must be so

*The world's largest liner, the* Queen Elizabeth *is 1,031 feet long and 118 feet in breadth.*

carefully designed that it will always carry its burdens in the required directions, regardless of slope. The men who design it leave nothing to guesswork by the men whose job it is to install it.

That is one instance out of the thousands in ship design where careful advance planning extends to every detail. Such planning requires technical knowledge; in addition, the designers must be endowed with the highest type of creative imagination. They must see clearly in their own minds the whole structure of every detail before the ship is ever

*Built in 1901, the* King Edward *was the first passenger steamer driven by a turbine.*

built. Hundreds of detailed drawings are required for a single ship, not counting the precise blue prints that are in constant use at the plants of ship-equipment manufacturers.

Such planning work keeps hundreds of designers busy for months and costs hundreds of thousands of dollars. When the master plans are completed, they are so valuable that they are kept in a fireproof vault. There are many blue prints taken off from these master plans.

When the plans are finally drawn and approved, the work of converting them into three dimensions of metal begins.

The plans for the various power plants of the ship will go to various machine shops. The plans for the ship's hull go to a unique room called the mold loft.

The mold loft is the place where the structural parts of a ship are made in paper or wood, for duplication elsewhere in steel or some other metal. A typical mold loft is 765 feet long and 185 feet wide, which is bigger than two football fields laid end to end. In this great room are made the templates, which are actual flat patterns of all areas of the hull. Each template has marked on it a curious jargon of symbols and signs. When the template leaves the mold loft for the fabricating shop, a glance at these symbols tells the men in the shop the character of the metal and answers such questions as how thick the metal should be. Other symbols clearly indicate where rivet holes are to be used and how twenty other different fabricating details are to be carried out. In the fabricating shop the template is simply laid on top of the proper metal, forming a perfect pattern.

The actual building of the ship is the end of the long process of preparation. The term "she slid down the ways" is a common one used in describing the launching of a ship, but most people don't know what a way is. Actually, it is nothing more than a long row of blocks of wood, about two feet on the side and the same distance apart. These keel blocks are laid on secure foundations, on an inclination, so that those farthest away from the water are highest. This will permit the vessel to slide easily into the water when she is completed. Vessels are built with their sterns toward the water, and the bow pointing toward the land. In a big shipyard there will, of course, be as many ways as there are ships being built at any one time.

First in the building of a ship comes the laying of the keel. In a steel ship this is a large, flat steel plate that is laid along the bottom of the hull. Above this plate is placed another plate, which is set on edge. This is called the vertical keel. On top of it is placed still another plate that bears the name of keelson. When these three plates are riveted securely together, they form the strong backbone of the ship. Upright "girders" are attached to this backbone at the stem and stern, and other curved girders are fastened along it to form the frames. To hold the frames securely and keep them from spreading, other girders are placed inside the ship, running across from frame to frame. These beams provide supports for the decks, just as beams under the floor of a house provide support for the flooring. For each deck there must be a set of beams. The beams themselves, since they are very heavy and must carry much weight, are given additional support by steel pillars underneath.

All these provide merely the framework of the ship. Now the skeleton

*Built in 1908 by the Germans, the* George Washington *became an American ship after World War I.*

must be covered. On the outside, steel plates make up what is called the skin of the ship. On big ships these steel plates may be nearly an inch thick. They are laid overlapping and are usually riveted together. This riveting makes a shipyard one of the noisiest places on earth, for thousands of riveting machines may be hammering away at once. In some ships the plates are welded together instead of being riveted. After the outer skin of steel is laid over the floor plates, it provides a double bottom that protects the ship from sinking in case the outer skin is damaged. The space between the skins has many practical uses as a container for fuel oil, water, and ballast. The ballast is sea water, taken aboard to make the ship sink low enough in the water to be manageable and to permit its screw propellers to operate sufficiently far beneath the surface.

When the skeleton has been constructed and the skins put in place, the ship is still far from being completed. Heavy steel platforms must be put in place for the engines. Special steel supports must be installed to support the long, heavy propeller shafts. Most important, the bulkheads must be built. These modern inventions are life savers for ships, and they have saved countless thousands of lives. The bulkheads are steel partitions that extend up from the inside skin of the ship to a point well above the water line. If a ship's side is torn open in a collision, the water can fill up only the space between these bulkheads and will not rush through the entire ship. Many special bulkheads are built for particular jobs. Regardless of whatever bulkheads the ship may have, every ship is required to have a continuous nonpierced bulkhead approximately five per cent of the length back from the stem. This is the so-called collision bulkhead which, in case the ship collides with another vessel or a shore structure, keeps her afloat no matter how badly her bow may be crushed. A bulkhead near the stern is designed to keep water out in case the tubes that house the propeller shaft are damaged. Bulkheads built around the engines and boilers give them extra protection. Although some ships have no doorways through bulkheads, others are equipped with water-tight doors, equipped to shut automatically or to be operated by electricity from the decks above.

Ships that are being built are always surrounded by scaffolding for the workers to walk on. This maze of scaffolding is placed not only outside the ship but inside as well. Over these scaffolds swarm a small army of workers, welders, electricians, riveters, and members of the thirty-six trades necessary to the building of even a small modern ship.

When the dramatic day of the launching comes, a ship may be at almost any stage of completion. Sometimes ships are launched after the outer skin has been put in place and the propeller and rudder installed. Sometimes the ship is completed on the ways. The preparation for the launching is a big task in itself. Usually two giant timbers are placed under the hull, some distance above the keel. These are called the ground ways, and they are heavily greased on top. These timbers slant down toward the water, with their ends projecting into it. To these

*Pride of the Dutch Merchant Marine, the* New Amsterdam *leaves Rotterdam bound for New York.*

timbers are fastened two other big timbers, the sliding ways. Then a cradle is constructed which fits up around the bottom of the ship. Before the launching the whole weight of the ship must rest in this cradle. To make this transfer of weight from the keel blocks, big wedges are driven between the launching ways and the cradle timbers until the ship is lifted clear of the keel blocks. Another method is to use powerful hydraulic jacks to lift the ship. Still another way is to use "cushion boxes," which are really boxes of sand placed on top of each keel block before the ship is built. To get it into the cradle, the sand is released from the boxes and the ship settles into the cradle.

Once the ship is in the cradle, the keel blocks are taken away, and the timbers holding the ground ways to the sliding ways are removed. The sliding ways and the cradle begin to move down the greased ground ways. The ship, snugly settled in the cradle, naturally slides too. Soon there is a tremendous splash as the ship, cradle, sliding ways and all, hits the water. Another ship has been launched!

CHAPTER 3

# THE STORY OF BATTLESHIPS

*The modernized battleship* Pennsylvania *showing her tripod masts.*

THERE are ships everywhere, as far as the eye can reach. The ships that make up the task force are ranged in orderly gray ranks. Steadily they plow through the calm Pacific, straight into the zone of danger. The cruiser screens are out; the destroyer flotillas are closing up.

In the forefront of the center column steams the monster flagship of the task force, a forty-thousand-ton battleship, the most costly and intricate craft ever to sail the seas. Aboard the flagship, dozens of enlisted men are already at the radio keys and earphones. From the planes of the aircraft carrier, some hundred miles ahead, messages are already coming through the air. "The enemy has been sighted!" the age-old message is now heard.

In accordance with immemorial sea tradition (and there are hundreds of traditions in every well-regulated navy), that thrilling message from the speeding observation planes is the signal for a general call to "chow" for all men, so that there will be no weakness from hunger in the grueling hours to come. This vital matter attended to, the general alarm bell starts ringing.

*An American battleship plows ahead through heavy weather.*

Now comes the order, "Clear ship for action!" Light bulbs are unscrewed; railings snapped down; everything that is movable is made fast. Sweating, half-naked turret crews test out ammunition elevators, buzzers, and telephones. Dressing rooms are made ready. The chaplain takes his post. The huge battlewagon's speed climbs up and up—twenty knots, twenty-five knots, thirty knots. Spotter planes take off and within a few minutes are calling back vital information to the mother ship. The battle will soon be joined, even though the ship itself may never come within actual sight of the enemy.

This is a far different picture from the old-time sea battles that took place in the early years of our country. The modern battleship (or "capital ship," to give the vessel its correct title) has grown until there is scarcely any resemblance between it and the sixty-gun frigates that won the freedom of the seas for our country.

The function of the battleship has also changed. It is no longer required to sail alongside its opponent until the gunners can see the faces of their enemies through the open portholes, and then fire broadside after broadside until one or both vessels are shattered hulks. Today the battleship is an observation post; an attacking force of inconceivably terrific hitting power; a strongly fortified position; an antiaircraft section; batteries of light, heavy, and antiaircraft artillery; a field hospital; and brigade headquarters all rolled into one. In addition, the modern battleship must be constructed so strongly that it can stand up under direct hits from bombs, torpedoes, and the heaviest shells, and still stay afloat and keep on fighting.

Warships have sailed the seas ever since those very early days when the long, narrow biremes of the Phœnicians, beaked like great sea monsters, sailed the Mediterranean and won control of that inland sea for the adventurous men from Sidon and Tyre. Gradually the warships grew larger. In Greek and Roman times there were triremes and even vessels with five and six banks of oars. By A.D. 1500 the highly specialized fighting ship with its muzzle-loading cannons arranged in tiers, never used as a merchantman or a transport, had made its appearance.

With the coming of the American Revolution the heavy three-masted cruiser, or frigate, carrying sixty and more guns, ruled the waves. Some-

*H.M.S.* Victory, *used as a naval barracks for enlisted men studying for commissions.*

*Nelson's flagship, H.M.S.* Victory, *led the British warships that defeated Napoleon's fleet at Trafalgar.*

time later, during the time when Lord Nelson sailed the seas and defeated all comers, the lumbering three-deck "ships-of-the-line," mounting more than one hundred cannons great and small and carrying as many as seven hundred men, were the standard battleships.

Between the time of Lord Nelson and his famous flagship *Victory* and the start of our Civil War, there were numerous experiments in battleship construction. Some nations were so progressive that they even took advantage of the power in the newly developed steam engine, combining steam and sail in one battleship, so that the propeller could help move the ship when the wind failed. France experimented with an armored warship, the *La Gloire*, in 1859, but naval experts thought very little of the idea of hanging plates of iron over the stout wooden sides of a warship. It remained for the United States to startle the world and to inaugurate a new era in the building and design of battleships.

It was in the early days of the Civil War, on Saturday, March 8, 1862, that the Union seamen on board a number of fine frigates and gunboats, which were successfully blockading Richmond, were dumfounded to see a monstrosity steaming into Hampton Roads. Small wonder that those men stared. The ship which was causing so much consternation had once been the United States frigate *Merrimac*, burned to the water's edge and sunk the previous April when the Federal soldiers had hastily abandoned the Norfolk Navy Yard. The Confederates had raised the hulk and altered it into something unique in the annals of sea warfare.

The *Merrimac*, now renamed the *Virginia*, had originally been built as the finest steam-and-sail frigate in the United States Navy. Now her charred hull had been cut all the way down to the water line; sails and masts had been done away with; and on the central section of the gun deck there had been erected a huge, slanting-sided casement of thick timbers and iron plates that completely enclosed all who worked the guns and the ship. The armor was four inches thick, a double skin of two-inch plates bolted together. There were six gun ports on each broadside and one each at bow and stern. To the submerged prow of the *Virginia* was bolted a heavy cast-iron ram—a holdover from the days of the triremes on this first of all true ironclads!

Most of the Confederate naval officers had sworn that the *Virginia* would sink of her own weight. The Union seamen soon wished that she would! The *Virginia* sailed straight at the Federal sloop of war *Cumberland*, firing explosive shells instead of round shot. Every Union ship that could bring guns to bear pounded the *Virginia's* sloping sides with solid ball and shells, but the shot rebounded like hailstones from a brick wall. The *Virginia* rammed the *Cumberland*, leaving in the ship's wooden side a gaping wound big enough to drive a horse and cart through. Sweeping down on the frigate *Congress*, the *Virginia* soon completely overwhelmed her, and the *Congress* eventually blew up. Other Federal ships, trying to run from this armored menace, went aground and hung there helplessly. The changing tide, however, called a halt to further fighting that day. When the *Virginia* steamed back to her base, the Union Army, and even officials in Washington, knew that only a miracle could save the entire Federal fleet from annihilation at the guns of this invulnerable monster.

*The battle between the* Monitor *and the* Merrimac.

That miracle happened. Returning the next day to complete her mission of sinking the helpless wooden ships in Hampton Roads, the *Virginia* was met by the oddest looking craft afloat. It was Captain John Ericsson's *Monitor*, and on that one frail craft were pinned all the hopes of the Northern navy.

The *Monitor's* armor was made of iron plates, five inches thick. The boat was 172 feet long and 41 feet across at its greatest beam, and had been placed on top of a wooden hull 50 feet shorter than the iron one. The deck was little more than a foot above the water line and was sharply pointed at bow and stern. Amidships there was a revolving turret 9 feet high and 20 feet in diameter built of eight layers of 1-inch iron plates and housing two 11-inch guns. This revolving turret was one of the most revolutionary developments in naval gunnery since the introduction of gunpowder. Always before, men had turned the ship to change the direction of their gunfire. The gunners aboard the *Monitor* turned the gun! Now the Confederates gasped with surprise.

For more than four hours those two primitive ironclads stood toe to toe and slugged it out. Crowded inside the small turret, Lieutenant Greene and some twenty men fired the *Monitor's* two smoothbore eleven-inchers as if they had been a pair of pocket pistols. The *Virginia* lashed this "Yankee cheese box on a raft" with all the metal she could throw. The Southern vessel even tried to ram her foe, but without

*One of Uncle Sam's most powerful battleships, the* South Dakota *drops anchor off Iceland's coast.*

*Battleships of the United States Seventh Fleet moving in formation in Lingayen Gulf, Philippine Islands.*

success. The *Monitor* answered with a steady stream of shells. There was little visible harm done to either ship. The shells exploded harmlessly against the stout iron walls, although a seaman in the *Monitor's* turret was knocked cold when he thoughtlessly leaned against the iron wall at the exact instant a shot struck it.

The battle was a draw, even though it was one of the most decisive naval engagements ever fought. Neither ship was badly damaged, and only a few men were hurt. Eventually both vessels withdrew to take on fresh supplies of ammunition but did not renew the struggle. What that battle did to the navies of the world is summed up in a statement that appeared the next day in the London *Times:* "Whereas yesterday England had 149 first-class ships fit for service, today we have only two." The ships referred to were experimental wooden ships protected in vital spots with iron plates.

Wooden warships were doomed. Then there developed an unlooked-for situation. Each of the large naval powers began to build ships, first with heavier guns to penetrate their enemies' armor plate, and then with increasingly thick armor to stand up under the shells of the enemy. Finally, in 1872, the Italians designed the *Duilio.* In this ship, all armor was concentrated around the central portion, leaving the ends unprotected. The ends, however, were divided into tiny cells so as to resemble two rafts. By saving weight in armor in this manner, the Italians were able to put armor 22 inches thick amidships and mount four monster naval rifles weighing 60 tons each.

Not to be outdone in this armament race, the British immediately set about building the *Inflexible*. Instead of mere 60-ton guns, this ship was provided with four muzzle-loading 80-ton guns. Then, to protect the vessel from the fire of the Italians, a terrific total of 24 inches of armor was packed onto the warship!

*A veteran of Trafalgar, the British warship* Implacable, *at her moorings at Portsmouth, England.*

The Italians rose grandly to the occasion. They ripped out their 60-ton guns and installed the largest guns ever conceived at that time—rifles that weighed 100 tons each! At this point the British gave up, explaining that at the moment they had no machinery with which to forge guns larger than 100 tons. It was reported at the time that they were afraid to pile any more weight on the already overloaded *Inflexible* for fear the ship would sink!

So the race went on, with warships growing more unwieldy and consequently more unseaworthy as the years passed. By 1890 things were in a turmoil. There was no agreement among the naval authorities of the world as to what constituted a good warship of *any* class, nor what the specific duties of each type of vessel should be. Then it was that the great American naval theorist, Alfred Thayer Mahan, began to make himself heard. His ideas—that a warship should be seaworthy, able to fight, and able to sail—were incorporated into the designing and building of warships. By 1898, when we fought Spain, the American navy was small but incomparably better than the Spanish collection of swift cruisers and torpedo boats, although some European authorities felt that the efficiency of the American navy was questionable.

Since that time, everything about the battleship has been improved. Accurate, breech-loading naval rifles have been perfected; ammunition has been improved and standardized; fire-control mechanisms (which cost a million dollars to install on a modern ship) were invented; and new ways were devised to make armor harder and stronger—to name just a few of the improvements.

Certain naval habits died hard, however. In 1905 the British started to build a warship named *Dreadnought,* which was the first ship *not* to carry boarding pikes! For many years the heavy guns of warships had made boarding in the old-time manner not only obsolete but out-and-out suicide. Yet in 1905 the British crews were still being trained in the boarding tactics used by the buccaneers and were also being drilled in the use of the cutlass.

Today the battleship is the most intricate mechanical device ever

*Like most other battleships the U.S.S.* Tennessee *carries seaplanes as scouts.*

*"Mighty Mo" the Navy calls her—the battleship* Missouri.

constructed by men. In order to get some idea of the vastness, yet orderliness, which exists on one of these vessels, let us now take an imaginary trip on board an average, modern American battleship.

To begin with, the ship will weigh between 35,000 and 45,000 tons; cost more than $65,000,000; and have at least nine 16-inch rifles each weighing about 125 tons. The ship is armored with 18 inches of alloy steel armor plate in its most vital sections; has several scouting planes that can be hurled aloft from catapults; and can toss 20 tons of steel at targets 20 miles away every minute when in action. Some 1,500 or more men find their homes aboard a battlewagon.

For the needs and conveniences of the men and officers, the average American battleship is stocked with such items as 30 typewriters; a complete soda fountain; 20,000-pound anchors; several barber chairs; a movable pulpit; motion-picture projectors; a garbage incinerator; and a printing press. It takes a lot of machinery to keep a battlewagon going efficiently. There are the mechanical conveyors and hoists to bring powder and shells into the turrets from the magazines hidden deep down in the ship. There is machinery that will whirl the giant turrets around at will; enormous steam turbines that propel the entire ship through the seas at a speed of 30 knots; and intricate electrical fire control. And, of course, there are complete machine shops for repairing anything that may break or wear out. All this machinery and other paraphernalia turns the battleship into something which is not adequately described by the names "Floating Fortress," "Floating Factory," or even "Floating City."

The modern American battleship is about 650 feet long, and it swells to the truly amazing width of over 100 feet amidships. There are only two decks that run the entire ship's length above the water line, although numerous passenger liners such as the *Queen Mary* have as many as six. The massive superstructures are not used as living quarters; instead, they hold navigating bridges, fire-control towers, workshops, and signal stands. Small wonder, then, that designers tell us that it requires thirty tons of blue prints to produce a battleship!

In the space below decks, room has to be found for a fair-sized city of men, including shoe cobblers, barbers, tailors, printers, dentists, soda jerkers, and many others. Because there are different classes of men aboard ship, the arrangement of the living conditions is much more complicated than it otherwise would be. Each separate class of the men has to have its own private mess quarters, galleys, recreation rooms, and even shore-going boats.

Feeding the members of a battleship's crew is no easy job, either. There may be 100 tons of beef aboard for one cruise. Enough loaves of bread pop out of the ovens in the battlewagon's bakery each week to feed a town of 8,500 people for an entire day. The bakery turns out an average of 3,800 loaves of bread, 700 pies, and nearly 10,000 cookies

*The U.S.S.* New Mexico *fires her 14-inch guns at Japanese defenses on the island of Guam.*

each week. For drinking and for sanitary purposes, as well as to supply the boilers and engines, about 120,000 gallons of water must be distilled each day.

Since the main purpose of the battleship is to inflict heavy damage on the enemy, let us take a quick look at the armament on the vessel before watching the ship go into action. The 14- to 16-inch rifles make up the main battery of the modern battlewagon. The 16-inch guns, however, are generally placed only on the 45,000-ton ships. These guns are arranged in double, triple, and even quadruple gun turrets. The triple arrangement seems to be favored for the larger battleships. In this system there are two turrets forward, the second from the bow being high enough so that it can discharge its guns over the first. In this way, two-thirds of the ship's great striking power is concentrated forward so that the ship can deliver crushing blows upon a fleeing enemy. A 16-inch gun will shoot a projectile weighing some 2,500 pounds for a distance of some 45,000 yards.

On some ships, the secondary armament consists of twenty 5-inch guns that hurl a 50-pound shell. On other ships, the 5-inchers have been replaced with batteries of 6-inch guns. Then there are various combinations of antiaircraft guns, heavy machine guns, light machine guns, and other weapons. For some years, now, the idea of how best to arm a battleship has been changing. For instance, the *New Mexico* has two forward turrets of three heavy rifles each, and the same number of turrets with the same number of guns aft, making a total of twelve heavy guns instead of the nine carried by the *North Carolina*.

The heavy guns in the turrets are loaded by first inserting the huge steel projectile, and then following it with several bags filled with the explosive charge. The bags containing the powder are made of raw silk because this material burns quickly and completely. Thus there are no glowing shreds of cloth which, when the gun's breech mechanism is opened to permit reloading, may cause an explosion that could easily wreck the entire turret.

To protect the rest of the ship from such a catastrophe, each turret has its barbette. The barbette is a cylindrical steel citadel that houses the turret proper, the gun machinery, and the ammunition hoist. The chief purpose of a barbette is to prevent enemy shell fire from penetrating into the handling rooms. If a fire should occur within the barbette, it would only be prevented from reaching the magazine by the flame doors. Such fires may be accidental or caused by an enemy shell. A hoist carries the powder bags and projectiles from the magazine in the depths of the ship into the individual turrets. Here the ponderous shells are handled mechanically.

Now that we have had a brief glimpse of the entire ship, let us return to the scene of action into which our ship was steering. We have seen that the vessel's 16-inchers can theoretically hit a target at the immense range of from 35,000 to 45,000 yards. However, actually doing so under conditions existing on the ocean at the time of battle is rendered uncertain by innumerable obstacles. If a heavy wind is blowing, even a 45,000-ton battlewagon will be an unsteady firing platform at the best. In the old days of wooden ships and muzzle-loading cannon, gun crews often misjudged the roll of their ship and discharged an entire broadside into the waves, having fired on the down-roll rather than on the upswing. A pitching battleship can easily throw its main guns off the target area by an even greater amount unless the conditions are taken into account when getting the range.

Then, too, the atmospheric conditions that exist around the ship are not the same as those in the upper regions of the air, where the shells do most of their traveling. Neither is the atmosphere the same around the enemy's fleet, fifteen or twenty miles away. If the weather conditions vary to any extent, then the flight path of the shell becomes such a complex curve that no mathematician could ever figure it, especially during a battle. Since the foe is not in sight, gunnery is dependent on spotter planes. These planes may be shot down, or the enemy's ships may be hidden by an overcast, whereas the ceiling may be high over our battleship.

Yes, the power of our battleship's broadside is staggering, but getting it on the target is a problem beset with many difficulties. To see how the modern miracle of accurate naval gunnery at immense ranges is brought about, we shall first have to go far down in the ship and enter

*A coxswain on a battleship pipes the crew to attention over the loud speaker system.*

*The captain of the* Missouri *giving commands from the navigating bridge.*

a highly secretive room. Constant information comes into this room from the fire control (gunnery) radar that is located about 120 feet above the water line and gives the range and compass bearings (direction) of the target. Messages come, too, from the enormous range finders that are installed in turrets and whose twin sights, spaced more than 40 feet apart, form the base of an isosceles triangle that has the target for its apex. Messages also arrive from the navigator, high up on the bridge, who reports changes of course and bearings; from the engine room, where reports are sent concerning the engine's revolutions; and, most important of all, from the radio hut where reports from the spotter planes are received, providing that the planes are still in the air. Each one of the individual feeding points is important in itself, but the plotting room far down in the ship's vitals is more important than any. Here is where all the information is put together in an attempt to hit the target.

The range-finder range must be corrected for atmospheric conditions and other elements until the "gun range" is found. Then, from the ship's speed and bearing in relation to the target ship, there is figured a "rate of change of range." That is, since at any moment either of the two ships may change course or speed, there are fresh mathematical problems to be worked out—a new rate of change of range—every time such a shift takes place.

We must now go topside from the plotting room to the director post, which may be located in the bulging quarters atop the cage. In this vital post, alongside the azimuth-recording and the deflection-recording instruments, there is a "master sight." This master sight, with the help of all the information passed up from the plotting room, tries to keep exactly on the enemy.

As the master sight is pointed and trained, its tiny motions are transmitted by means of indicators to the turrets, which by this time have rolled around in their barbettes to point approximately at the enemy. In the turrets, the gun captains and gun layers follow the instructions received, until their guns are trained precisely according to the angles indicated. The men behind the guns no longer fire them, however. Up in the tower, the control chief waits for that instant when the ship has leveled off after making a roll and then presses the trigger which releases an entire salvo.

As in land artillery practice, the gunnery chief tries to "straddle" the enemy with salvos and then find the proper range between. Generally he does not fire the entire weight of the ship's primary batteries until he is well on the target.

The entire problem of gunfire on board the battleship is complicated by the fact that the vessel may have to swerve suddenly to escape a

*First of the Navy's super battleships, the 45,000-ton* Iowa.

torpedo, a maneuver which will throw all aiming out of gear; or an enemy shell may blow up the entire control system. In this case, other means of fire control will have to be substituted.

The other batteries of the battlewagon—the 5- or 6-inch guns which are particularly effective against destroyers; the antiaircraft guns; the multiple pompons—all have their separate director posts. These systems, too, must have their emergency setups. Moreover, arrangements have to be made to keep up communications throughout the ship by signaling, or by runners in case (as frequently happens) the telephone cables or speaking tubes are smashed by enemy fire.

In the middle of all this intricate mechanism, the battleship's commander must at all times keep some idea as to where he is in the battle area in relation to his own ships and to those of the enemy!

Many naval experts claim that the day of the great battleship is over, that these enormous vessels have been rendered obsolete by the bomber and the atomic bomb. Other men, equally expert in this field, claim that the battleship is entering a new era of power and urge the construction of 65,000-ton vessels. Actually, no one really can foresee the future of the battleship.

# CHAPTER 4

# DESTROYERS AND CARRIERS

*A Navy fighter moves through the "nimbus" caused by crystallization of vapor on its propeller tips.*

BATTLESHIPS and their younger sisters, the cruisers, are not the only ships which play an important part in modern sea battles. The swift little destroyers and the great aircraft carriers, with their swarms of deadly aircraft, often outshine the big battleships.

The destroyer well lives up to her name, for she is a deadly fighting craft. She moves fast, carries enormous fire power, and plunges into the thick of battle with a daring that easily makes her one of the most spectacular warships of the modern navy. Watch a destroyer in motion, and you will see the spray hissing high as she knifes through the water, her powerful engines hurtling her 2,200-ton bulk forward at a speed of 40 knots. She is long and narrow, streamlined to produce speed that is impossible in larger ships. Her mobility is one of the characteristics that make the destroyer such a useful sea weapon against planes in the sky, ships on the sea, and submarines under the sea.

*Armed with torpedoes and guns, the destroyer is the greyhound of the sea.*

The modern destroyer, with all her deadly armament, began as a torpedo boat in the Civil War. The Confederate ramming ship, the *Albemarle,* was playing havoc with Union shipping in 1864. Somehow she had to be destroyed. Even though she lay at anchor all through the summer and fall of that year, she was such a menace that Northern shipping was seriously disrupted for fear of attacks by this powerful Confederate ship. Yet there seemed to be no way to reach the craft as she lay in a secure position near the mouth of the Roanoke River. A bold young Union naval officer suggested a plan reminiscent of the daring of young Stephen Decatur when he proposed to burn the *Philadelphia.* "Why not try to destroy the *Albemarle* with torpedoes?" asked Lieutenant William B. Cushing. How could the torpedo be taken within reach of the ship he proposed to destroy? Cushing's answer to that question was that he was sure a ship could be designed to carry one or more torpedoes. At last he was given permission to go ahead, and went to New York to find vessels that could be fitted up as torpedo boats. He selected towboats that were open launches about 30 feet in length, with small engines, propelled by a screw. A 12-pound howitzer was fitted to the bow of each, and a boom was rigged out some 14 feet in length, swinging by a goose-neck hinge to the bluff of the bow. At the end of this boom an iron slide was fitted up to receive the torpedo. The type of torpedo used by Cushing was the spar torpedo, which consisted of a copper cylinder at the bottom of which was a cone containing a fulminate cap. Within the cylinder was a tube running the whole length, in the end of which a grape shot, held up by a trigger pin, was arranged so that a slight pull would remove the pin. The grape would then fall on the cap in the cone and cause it to explode some fifty pounds of powder placed in the space between the outer cylinder and the tube. The spar could be swung under water, and a special air chamber permitted the torpedo to float in an upright position. It was a complicated piece of apparatus, a far cry from the torpedo tubes that launch torpedoes from modern destroyers and submarines. To make it effective, it was necessary, of course, to swing the boom in under the overhang of the vessel being attacked, a most delicate maneuver in which the torpedo boat had to be stopped at just the right point.

For his attack, Lieutenant Cushing selected a dark, rainy night. Cautiously he made his way upstream. His own account of what happened makes interesting reading, especially when compared with the account of a modern destroyer action which is recounted later in this chapter.

We passed within thirty feet of the pickets without discovery, and neared the vessel. I now thought that it might be better to board her, and "take her alive,"

*A destroyer shows its seaworthiness during heavy weather in the Pacific.*

*A torpedo bomber seeking the enemy leaps from the edge of a carrier's deck.*

having in the two boats twenty men well armed with revolvers, cutlasses, and hand grenades. To be sure, there were ten times our number on the ship, and thousands near by, but a surprise is everything, and I thought if her fasts were cut at the instant of boarding, we might overcome those on board, take her into the stream, and use her iron sides to protect us afterwards from the forts. Knowing the town, I concluded to land at the lower wharf, creep around, and suddenly dash aboard from the bank; but just as I was sheering in close to the wharf a hail came, sharp and quick, from the ironclad, and in an instant was repeated. I at once directed the cutter to cast off, and go down to capture the guard left in our rear, and, ordering all steam, went at the dark mountain of iron in front of us. A heavy fire was at once opened upon us, not only from the ship but from men stationed on the shore. This did not disable us, and we neared them rapidly. A large fire now blazed upon the bank, and by its light I discovered the unfortunate fact that there was a circle of logs around the *Albemarle,* boomed well out from her side, with the very intention of preventing the action of torpedoes. To examine them more closely, I ran alongside until amidships, received the enemy's fire, and sheered off for the purpose of turning, a hundred yards away, and going at the booms squarely, at right angles, trusting to their having been long enough in the water to have become slimy—in which case my boat, under full headway, would bump up against them and slip over into the pen with the ram. This was my only chance of success, and once over the obstruction my boat would never get out again. As I turned, the whole back of my coat was torn off by buckshot, and the sole of my shoe was carried away. The fire was very severe.

The captain hailed us during a lull of the firing, again demanding what boat it was. All my men gave comical answers, and mine was a dose of canister from the howitzer. In another instant we had struck the logs and were over, with the headway nearly gone, slowly forging up under the enemy's quarter port. Ten feet from us the muzzle of a rifle gun looked into our faces, and every word of command on board was distinctly heard.

My clothing was perforated with bullets as I stood in the bow, the heel jigger in my right hand and the exploding line in the left. We were near enough then, and I ordered the boom lowered until the forward motion of the launch carried the torpedo under the ram's overhang. A strong pull of the detaching line, a moment's waiting for the torpedo to rise under the hull, and I hauled in the left hand just cut by a bullet.

The explosion took place at the same instant that one hundred pounds of grape, at ten feet range, crashed among us, and the dense mass of water thrown out by the torpedo came down with choking weight upon us.

The attack succeeded. The *Albemarle* was sunk, and the torpedo had won a place in the modern navy. Our first special torpedo boat was quite fittingly named the *Cushing* when she was commissioned in 1890. During the Spanish-American War torpedo boats were made much larger, and the name destroyer came to be applied. The torpedo-boat destroyer of that period was a small craft with a displacement of only about 325 tons. By the time the United States entered World War I, our Navy had 52 destroyers fit for service. These destroyers had grown to a length of something like 315 feet, displaced 920 tons, and had 4 torpedo tubes as well as four 4-inch guns. They could travel at 35 knots. They were good, sturdy fighting ships, these World War I destroyers, and they turned in a grand record of success in battle. They guarded the convoys that crossed the Atlantic, fought submarines, protected the Grand Fleet, and harried the enemy wherever his ships were found. Impressed with the great fighting capabilities of the destroyer, our Navy rushed to build 238 of them during World War I. A few of these

*Planes from the aircraft carrier* Enterprise *destroyed many Japanese warships.*

*Testing a new Navy destroyer by making her travel full speed astern.*

were completed during the war, but most of them proved their worth in World War II. Fifty of them went to hard-pressed Britain in 1940, when that country stood fighting with her back to the wall.

In 1940 the United States began a big building program to produce the modern super-destroyer of the *Fletcher* class. Go aboard a modern destroyer of this class, and you will find that it is an astonishingly efficient and complicated fighting machine. Every destroyer is divided into four sections, lettered *A*, *B*, *C*, and *D*. Below deck in the *A* section, which is forward, are located the quarters of the chief petty officers, fuel oil tanks, underwater sound room for the detection of submarines, the forward magazine. On deck are two 5-inch guns and the bridge with the forward director station. The *B* section contains the boiler rooms, fuel, and fresh-water tanks, storerooms and workshops. Below deck in the *C* section are the engine rooms, distilling plant, generators, and pumps. On deck are the all-important torpedo tubes. The *D* section, located aft, contains some living quarters, storerooms for food, more magazines, and more fuel oil tanks. On deck are three more 5-inch guns, and far aft are the racks that contain the "ash cans," the deadly depth bombs used to destroy submarines.

The modern destroyer depends upon her speed for her usefulness in battle. Her ability to charge through the water at a speed of forty knots is made possible by amazing power plants that use high temperature steam. In the twin engine rooms of a destroyer are powerful steam boilers that develop steam superheated to 725 degrees, with a pressure of 600 pounds. Every hour these boilers convert 150,000 pounds of water into steam. This steam thunders through turbines at 150 feet a second, driving against the razor-thin blades with the fury of a hurricane. The blades are thus made to spin at enormous speed, and their spinning turns the crank shaft, which can send the destroyer racing forward at speeds that make other ships look slow by comparison.

Although her torpedoes continue to be an important part of her armament, the modern destroyer carries a formidable array of other weapons. A destroyer's complement of 5-inch guns, of which there will be five or more, can hurl some twenty shots a minute at sea or air targets. On some destroyers there is a plotting room, which is always found on battleships and cruisers. In this room are all the electro-mechanical instruments that permit miracles of marksmanship.

It takes a hardy sailor to stand the rolling of a destroyer in heavy seas. Because of her long, knifelike shape, her narrowness in proportion to her length, the destroyer rolls far over on her sides. In the chart house of any destroyer you will find a clinometer, a device that registers the exact roll in degrees from the vertical. The clinometer of a destroyer will reveal that she quite commonly rolls forty-five degrees from the perpendicular. An old United States destroyer, taken over by the British and renamed the *Skerwood,* at one time claimed to have the world's record for roll when she recorded a sideways tilt of seventy-one degrees. There are many unofficial claims for records, some ranging as high as eighty-two degrees. The destroyer is possessed of other movements besides roll. When seas are high, her bow will dig deep into waves; whereupon her stern will come out of the water. Then the bow will rear high in the air, sending green sea water rolling down over the bridge. On really big waves, she may slide sideways into the trough of waves, only to climb a moment later high on their crests. Going any place aboard a destroyer under such circumstances takes sea legs of the sturdiest variety and a strong grip to hang onto the nearest solid support.

"Pilots, man your planes!" This command could be heard on no other ship in the world but an aircraft carrier. No other ship, with the possible exception of the submarine, has changed sea warfare in general so greatly as has the carrier, wartime's floating airfield.

*Blowers keep this petty officer cool as he stands at the controls in the 110-degree heat of a destroyer's engine room.*

*Hand signals tell the incoming pilot whether he is approaching the carrier's deck properly.*

The seagoing landing fields that today we call "aircraft carriers" have had a skyrocket-like rise to prominence since the day when a converted English Channel steamer, the *Engadine*, sent up an observation plane to scout the opening phase of the famous Battle of Jutland during World War I.

Back in 1910 the U.S.S. *Birmingham* launched the first land plane to be successfully sent aloft from a seagoing vessel. In 1911 the pilot of that same plane made the first successful "carrier landing." In this case, the carrier was simply the U.S.S. *Pennsylvania* with a temporary flight deck erected on it. As early as 1915 the United States Navy's General Board recommended the construction of aircraft carriers. It was not until *after* the First World War, however, that any action was taken on this recommendation. Then the old collier *Jupiter* was made over into one of the very first true carriers in history. It was appropriately rechristened the *Langley*.

At first carriers were designed to be nothing but floating airdromes. Today, however, they are the keystones of any naval task force, and they played a dominant part in naval operations in the Pacific throughout World War II. Neither are the flat-tops, as they are affectionately called by the men who serve aboard them, any longer a defenseless target for enemy guns as they were in the early years of their history. In many ways, among which is the addition of large numbers of improved anti-aircraft guns to their armament, aircraft carriers have been made far more dangerous as weapons of war than they once were.

The prime job of any carrier is a wartime job, in which the carrier's duty is to "get and report vital information and to strike swift blows early in the conflict." To this end, the carriers of today are very fast and extremely seaworthy. When in action, they are now effectively screened by cruiser and destroyer escorts to avoid being badly damaged. They carry large numbers of planes that can make lightninglike smashes at enemy ships and bases. Due to the slashing speed of modern carriers, they can send their planes aloft well out of the reach of even the most powerful naval guns. These planes—equipped to drop bombs, to fight off attacking enemy planes or to launch torpedoes—are an important factor in any kind of naval engagement.

In simple terms, the regulation aircraft carrier is a ship only slightly smaller than a battleship. It averages 750 feet long by 88 feet wide, although some of the later craft are 880 feet long and displace 33,000 tons. The 33,000-ton class is fairly standard for a United States Navy carrier, with the exception of the three large 45,000-ton *Midways*. The carrier has a full-length flat deck on which planes land and from which they take off. The "island" is the only break in the whole deck. This "island" is the superstructure on the starboard side, consisting of stacks, conning tower, heavy guns, and other such necessary gear.

Below the smooth flight deck of the aircraft carrier is the hangar deck. Here, with folded wings, the aircraft are stored between missions. Mammoth elevators connect the hangar deck with the flight deck, permitting the rapid movement of the ship's swarm of planes.

Below these two huge decks is a compact maze of rooms containing engines, boilers, huge stores of aviation grade gasoline for planes and fuel oil for the ship, crew and officer quarters, and the many other elements that go to make up these mighty "eyes" of the modern naval task force. Because of their enormous size, today's carriers can carry an unusually large supply of ammunition, bombs, torpedoes, fuel, and food, thus enabling the ship to keep to sea for long periods of time without having to waste time by stopping to replenish supplies.

Normally, a carrier is equipped with planes for scouting, reconnaissance, bombing, and launching torpedoes. These planes are so designed as to be interchangeable if need arises. Thus a bombing plane can be used for scouting, and a scouting plane can be used for bombing.

*The pilot of a torpedo bomber taking off from the flight deck of the U.S.S.* Saratoga.

The average-sized United States carrier transports between 80 and 100 aircraft, 2,000 or more men, and can make 35 knots. That's a lot of speed for a 30,000-ton ship carrying 500,000 pounds of aircraft!

Aircraft carriers have to meet so many emergencies in modern sea warfare that their design is a "series of compromises." Every knot of speed possible must be gotten out of them, and this makes it impossible to carry as much armor as a battlewagon. In fact, an aircraft carrier's armor is so light that it affords a minimum of protection. This armor is usually placed in the form of a belt over such vital parts of the ship as the ammunition magazines and the engine rooms. Similarly, light armor is placed over the control stations and the gun locations.

The largest of our present carriers are armed with twelve 5-inch antiaircraft guns; and many batteries of machine guns. Other carriers are equipped with sixteen 5-inch guns backed up with numerous 40 mm., 20 mm., and smaller antiaircraft batteries. All in all, today's carriers can deal out terrific punishment—and take it too!

Amazing as are the aircraft carriers in design and construction, the orderly activity that takes place while these ships are in action is even

*Dressed in oilskins, a seaman stands watch as a storm approaches a destroyer.*

*In wartime, destroyers are assigned the task of protecting convoys against submarines.*

more wonderful. It requires a whole host of specialists just to man the flight deck. One of the first things to meet the eye here is the color and variety of uniforms worn by the men.

The plane handlers wear blue jerseys; the chockmen wear purple; gas crews sport red helmets; and the plane directors show both body and head swathed in yellow. The crew manning the arresting gear have green helmets and jerseys and the members of the catapult teams also show green headgear. The fire-fighter crews—armed with foam and salt water hoses and with carbon dioxide extinguishers—wear the time-honored red helmets and red jerseys.

This complex organization is only on the flight deck proper. Below this deck are the equally complex yet smoothly efficient operations of the hangar deck and engineering, the servicing division for ordnance and fuel, the briefing rooms, and the stores and maintenance shops. All these and more contribute directly to the flight operations and are separate from the organization of the ship itself.

Among the many specially engineered devices that have made United States carriers the deadly weapons they are, perhaps the most outstanding is the arresting gear that halts a plane on the deck and that has done much to establish the enviable record of bringing in several squadrons of planes with each plane only half a minute apart. In fact, it is claimed that without this arresting gear—capable of stopping a sixteen-thousand-pound plane in a limited deck space—it would be practically impossible to operate carriers under modern battle conditions.

The arresting gear is somewhat intricate in its structure. At the stern of the flight deck there are twelve single cables stretched at twenty-foot intervals and held about five inches above deck level by inverted V-shaped supports. These supports are known as the "yielding elements" or "deck pendant supports." The cables themselves are the deck pendants. In such a position, the cables can be caught easily by the arresting hook. This hook is a simple, solid steel hook that trails from the plane's tail as it approaches the arresting gear for a landing.

As the plane settles to within a few feet of the landing deck, the hook catches a cable which appears to stretch out like a strong rubber band. Actually, the plane is drawing the cable forward across the deck. This deck cable is attached to a "purchase cable." The purchase cable operates a hydraulic cylinder full of fluid, located on a deck below the flight deck. As the purchase cable is pulled out on the flight deck by the airplane, it causes the ram in a hydraulic cylinder to force fluid out of the cylinder and through a control valve. Thus, it is the liquid that actually absorbs the force of the plane's stopping, and the plane is thereby brought to a halt gradually instead of quickly. After the deck cable has been unhooked from the plane, the whole mechanism can be made ready to stop another plane in less than half a minute.

The record of such famous carriers as the *Enterprise,* the *Hornet,* the *Saratoga,* and the *Franklin* has proved the right of the carrier to a secure place in naval history as a gallant fighting ship.

# CHAPTER 5

# UNDERSEA SHIPS

*Like all American submarines, the U.S.S.* Jack *has a long cruising range.*

IN 1620 a Naval officer appeared before King James I of England. "Your Majesty," he said scornfully, "this man claims that he has a boat that can travel *under* the water."

The king, however, was not so scornful. He was not only interested in the strange invention of one Cornelius van Drebel, a Hollander living in London, but he insisted on being the first passenger on what seems to have been the world's first true submarine. It was a quaint craft, built of wood, covered with leather, with the joints sealed with tallow to keep the water out. It was propelled by twelve rowers, making it an underwater galley. It is not exactly clear from the records just how it was submerged, nor how far. Some experts believe that it traveled along just under the surface; others claim that it was submerged as much as fifteen feet. Old records indicate that, like modern submarines, it had a means of purifying the air, described as "a chemical liquor which would speedily restore to the air such a portion of vital parts as to make it again fit."

The story has it that in this device King James made a trip down the Thames River. Half a century later, John Wilkins, an Englishman, wrote about the possibilities of the submarine in naval warfare. He commented that the submarine "may be of very great advantage against a navy of enemies, who by this means may be undermined in the water and blown up."

It took American ingenuity to make this prophecy come true. In 1776 an American inventor, David Bushnell, became interested in the

*As a submarine dives, her Diesel engines stop and electric motors are thrown into gear.*

possibilities of constructing an undersea craft. He succeeded in building a curious one-man submarine, which he named the *Turtle*. Its performance won him the title of "Father of the Submarine." His little submarine was equipped with propellers fore and aft. These were turned by the occupant, and their motion drove the craft through the water. The daring Bushnell promptly put his submarine to work by a bold attack on a British vessel. Among the British ships lying at anchor in New York Harbor was the sizable *Eagle*. This craft Bushnell proposed to destroy. A time bomb was attached to the outside of the *Turtle*, manned by Sergeant Ezra Lee, and then the submarine was propelled underwater to a point under the *Eagle*. There Lee started to turn the screw that was supposed to bore into the warship's hull, thus attaching the time bomb. However, it turned out that the drill would not penetrate the tough copper-covered hull. Lee continued to try as long as he dared, knowing that at any minute the bomb would explode. At the last minute he propelled the *Turtle* away from the enemy warship as fast as he could. He had barely reached a safe distance when there was a terrific explosion that did not damage the *Eagle*, but rocked her badly and startled the English seamen who were mystified completely as to the source of this strange blast. Other attempts were made, and, although they did not actually destroy any battleships, they did make the harbor so unsafe that the British ships departed. Bushnell was awarded high honors by General Washington for his services in building this new kind of warship.

The idea of the submarine was a challenging one to many inventors. Soon after the Revolutionary War a great inventor, Robert Fulton, turned his attention to undersea navigation. Ten years before Fulton startled the spectators along the Hudson River with his successful steamboat, the *Clermont,* he succeeded in constructing a successful submarine. He built the craft in France, where he had hopes of selling her to Napoleon as a ship-of-war. The *Nautilus* was a much larger craft than the little round affair constructed by Bushnell. It too was propelled by a screw-type propeller, operated by hand. Although made of wood, the hull was covered with copper plates, and there was a crude conning tower covered with glass. Fulton demonstrated the *Nautilus* for Napoleon, who, for all his military genius, could see no possibilities in the craft. The disappointed Fulton then went to England, but the English were equally unimpressed. Fulton's efforts to sell his submarine to the American Government likewise met with complete failure. The naval experts of the period were blind to the capabilities of the submarine.

The progress of the submarine was slow. During the Civil War various kinds of submarines were built, but they were not very successful. The only one with a victory to its credit was a Confederate submarine, the *David.* Boldly it made its way into the harbor at Charleston, South Carolina, in 1864, and succeeded in delivering a torpedo against the U.S.S. *Housatonic* as she lay at anchor. The *Housatonic* was fatally struck, and sank. As the *David* turned to escape after her victorious mission, something went wrong with one of the crudely designed hatches, and water burst into the submarine, drowning her six-man crew. Even though steamships had become familiar craft and were steadily driving sailing ships from the seas, no one succeeded in applying steam power to submarines of the period. The *David,* like her contemporaries, was propelled by hand, very much in the manner employed by Bushnell in his *Turtle,* built almost a century earlier.

There was a very good reason why steam could not be used under the sea. The designers were baffled by the problem of how to fire steam boilers in a craft running under the water. One inventor found a possible answer in 1880. The English Garrett submarine was steam propelled, a feat accomplished by equipping the craft with a collapsible smokestack.

The method of operation was to have the submarine steam along the surface with her fires burning furiously. Steam pressure was built up fast, to the limit of safety, then the smokestack was taken down and equipped with a water-tight covering. With the boiler doors sealed tight, and the hatches shut, it was possible for the Garrett submarine to steam for a number of miles under the pressure of the accumulated steam. Another experiment in steam-propelled submarines was carried out by a Swedish gun designer, named Nordenfelt, who made a craft that was capable of submerging to a depth of fifty feet. He took a long step toward making the submarine the truly deadly craft it would one day become by installing torpedo tubes.

Meanwhile, a great designer of submarines had appeared on the scene. He was John P. Holland, an Irish-born American who built his first submarine in 1875. It was a cranky ship, with many defects, but Holland courageously determined to perfect the craft if it took him the rest of his life. The United States Navy was interested in his work and finally agreed to have him build a submarine that would embody all the information that Holland had gathered through a series of heartbreaking failures. As work progressed on the *Plunger* in 1895, Holland saw that even yet he had not learned enough. He started all over again to build a workable craft, and at last produced one that satisfied the Navy. It could dive to various selected levels and make a slow but steady forward progress at these levels. It was an extremely hard craft to control, because it rolled and pitched violently. Submarines of the early Holland design were small, only 63 feet long with a beam of 12 feet. Compared with modern giants, which are 300 or 400 feet long, they were tiny.

While Holland was at work on his submarines, another American who had big ideas about this type of craft was also making progress toward a different objective in submarine design. He was Simon Lake, who at first did not think of the submarine as a warship. His idea was to build a submarine that could run on the bottom of the sea. By 1895 he had constructed a fourteen-foot submarine mounted on wheels. It had a hand-operated propeller. In a sense, this craft, which Lake christened the *Argonaut*, was not a true submarine, because it could not operate on different levels under the sea. It was designed to sink to the bottom, where it could run on its large wheels. With the *Argonaut*, Lake actually made several trips on the sea floor of Chesapeake Bay. Eventually the Navy combined the great stability of the Lake submarines with the ability of the Holland submarines to operate at different levels under the water.

Although all navies had some submarines before World War I, it remained for the Germans to turn the U-boat into a truly frightful weapon of war. On September 22, 1914, a little German submarine, the U-9, commanded by Otto Weddigen, performed the astonishing feat of sinking three big British cruisers, the *Hogue*, the *Aboukir*, and the *Cressy*. This was a staggering blow to the British Navy, and it showed plainly that any modern naval force must not only have its own submarines but also must be prepared to fight off enemy submarines. The U-9 was not much of a submarine by modern standards, for its displacement was only 450 tons, and it carried a crew of only 22 officers and men. Yet in spite of its small size it had sunk three powerfully armed cruisers that would have been a match for some of the biggest warships of their time. Submarines grew swiftly in size and deadliness as the First World War progressed.

The modern submarine is a compact, highly efficient machine that often takes fifty or more men to operate it. A 400-foot long submarine costs more than $5,000,000 to construct. Its surface speed is 27 knots; its underwater speed, about 13.

Amidships it has two hulls, with the space between used for ballast and fuel tanks. The hull, which is single at bow and stern, is strong enough to withstand the pressure at 350 feet below the surface. A 15-foot conning tower juts upward amidships. The long narrow deck of the submarine is only 8 feet above water.

If you climb the short iron ladder from the deck to the bridge above the conning tower, you will find a short semiprotected platform with navigating instruments. This is the skipper's post when the ship is on the surface. Descend a ladder through the conning tower hatch, and you will enter the control room, the nerve center of the boat. There you will see the navigating instruments, the master gyrocompass, meters to indicate depth, speed, rudder positions. There are also red and green lights to register whether valves

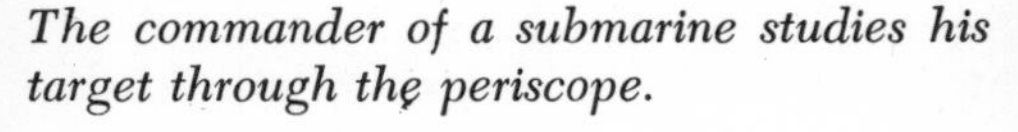

*The commander of a submarine studies his target through the periscope.*

and hatches are opened or closed; large wheels to control the diving rudders, gas indicators, and gauges of fuel and water.

The radio room, a closetlike space, is in a corner of the control compartment. Here the communications officer contacts the submarine's base or other ships while on the surface. Underwater signaling is done with an oscillator that transmits sound waves ten miles or more.

Space is scarce on even the most modern submarines, so you must bend to go through the steel partitions to the other seven compartments of the submarine. One water-tight oval doorway hardly large enough for an average-sized man is the only connection between compartments. Any compartment, in case of trouble, can be sealed off from all the others.

In the bow is the forward torpedo room, with its many breech doors of the tubes from which the torpedoes are loosed. In side racks are stored the reserve torpedoes. In wartime each tube is filled with a torpedo, ready for instant use.

Just back of the forward torpedo room is the forward battery room below whose decks are the great electric storage batteries that furnish power for the ship when it is submerged. At moderate submerged speed this submarine can run nearly sixty miles before its batteries must be recharged. Above the battery storeroom are the surprisingly compact quarters of the officers. The largest cabin, the captain's home, is about six feet square. It contains berth, desk, drawers, and a washbowl with running water. It includes also a compass dial, depth gauge, telephone and other instruments, so that even in his quarters the captain can at once take full charge of his submarine.

The wardroom or saloon of the submarine is a bit longer. At its dining table eight men can be seated. Its cupboards contain the sub's tableware and linens and the short bookshelf that holds the ship's library.

Returning through the control room, you pass directly aft into the small mess room of the crew, furnished with narrow folding tables and settees. The crew must eat in shifts because of the limited space. Under the mess room are the food storage rooms and the ammunition magazines. Back of the mess room is the crew room, jammed with tiers of metal-springed bunks. The compartment cannot accommodate the whole crew, and other bunks are scattered about the submarine wherever space is available. Adjoining the dormitory is the washroom, with its tiny showers.

Backing from the crew space, you enter the engine room with its masses of Diesel engines and electric generators. In the maneuvering rooms farther aft are the electric motors that drive the propellers. At the stern is the after torpedo room, similar to the forward torpedo room. Not an inch of space is wasted on this complex naval machine.

The captain keeps the submarine's position in the water, or makes it dive or rise, by letting water into and out of the ballast tanks. Cargo and passenger vessels have a large reserve of buoyancy so that they can take on heavy cargoes and still be light enough to float safely. Submarines have little reserve buoyancy. On war patrol this buoyancy will increase as the submarine is lightened through consumption of fuel, stores, and the firing of torpedoes, which weigh thousands of pounds. The rule, therefore, is to keep the weight of a submarine the same and equally distributed, to avoid new calculations for changed buoyancy.

The captain sees to it that water is added to the trimming tanks to take the place of weight expended. Compensation for fuel consumed is made automatically. As the fuel, which is stored in eight or more tanks in several groups throughout the ship, is consumed by the Diesel engines, sea water automatically enters through the bottom of the tank, carrying the lighter fuel oil above it and forcing the fuel back to the

*Crew members stand ready at the various controls while the commander looks through the periscope.*

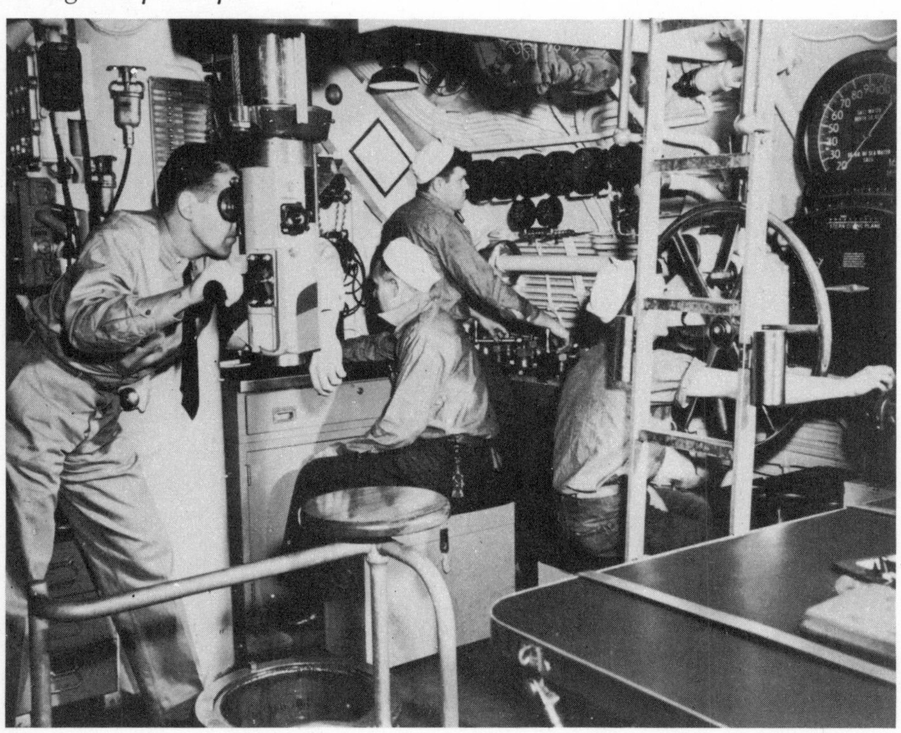

*Besides torpedoes the U.S.S.* Nautilus *is armed with deck guns fore and aft the conning tower.*

Diesels. Ballast tanks that are built into the bow, the stern, and amidships maintain the desired trim or balance of the submarine.

The weight and position of all fuel and supplies aboard are carefully recorded. Compensations are made frequently as these are consumed; so the submarine always remains in trim. Once the diving officer gets "the feel" of his boat, he knows at once if the submarine is out of trim and makes adjustments through the variable ballast tanks. An experienced diving officer can sense differences of a few hundred pounds in a five-million-pound submarine.

On the regular dive, when the Kingston valves are opened to admit the flood of water ballast, the air vents are opened to permit the escape of air. In the quick dive, however, the skipper orders, "Ride the vents!" This means that the flood valves are opened, but the air vents are kept shut to counteract the sharp increase in water pressure.

Both air and water manifolds are operated from the control room, under the direction of the skipper. Here are the depth gauges, a vital instrument on the submarine, for the captain must always know exactly how far under the surface the submarine is. Should it sink to too great a depth, the sub would flatten like a deflated tire.

Two large control wheels in the central compartment turn the flat diving wings which project on either side of the bow and stern from horizontal to an angle of thirty degrees. In diving, as the ballast tanks are flooded, the bow hydroplanes are tilted forward, forcing the bow down, while the stern hydroplanes are turned backward, forcing the stern up. The greater the tilt and the greater the speed of the submarine, the faster the dive.

The control room also houses the aneroid barometer, which indicates the air pressure within the boat itself. This pressure is slight, just enough to make certain that the boat is water-tight and that no air is escaping through some tiny leak. Here, too, is the clinometer, which tells the degree of the list or slant of the vessel.

In the engine room the power sources are compact, light in weight, and powerful. Gasoline engines, similar to those of automobiles, were used on early submarines. But the mixture of gasoline, vapor, and air is highly explosive and several disasters occurred. Today the Diesel engine is used to power all modern undersea boats. The Diesels are operated only when the sub is on the surface. Below the surface submarines are operated by electric motors, on current from storage batteries. Hydrogen gas, a serious danger aboard a submarine, is released during recharging. The battery compartments therefore have their own ventilating system to change the air.

Surface boats sail only in two dimensions, the length and breadth of the seas. In submarine navigation a third dimension is added—depth. In all navigation, a course must be plotted. The speed of the vessel, wind, and current must be taken into account. The location of the ship must be frequently checked and compared with the plotted course.

For a patrol the captain of a submarine plots a course like the skipper of any surface ship. He reckons distances and directions with the help of charts and tables. With his course plotted, the captain allows for deviations to avoid currents, winds, danger from icebergs. At intervals he will determine his position to see if he is on course, using an accurate clock set to Greenwich time, called a chronometer, and a sextant to "shoot the sun" or measure its distance from the horizon. He also uses the compass, direction finder, log, and radio to check on the latitude and longitude of his ship. In wartime, radio must be used with caution lest it tip off the enemy to the position of the submarine. During the day the submarine may have to remain submerged. But measurements may be made at night from observations of the moon and stars.

A magnetic compass gets out of order easily on a submarine, because the steel hull, magnetic fields of motors and wires, all attract the needle. The gyroscopic compass is therefore essential for submarine navigation. Unaffected by the steel of the boat, electric magnetic fields or magnetic storms, the gyroscope compasses give faithful service.

A submarine would have little value in wartime if it had to surface to spot enemy shipping. For then the element of surprise on which it depends for attack, as well as the concealment on which it relies for protection, would be lost. The eye of the submarine, the periscope, enables the boat to see without leaving its hiding place.

Basically, the periscope consists of two mirrors, one above the other, at angles of forty-five degrees facing opposite directions. A horizontal beam of light striking the upper mirror is reflected downward at right angles. The lower mirror catches this image and passes it on at right angles in a horizontal direction to the view of the submarine officers.

The highly perfected modern periscope gives the submarine a wide vision of the surface when the boat is at a depth of fifty feet. To get a view of a large area, a reverse telescope arrangement of lenses is placed in the upper end of the periscope. A prism then bends this light at right angles and sends it down the tube, where another telescope arrangement of lenses, this time in the natural order, restores the view to normal size and, in fact, even magnifies it slightly, making objects one and a half times as large as they really are.

To get a view in the opposite direction, captains of the early submarines would "walk the periscope around," turning it with hand grips. Modern periscopes, through the use of complicated lenses and prisms, provide a full circle of vision.

The mechanical parts of the periscope have also been improved. The early periscope was a single tube running through a stuffing box in the hull. At first it was a fixed tube, but soon it was designed to be raised and lowered. The early tube, however, was slightly bent by water pressure when the submarine traveled at a fast speed and was thrown out of adjustment. The modern periscope is a double tube. The outer tube resists the water pressure, protecting the alignment of the inner tube, which encloses the lens arrangement. Modern periscopes are raised and lowered electrically.

Large submarines carry as many as three periscopes. One of these has special night lenses to counteract the darkness that so often dims the view. Although modern submarines can dive down three hundred feet, the periscope is used only at depths of fifty feet. The maximum depth at which the boat can submerge with the new periscope still functioning is known as the periscope depth. If conditions permit, the captain can bring the boat closer to the surface, increasing the height of the periscope and extending the range of its view.

Recent periscopes are usually seven inches in diameter with the top section decreased to a diameter of some three inches. The periscope is practically unnoticeable at periscope depth where only a foot of tube protrudes above the water. At periscope depth only a near-by view is obtained. Much of the time the observer will see nothing but water because of wave motion. With the entire narrow part above water, however, he may see several miles.

In a naval battle, the captain, after discharging his torpedoes, will usually order a quick dive to three hundred feet and stay there quietly awhile to avoid depth charges. When the sound detectors on the submarine indicate it is safe above, the captain may order the submarine to periscope depth, where he will take a quick look to see whether the coast is clear. If it is, he may rise a little higher to examine the results of his shooting. This underwater shooting depended on his periscope. Through the periscope he spotted the enemy craft and estimated its direction and speed. He based these calculations on the size of the image reflected on a sheet of glass ruled with vertical and horizontal lines. This measuring device of the periscope is called a telemeter. In addition to estimating the direction and speed of the target, the captain must consider the submarine's speed and direction. Only then can he aim the torpedo with any hope of scoring a bull's-eye.

The submarine uses a number of special signaling devices designed for underwater use, so that the submarine can communicate with other submarines and with surface ships. The devices use sound waves, because sound waves travel much faster through water than they do through air.

In wartime, sound waves so high-pitched as to be unheard by the human ear are beamed through the water by the submarine in a supersonic method. When the beam hits an enemy vessel it is reflected back and is received with a detector. By calculating the direction and distance of the ship from these observations, the submarine has a good opportunity to torpedo it. Unfortunately, the device can also be used by the ship to locate the submarine. Then the underwater boat has to face the hazard of depth charges.

Modern undersea craft have crews of more than fifty men. Men are

*Crewmen operating the elevators which regulate the submarine's depth in the water*

*A machinist checks the twin Diesels in the engine room of a submarine.*

needed in the engine rooms, motor room, torpedo rooms, and control compartment. The radio, periscope, diving controls, and innumerable other instruments must be faithfully watched. Men are needed from bridge to galley. Electrician, torpedoman, radio operator, oiler, wiper, and cook, each has his routine duty to perform. Although an oiler's task may seem trivial, it is necessary for the harmonious operation of the whole. For an emergency job, the entire crew might be called to pitch in. Then hours of duty are uncounted.

The danger of undersea operation is exemplified by the United States submarine *Squalus*. On May 23, 1939, she left the Navy Yard at Portsmouth, New Hampshire, for diving practice. The captain radioed his base before diving, according to regulations. When time passed and no message of her surfacing came, the Navy began a search, enlisting many vessels from the Portsmouth area. Meanwhile, the rescue and salvage ship *Falcon* was speeding for Portsmouth from the naval base at New London, Connecticut.

When the *Squalus* made her practice dive, her main engine air supply valve jammed and a flood of water poured through the valve opening. Water-tight doors forward of the engine room were immediately shut, which confined the flood to the rear compartments. Weighted with water, the *Squalus* settled on the bottom at a 240-foot depth. The ship could not be brought up by blowing the tanks.

The captain sent up a signal buoy with telephone connections, then signal floats, which spouted red smoke as soon as they reached the surface. The signals were sighted and contact was made through the telephone buoy. As soon as the *Falcon* arrived, divers went below to clear deck wires and to attach the down-haul cable for the rescue chamber. These preparations required a day. Then the rescue chamber was sent down to the submarine. Almost an hour and a half later the rescue chamber returned with seven of the crew from the *Squalus*. Three other trips followed, and thirty-three of the crew of fifty-nine were saved in the first underwater rescue chamber operation of its kind in history.

The *Squalus* was raised after months of difficult salvage operation, refitted at a cost of about a million dollars, and recommissioned as the *Sailfish*. Events during the Second World War proved the wisdom of this expensive repair job, for with the submarine *Bowfin*, she sank seven Japanese ships.

A sister ship of the *Squalus* was the 1,480-ton *Seawolf*. For the story of what a submarine action is like, we turn to the account of the *Seawolf's* sound man, Chief Radioman Joseph Eckberg, which has been reported by Gerold Frank and James Horan:

> On the seventh night came another urgent message: the Jap force had been sighted. An armada of Jap men-of-war and transports was racing full speed for the Lombok Straits. The *Seawolf* was ordered to meet it head on. We halted our battery charge and at terrific speed knifed our way on the surface northward for the straits, plunged into them, and did not ease our Diesels until the dull mass of Nusa Besar, a small island in the middle of the channel, came into sight. We waited, watched, waited. . . .
>
> "Something one point on the starboard bow, sir!" It was the bow lookout. The time was 2:00 A.M.
>
> "Clear the bridge! Stand by to dive!"
>
> Wang! went the klaxon horn signal. Men tumbled down the ladder, the hatch was wiggled tight, we crash dived, and leveled off.
>
> Now, on sound, I heard pinging all around. We'd gotten into a hornet's nest, all right. We didn't realize it then, but we had penetrated through the outer screen of Japanese destroyers—their first defense, specifically set up to intercept any enemy force—and were in the middle of the Jap task force.
>
> Captain Warder upped his periscope carefully. "It's pitch black up here," he said. "I can't see a thing . . . not a thing."
>
> But in the sound shack, phones pressed against my ears, I heard the chorus of beating screws. Maley, who'd been dozing just before the diving alarm sounded, joined me. His long nose seemed even longer.
>
> "I hear we're really in it," he said soberly.
>
> "You're not kidding," I said. "We've got a whole nest of them up there."
>
> "I understand from the talk that we're heading right in. The old man's waiting until it comes light so he can see what he's doing. He's not interested in these destroyers anyway. He wants the troopships."

Overhead the Jap screws churned the sea. Their sound came down through the water and penetrated the ship's hull. Everyone heard it.

Maley inhaled deeply. The subdued light of the radio shack etched the hollows under his cheekbones. "It's going to be a long day," he said. . . .

At dawn the skipper brought us up to periscope depth. He scanned the sea. "Well," he said. "What do you think of that? Down periscope." Then, to Ensign Mercer: "Jim, there's nothing up there now. Nothing at all. Let me see those charts."

It was evident that the destroyers had spread out and were running an entrance patrol, completely unaware that we were already inside. I was right. We were locked in the straits.

Silence for a moment, then Captain Warder's voice again: "We dove at this point, didn't we? We've been making one-third."

"That's right, sir," came Mercer's voice.

"Up periscope," said the captain. "I don't think I'm lost. I can't spot Nusa Besar. I see some land over there, but I don't know where it is on the chart. Do you suppose this current has thrown us off again? . . . H-m-m-m. Well, we're bound to run into them if we continue up the straits. We certainly can't miss them. There's too many."

We moved on slowly, hour after hour. We were moving north in the straits, but we did not know our exact position. The skipper took frequent periscope observations.

"Aha," he said, some minutes later. "I see the masts of several big ships. They're close to the beach. They're probably where we thought they were, over near that Bali airfield. They look as if they're at anchor. Now, Jim . . . if that's the airfield, mark my bearing." He estimated the distance. "Range, 16,000 yards." Then: "Now we ought to get an idea where we are. Don't sound battle stations yet. I want to get this navigational problem fixed up before I attack. I've got to make sure of what I'm getting into here, and I've got to find a way out."

Minutes passed. The skipper and Mercer were working at the plotting table. This was an important operation for the *Wolf*. If we could stop the Japs from landing on Bali, we could throw them off their time-table and delay their entire East Indies invasion. At this very moment the United Nations were pouring troops and munitions into the vital ports of Moresby and Darwin, building them up as supply bases. Every hour counted.

"All right!" Captain Warder sounded satisfied. "We'll get on the course to close with them. Tell the crew to stand easy. It'll be quite a while yet before we get in to where I'm going to fire."

We maneuvered slowly. We knew we were in treacherous waters and going into still more dangerous ones. Over my phones I heard the roar of shallow water eddying and swirling around the high coral shoals. The *Wolf* was weaving her way with infinite care through a subterranean maze of jagged, razor-sharp reefs, any one of which could rip her hull from stem to stern. The slightest error in navigation would be fatal for all of us.

My watch showed a few minutes after 7:00 A.M. Gus Wright, battle telephones on his ears, was in the after-battery compartment, ready to pass on all orders from the conning tower. We were ready to leap into action. We glided forward smoothly. Suddenly the *Wolf* lurched. The lights flickered. I was thrown off my stool. There was a grinding, grating noise.

"We're aground!" someone shouted.

It echoed thinly through the ship.

Captain Warder's voice said: "All back emergency!"

The *Wolf* shuddered. We heard the grating noise again forward on the keel. Suddenly we were free. Down below we began breathing again.

"Well, Jim," said Captain Warder conversationally, "I guess we just won't go in that way. We'll have to find some other way in here."

We reversed our course. We inched backward. Suddenly, another lurch, a jar, and the *Wolf* was stuck again, this time at periscope depth. Ten full minutes the skipper made use of all the tactics he knew for such an emergency. No one did much talking. We were in a spot. We were trapped, we were lost, and above us prowled Jap warships loaded with depth charges. Captain Warder, at the control-room periscope, scanned the sea. The sun was shining, the day was bright. He could see the ships he wanted to attack, and he couldn't get at them.

"I can't keep this up," he said. "I'll hurt her. She's going to get damaged. There are ships in there, and I've got to get them." He stepped back from the periscope.

"Surface!" he snapped, and shinnied up the control-room ladder like a monkey.

Sitting in the sound shack, I felt my stomach turn over. I went ice cold. For the first time in my life I think I knew absolute, craven fear. Here it was bright daylight, and Captain Warder was bringing us up in the middle of a Jap task force that could blow us to bits with a single salvo.

The *Wolf* broke water. The hatch sprang open. The captain raced to the bridge. I waited instinctively for the first shells to scream over.

Captain Warder's voice came down evenly: "Put two main engines on propulsion. Put two on quick battery charge." Then: "Send raincoats to the bridge."

Nothing made sense any more, and then all at once it did.

As we surfaced, a tropical squall had struck us, as if in the *Wolf's* extremity someone had cast a huge gray blanket over us, shielding us from the Japs. "An act of God," Captain Warder called it later. Dangerous as the surfacing appeared to us below, the skipper was correct in his analysis of what had to be done. If we continued underwater, we might be caught on the coral reefs. Far better to risk getting out of these dangerous waters, with the chance of fighting it out on the surface, than to be set up like a sitting duck on a rock for the Japs.

We ran toward deeper water on the two engines, full speed, for about half an hour, and then we dove. It was our eleventh night out of Surabaya. As soon as we leveled off, I began searching for ships. Something was wrong. The familiar background of water noises was missing. The number two projector was dead. It must have snapped off the end of the second sound shaft when we ran aground. Now the *Wolf* was crippled in sound, badly crippled. There was nothing we could do to fix it. Now sound had only one projector with which to search and find the enemy, look out for other ships, and trace the trail of our torpedoes. I reported it to the captain.

"Carry on the best you can, Eckberg," he said.

We moved in toward the beach. It was now 11:00 A.M. Captain Warder upped periscope. He saw three big transports jammed with Jap troops. He kept up a running report:

"A destroyer over there. . . . He's firing his main batteries. There they go. I can see the burst and flame and smoke. . . . Is he firing at me? He's firing in this direction, all right. . . . He can't see this periscope! . . . Oh-h-h-h. They're firing their antiaircraft! There's something up there. Well, that's fine!" He chuckled. "That

*The helmsman gets instructions from the commander over the submarine's telephone.*

takes the pressure right off us. Now we can really sneak in." Pause. "There's some Jap Zeros there too."

We closed with the transports. We reached a point where the water was so shallow we could go no farther at periscope depth. Captain Warder ordered the *Wolf* swung about so that he could fire from the stern tubes and be headed out at the same time for a swift escape.

"Stand by!" came from the conning tower. Captain Warder coached Rudy at the helm. "Right a little . . . Left a little . . . Steady . . . steady . . . steady . . . steady . . ." This was a long-range shot. It had to be right. "Fire six!" A pause. "Fire seven!" A pause. "Fire eight!"

I picked up the torpedoes as they went.

"They're running hot, Captain," I reported. "I can hear them—"

"Yes, they're running straight too, Eckberg," came Captain Warder's soft voice. "I'm watching them."

A minute later: "Down periscope. Rig for depth charge attack!"

Captain Warder, slow and deliberate, broke in: "Now, Eckberg, here comes a destroyer. I want you to pick up those propellers, and I want you to give me bearings. Give me all the information you can in regard to this ship."

Under his words I heard three distant muffled explosions. Our fish had hit home. I answered him, surprised at my calm voice: "I sure will, Captain. I've got him now. I've got his screws. They're bearing one six zero, they're fast, and they're getting louder."

The whish-sh . . . whish-sh . . . whish-sh of the destroyer's screws was clear in my phones.

"Good!" said the captain.

"He's coming portside, Captain, he's coming fast."

"Very well, Eckberg. Keep talking."

"Aye, aye, sir."

Now every moving thing in the *Wolf*—every bit of machinery, every source of sound—was turned off. The air-conditioning machinery was switched off, lest its sound betray us. The whir of the fans ceased. The blowers stopped. The hydraulic pump jarred to a halt. The whine of the electric generators died away. The men took off their sandals lest a footfall betray us. In the galley the mess cooks silently shifted pots and pans from the stove to the floor, lest an accidental push send them clattering down. Throughout the ship the buzz of conversation stopped. We waited. The heat began to increase. The *Wolf* was as silent as a tomb save for the low grind of my sound controls as I spun dials, worked my wheels frantically to keep the Jap clear in my phones.

Now he was five thousand yards away. I must know where he was every second and where he would be. The perspiration began to roll off me. It seemed as if someone was pouring water down my back.

Four thousand yards . . . three thousand . . . two thousand . . . one thousand . . . The temperature within the *Wolf* was at least 110 degrees . . . five hundred yards . . .

I began to say, "Bearing two five five," but I never pronounced the second five. The first depth charge exploded. Everything suddenly turned upside down. It was the loudest sound I had yet heard. It was as solid as a blow on the skull; it was like a thunderclap between my ears. I found myself on the floor, my stool unturned. Maley was on the floor beside me, scrambling to his feet. We were in a snowstorm—paint chippings and cork from the bulkheads filled the air. Paint flew off corners. Overhead, electric bulbs shattered in their sockets. The lights flickered off, then on again. The wall opposite me billowed in toward me; the force of the concussion was so great it had contracted the *Wolf's* hull like a rubber ball. It was as if a gigantic hand had reached under the sea, grabbed the *Wolf* about the middle, and shaken her.

I was sitting in a puddle of my own perspiration, one hand flung back to break my fall. I tried to get up. I reached forward to grab my bearing-control lever, and an electric shock jarred me from head to toe. I was grounded in my own sweat. I tingled to my fingertips. And all the time from that terrific explosion it seemed that somewhere, deep in my skull, behind my eyes, my brain pan jangled like a struck bell.

All this could have taken only a few seconds. As from a great distance I heard Captain Warder's voice, asking insistently, "Where is he now, Eckberg? Where is he now?"

I put my hands to my phones to adjust them and found them over my temples. I pushed the left phone over my ear—and another charge exploded.

This was even closer than the first, right off the beam of the ship. I can hear today only because the phones were not on my ears. The *Wolf* lurched sharply. There was no screaming, no panic. I listened hard, balanced on the edge of the stool, and I caught the Jap screws again. He had passed our beam. He was going up our port side. He was driving up on the bow. I managed to call out his bearing.

"Good work, Eckberg," said the intercom. "Keep it up. Good work."

A moment later Captain Warder's voice came to me again, surprisingly clear. He had abandoned the conning tower and taken a stool in the control room just outside my shack. The conning tower had been sealed off. Now we could see each other if he leaned to the left and I to the right. Here he could talk directly to me, and from here he could control the *Wolf's* activities.

A third depth charge landed. It wasn't as close. I could hear the Jap's propellers through it. Now more charges, each a little farther away. I was shouting bearings, and Captain Warder was snapping orders.

Our depth gauge had to tell us much. If a charge exploded above us, it drove us down. If the gauge showed eighty feet and a moment later one hundred feet, the charge had exploded above us. If we bounced up, it had exploded under us. The Jap was trying to land them so close that the concussion would rip open the *Wolf's* seams. If he managed to explode one directly under us, we'd ride the bubble of air right to the surface, where he could finish us off with his deck guns.

"She's gone away, Captain," I finally announced.

The skipper passed a hand over his forehead. He clenched and unclenched his left hand. "Dick," he said, "pass the word. Have the mess cooks run coffee through the ship for all hands." . . .

We gulped down our coffee. Then the entire crew began digging into corners looking for leaks. Zerk and Dishman and Snyder were crawling about in grease and slime, and Zerk came crawling out of a corner with a grin to announce, "Well, she held together down here, anyway."

Dishman, who had No. 1 engine, would take no one's word that she was all right. He swarmed around her like a mother hen looking out for her brood, inspecting every nut and bolt, feeling, listening, watching.

Still submerged, we ran for the southern exit of the straits. We thought we had sunk two ships. We knew the *Wolf* had been hurt by the depth charges—probably not badly, but a few air and water lines had sprung small leaks, according to the report from the men crawling about. We wanted to reach the open sea to surface and recharge batteries, to examine the *Wolf's* injuries, and to send a report to the High Command of what we had done. We dared not use our transmitter in the straits because the Japs could put direction finders on us. Out at sea, by the time they determined where we were sending from, we'd be away from there with all the ocean to hide in.

# CHAPTER 6

# PIRATES AND BUCCANEERS

*Archers with crossbows ascend the rigging to battle stations from which they fire their arrows.*

THERE have been pirates on the seas nearly as long as there have been sailing ships to carry cargoes that lawless men might covet. Four thousand years ago the Mediterranean was thickly infested with pirates of all nations of the ancient world. At one time the navy of the then-mighty island nation of Crete succeeded in scourging the pirates from the seas. But when the gay and exciting Cretan civilization was finally blotted out by the barbaric hordes from Europe, piracy again flourished unchecked. In fact, during the reign of the Phœnicians and the Greeks on the sea, the merchants were pirates when trade was dull and honest tradesmen only when it was to their advantage.

When Rome came into power, the pirates practically owned the Mediterranean Sea. They even went so far as to capture Julius Cæsar and hold him for ransom. Cæsar, who at that time was a young man, was returning to Rome from the East. Off the coast of Asia Minor his ship was boarded by the band of ruffians captained by Spartaco, who for years had terrorized that part of the world.

*Favorite pirate tactic was to close in and smash the oars of a ship before boarding it.*

"You'll pay us twenty-five thousand dollars, or we'll slit the throat of every man on board!" roared Spartaco to the owner of the ship, a fat, cowardly merchant.

The young Roman to whom Spartaco gestured in contempt glared at the pirate with eyes that suddenly were like two sword points. "It's plain to be seen that you don't know your business!" snapped the man who later was to become the most famous general in history. "Anyone can tell that I alone am worth fifty thousand dollars!"

In the end, the surprised pirates took Cæsar back to their camp on shore to hold as a hostage while the ship continued on its way to Rome, bearing Cæsar's letter ordering his family to send the fifty thousand dollars to Spartaco.

That rough gang of pirates soon found that the young Roman was a better man than they. He ordered them about at will and dared them to kill him, well knowing that they would not throw away a chance of getting fifty thousand dollars. Cæsar beat them all soundly at fencing, for he was one of the finest swordsmen Rome ever produced. He made them play ball and race with him; he ordered them to tell him stories of their misdeeds; in short, he completely ruled the pirate camp. His bearing at all times was so lordly and superior that not even the roughest pirate thought of disobeying him.

Time after time Cæsar promised to hang them all (there were four hundred in the band) once he was ransomed. The pirates never tired of this "joke." Eventually the ship arrived from Rome, Cæsar was ransomed, and apparently went out of the pirates' lives forever. Later, however, as the pirates feasted in celebration of the fortune they had just received, Roman soldiers surrounded them and captured every one of them without a struggle.

When Spartaco saw the tall slim figure with the cold eyes, he burst into a rage. "He said he'd hang us all, and he will!" the pirate chief cried. That is just what happened. In time, Rome wiped out piracy in the Mediterranean.

Most famous, perhaps, of all the pirates in ancient times were the Vikings, those hardy sea rovers of the north who lived only to fight and plunder. They were the most ferocious warriors of their times and were protected by shirts of stout chain mail and carried heavy spears and five-foot long swords. Between A.D. 700 and 1000 they ravaged Ireland, conquered much of England, besieged Paris on numerous occasions with well-organized armies, and even made their wrath felt on the shore of the Mediterranean, where there was no longer a mighty Roman navy to keep the peace. Ultimately numbers of Vikings gathered together in Constantinople, where they formed the "Varangian Guard," a body of men who protected the emperor from assassins.

Even the bloody deeds of the Vikings are overshadowed by the feats of arms performed by those pirates who looted and robbed during the early days of our own country. Spain had conquered and settled the rich lands of Mexico, Central America, and parts of South America, as well as the islands of the West Indies. From these hot lands poured gold, silver, and precious gems in a torrent such as the world had never seen. Spain soon came to be envied and hated by all the other nations because of this newly acquired wealth.

During the long reign of Queen Elizabeth, a number of daring English sailors—among whom the most noteworthy were Drake, Hawkins, Frobisher, and Clifford—waged a private war against Spain. These men

*A Spanish caravel preparing to sail from Panama harbor with a cargo of gold.*

*Mediterranean pirates fire a broadside at a merchant galley* (left).

fitted out ships and enlisted crews, then captured Spanish galleons and merchant ships on the high seas, and even looted a number of Spanish towns in the West Indies and on the mainland of what is now Central America. These English captains were not regarded as pirates, although their deeds seem to have been piratical enough, because they had the sanction of Queen Elizabeth, who was great enough to challenge Spain's right to own the whole of the New World. Instead, men like Drake and Hawkins were regarded as patriotic soldiers and sailors who served their queen faithfully.

By the year 1600, however, the great age of the Elizabethan "explorers" was over. The cruelty of the Spanish and their disregard for properly colonizing the lands they had conquered had stripped the islands of the Antilles of the greater number of their original riches and population. For example, the once-flourishing island of Puerto Rico was entirely uninhabited in its center and northern sections. Horses, oxen, pigs, and dogs ran wild in this territory; so it was not long before hunters came, the hunters of wild cattle and boars who later were to become the famous "Filibusters" or "Buccaneers."

These hunters were probably shipwrecked seamen, marooned sailors, or runaways. No matter what their nationality, English, French, or Dutch, they were all wild fellows. In the early 1600's they settled on the north coast of Haiti and in Puerto Rico, as well as on other smaller islands that had been completely abandoned.

The men lived in groups of from two to five in huts built of logs, brush, and hides. They had neither wives nor children, and they had no possessions save their weapons and a few cooking utensils. Even these things, however, were considered common property. They had certain unwritten laws, the highest of which was comradeship. Neither huts nor chests were locked and all quarrels had to be settled by a duel.

These men cured the meat of the animals they killed by smoking it over fires in a manner they had learned from the Caribbean Indians. The Indians called meat smoked in this manner "bucan" and to the white men the process came to be known as "buccaneering." The word was later applied to the hunters themselves, who became "buccaneers." But at first, the buccaneers were nothing but hunters and butchers.

The buccaneers had a kind of uniformity in the way they dressed, although by no stretch of the imagination could the clothes they wore be called a "uniform" as we know uniforms. The buccaneer of those days wore a Spanish hat, the brim of which had been carved away except for a peak over the wearer's eyes to protect them from the fierce sun. A coarse cloth shirt hung down over knee-length trousers. He wore leather boots and a wide belt into which he thrust his butcher knives, powder flask, and other possessions. His main piece of armament was his long, heavy-bore gun, which he carried at all times. These guns were famous for their power and accuracy and the heavy musket balls they fired.

At first the buccaneers ate most of the meat they prepared. Later they traded some of it to smugglers and other lawless men for ammunition, knives, and money, since this smoked meat was excellent food to carry on a long sea voyage. Thus trade developed, and the numbers of the buccaneers increased so rapidly that soon Spain decided that these wild men were a menace to Spanish possessions. So Spain began to wage war on the hunters, killing many of them and exterminating all the wild cattle from many of the islands in the West Indies.

In revenge, the buccaneers began to chase the Spaniards as well as the wild oxen; thus was started a colonial war that lasted nearly one hundred years. One of the first concerted moves the buccaneers made was to select a base from which they could make their raids on the

Spanish. They chose the island of Tortuga, which stands out of the water like a fortress. It can be approached only from the south, where there is a bay, flanked on either side by steep headlands, so deep as to be suitable for all sizes of ships.

Soon a colony was established on Tortuga, where the buccaneers traded what smoked meat they could produce to smugglers and to the seamen on English and French ships that called there to get rid of smuggled goods. Finally, a French trading company sent a man named Bertrand d'Ogeron to Tortuga who united the buccaneers. Under the influence of this D'Ogeron, Tortuga and the buccaneers flourished.

When the buccaneers decided to go in for piracy, they lived under the same general rules that had served them while they had been hunters. A group of them would elect the greatest rogue among them as captain. He commanded only during the action, however, and at other times was no different from the rest of the men. The band, which at first never numbered more than twenty or thirty, would procure a large native canoe by one means or another and put out to sea.

The equipment of the buccaneers was primitive but effective. They took their muskets, pistols, and long knives. They had no cannon, and at that period probably would not have known how to load and aim it properly even if the canoes had been large enough to stand up under the firing.

The buccaneers usually took along a good supply of food, but were never able to ration themselves. Consequently, they often ate up everything they had during the first few days and literally starved for the remainder of the voyage. Life was hard on the outbound trip. The canoes were so crowded that there was little if any room in which to lie down. If the craft boasted a shelter or cabin, it was turned over to the officers. During the day the men would take turns sitting on the oar bench and row with a long, steady stroke for hours on end, for most of the buccaneers were stronger even than ordinarily strong men and were accustomed to the terrible heat of that part of the world.

A good lookout was kept for ships, and true buccaneers never attacked any but Spanish craft. The steersman tried to keep the masts of the ship in a straight line and approach the quarry from the stern, where at best only a couple of "stern chasers" could be brought to bear on the pirates. In those days naval guns could not be swung about at will; the entire ship had to be turned.

The pirates sent their best shots to the prow of their canoe, where the musketeers kept up a continual fire, shooting through open portholes and at every man who showed himself on board the ship. When the canoe had run alongside the quarry, the buccaneers swarmed aboard, long knives held in their teeth just as they are portrayed in pictures.

Once on board, these terrible fighters soon swept all opposition aside with their knives and pistols and that famous weapon of boarding parties, the cutlass. The cutlass of the buccaneers was a wide-bladed, curved sword with a basketlike hilt made of leather or steel. It was short enough so it would not hamper a seaman boarding an enemy ship, yet heavy enough so that when swung by a strong arm it easily lopped off arms and heads.

Any prisoners taken by the buccaneers were usually set adrift in a small boat or sold in the nearest port as slaves. Each pirate had the privilege of taking a complete suit of clothes from the prize. The rest of the booty was dumped together and distributed according to the strict buccaneer code. This code declared that a captain should receive six shares; the master's mate, two; and other officers and men in proportion. The first man to sight the prize; the man who struck down the

*Buccaneers aboard a captured vessel make ready to attack a Spanish treasure ship.*

enemy's captain; the first boarder on the enemy's decks, all were given extra awards.

A sort of crude "accident insurance" also existed among these men who so often risked their lives and limbs. If a man lost an eye in action, he was given one hundred crowns or one slave extra. The loss of both eyes meant six hundred crowns or six slaves extra; the loss of both hands or both legs, the same; the loss of a foot two hundred crowns or two slaves; and so on. These shares were passed out before the general division was made. Before the division, however, every buccaneer had to swear that he was concealing nothing from his fellows. If a man swore falsely, he was immediately marooned on a barren island with a small amount of food and ammunition. Marooning frequently meant death by starvation. Few buccaneers were as fortunate as Ben Gunn of *Treasure Island*, who lived for years off the wild goats on his island.

The buccaneers generally sank their own canoe and took over the first prize that was fairly large and well armed. Then they continued their voyage in search of more booty. The men did only the most necessary work, such as making sail, steering the ship, and keeping their arms in some sort of condition.

Quarrels were always settled by duels ashore. The favorite method of fighting was with pistols, the two men standing back to back at a distance of ten paces and turning to fire at the word of command. If both shots missed, they finished the matter with their cutlasses. Another manner of settling such debates was to tie the two men together, leg to leg, and let them argue the question with knives.

The cruise continued until the buccaneers agreed that they had secured enough booty. Then they put in for Port Royal or Tortuga, divided the loot, and turned it into cash among the merchants of the town.

The first important captain among the buccaneers was an ex-slave named Olonner or L'Olonnais because he came from Port les Sables d'Olonne. His real name was Jean David Nau. After serving his slave years, Olonner became a hunter of wild cattle on the island of Haiti and finally a pirate. He was so successful in his early voyages that he drew numbers of men to him, for the buccaneers were superstitious and would follow only a "lucky" captain. Olonner was also called the "Spaniard's scourge" because he killed all Spaniards whom he captured.

Once, however, the Spaniards nearly had their revenge. Olonner's ship was wrecked on the coast of Campeche, in Central America. His men were attacked by Spanish soldiers and most of them killed. Olonner

*The crew of a Spanish galleon loading its guns to repel a swift pirate ship.*

was badly wounded several times, but smeared his face and body with sand and blood and hid among a heap of dead men. Thus he escaped detection. He eventually worked his way back to Tortuga, where he soon obtained the use of a canoe and raised a score of buccaneers to sail with him on fresh ventures.

The Spanish governor of Havana, Cuba, learned that the dreaded Olonner was back on the job again and sent an armed ship to capture him. Olonner turned the tables on his hunters, for he boarded their ship one night and killed the entire crew with the exception of one man. Olonner spared him only so the wretch could tell the governor of Havana what had happened to his ship!

Olonner took command of the Spanish warship, which was a fine, swift frigate and well armed. He cruised in this for a time, plundering and sinking every Spanish craft he sighted. Soon he was rich and famous. Now a new idea entered Olonner's head, which was to raise him far above the average buccaneer. Before this time, the most that the buccaneers had done was to loot and sink individual ships, but Olonner had more spectacular ideas.

Olonner persuaded all Tortuga to contribute to an unheard of scheme. In April, 1667, Olonner's fleet of eight ships, with four hundred picked men, sailed from Tortuga, heading for the rich Spanish city of Maracaibo on the coast of Venezuela. Olonner and his men captured a heavily armed fort outside the town and then bombarded Maracaibo proper. After the city had surrendered, Olonner and his men looted the place for two weeks and then marched on the near-by city of Gibraltar. Here the fighting was more severe, but again the Spanish soldiers could not withstand the fury of the buccaneers. For a whole month Olonner and his ruffians lived in the palaces of Gibraltar, then forced the Spaniards to ransom the town and themselves separately. Marching again to

*Henry Morgan, often called the king of the buccaneers.*

Maracaibo, Olonner received twenty thousand pieces of eight as its ransom.

Olonner was now the greatest hero Tortuga had ever seen. He had no difficulty in raising six stout ships and seven hundred men. With this formidable fleet he sailed to the mainland of Central America, along which the buccaneers marched, burning and looting every town in their path. Eventually Olonner besieged the city of San Pedro and took it only after losing many men. But there was no trace of gold in the town, only a great store of indigo! Olonner burned the entire city and marched back to the coast. Sometime later the buccaneer captain was shipwrecked, and he and his crew were hacked to bits by the Indians.

This was only a start of land attacks by pirates. One of the earliest leaders of such ventures was John Davis, a native of Jamaica. He had one ship and ninety men when he landed on the coast of Nicaragua. He left ten men to guard his ship. The others procured three canoes and sailed boldly up the river leading to the interior city of Grenada. They met sentinels, but spoke to them in Spanish and so passed as peaceful fishermen. They landed at the town without trouble and immediately cut down the soldiers who had gathered to watch them disembark.

Having penetrated to the middle of Nicaragua without harm, Davis' men separated and proceeded to steal everything that wasn't nailed down, both in homes and in churches. Eventually the aroused population assembled and tried to protect what little wealth was left. Davis had too few in his crew to risk a real fight; so the buccaneers piled into their canoes, sped down the river to their ship, and safely put to sea with silver and jewels worth more than forty thousand piasters.

The honor of surpassing both Olonner and Davis in great feats of arms and all-round villainy belongs to Henry Morgan, often called the king of the buccaneers. Morgan was a Welshman, son of a rich man, but his love of adventure took him to sea at an early age. As Morgan grew older, he served as an under-officer to Mansfield, who seems to have been a very ordinary sort of pirate.

Morgan spent some time in making rather fruitless attacks on ships and some villages in Cuba before his first great expedition. Then he decided to storm the town of Porto Bello, on the mainland of Central America. This town was exceptionally well fortified and had an almost impregnable citadel in the town proper. But Porto Bello was well worth attacking, for it was to this city that the Spaniards sent all the gold from the land of the Incas as well as the silver from the Potosí and Darien mines to be stored until the yearly treasure fleet of great galleons transported it to Spain.

Morgan anchored his fleet near the town and landed his four hundred men. That night they surrounded the fort, attacked, and overwhelmed the Spanish soldiers by the very savagery of their attack. Morgan then locked all the Spaniards left alive inside the fort, fired the powder magazine, and blew fort and soldiers to bits. The buccaneers stormed into Porto Bello after this outrage, but were met with a storm of musket and cannon balls. The governor, the soldiers, and most of the civilians were making a determined stand inside the citadel!

Morgan ordered an all-out attack. The fight raged for hours under a boiling sun. Morgan made grenades out of pots filled with gunpowder and his men hurled these over the stout walls of the citadel. The Spaniards answered by pouring kettles of boiling tar onto the pirates. Eventually the buccaneers scaled the wall and looted the city.

When the buccaneers sailed away, they had two hundred and fifty thousand pieces of eight and an enormous amount of valuable merchandise.

On his return to Jamaica, Morgan learned about Olonner's escapade at Maracaibo. So, with five hundred men and eight ships, the Welshman decided to imitate the earlier pirate's venture. For several weeks Morgan and his men marched and fought bloody battles in the region of Maracaibo and Gibraltar. At every turn he was outnumbered by the Spaniards, but still Morgan outfought and out-thought the enemy. He left looted towns and tortured people in his wake but returned to Jamaica the undoubted king of the buccaneers.

Morgan now had no difficulty in rallying two thousand men and thirty-seven ships to his standard. This was an armed force that any country in Europe at that time would have been proud to own, for the very ferocity with which the pirates fought made them equal to several times their number of professional soldiers.

Morgan decided to attack a town that had never been conquered but which was undoubtedly the richest city in the New World. This was Panama, the natural center of all Spanish possessions in America. The town was built on the narrowest part of the Isthmus of Panama in the middle of a productive gold country. Through Panama passed all the gold from South America on its way to the shipping point, Porto Bello; naturally, some of the treasure always remained. In addition, Panama was rich in cattle, coffee, cocoa, and timber.

Morgan decided to travel by small boats up the River Chagres to Venta Cruces and then push overland to Panama. The captain did not take any food with him, since he claimed the men could capture Spanish stores along the way. So for twelve days the buccaneer army pushed along through some of the worst jungle in the world. The Spaniards fled before them, hiding their treasure and destroying their food.

For twelve terrible days the buccaneers ate cats and dogs and even boiled up some old leather bags they found to keep from starving. But they did reach Panama and, in a two-day battle, probably the greatest pitched battle ever staged by pirates, took the city. A few weeks later Morgan's men marched away, driving before them one hundred and seventy-five beasts of burden loaded down with sacks of gold, silver, and jewels.

Morgan sailed with his fleet to a near-by island to divide this enormous booty according to the strict code of the buccaneers. The Spaniards claimed the loot amounted to more than a million and a half dollars. Morgan calmly told his men that each one was to receive fifty dollars as his full share! Then, while the men were arguing and threatening to kill

*Pirates captured by Spaniards were condemned to death or slave labor.*

*Caribbean buccaneers at a secret island hideout.*

their leader, Morgan sneaked away with some friends in the ships, taking *all* the money with them and leaving the greater portion of that big buccaneer army stranded!

Morgan was now so dangerous that the English king called him to London, where the pirate was knighted and made lieutenant governor of Jamaica. But he ended his life in the lowest taverns, without friends or money.

After Morgan's time the great companies of buccaneers broke up and went back to sea voyages, chasing Spanish ships on all the seven seas. Edward Davis did manage to muster one thousand men and ten ships for another attack on Panama, but he blundered into a Spanish fleet of warships. Lack of discipline among the buccaneers gave the victory to the Spaniards and the remnants of the battered pirate fleet sailed away to the south. With them went the power of the buccaneers. They had threatened the power of Spain in the New World, but had failed to break Spain's hold on her colonies.

There were still occasional pirate captains of note after Morgan and Davis, however. Most interesting, perhaps was Blackbeard. He was an Englishman whose real name was Drummond, although he always called himself Edward Teach. Others called him Blackbeard for an excellent reason. He was everything a pirate chief is supposed to be, in looks and in actions. He was far bigger even than the average buccaneer and his strength was so great that it was a byword among his men. His black beard grew up to his eyes, and he wore his beard in separate braids tied with bright ribbons. His eyebrows were so heavy that he looked like a gorilla. When Blackbeard went into action, he wore a lighted fuse or "slowmatch" coiled about his head to light up his satanic features. He also carried a bandoleer into which were thrust half a dozen pistols and several knives and swords.

Blackbeard looted, burned, and murdered up and down the Atlantic coast of the new American colonies until Virginia fitted out two ships and placed them under the command of young Lieutenant Maynard with the command to settle Blackbeard once and for all. Maynard gave the pirate a thrilling chase and finally met the pirate chief sword to sword in a furious combat. Maynard proved to be the better swordsman, although before he killed Blackbeard, he received twenty sword wounds and five pistol bullets in his body!

One of the last of the true pirates was William Kidd, a man far more notorious than his deeds warrant. Kidd was a Scottish minister's son who became a sailor. He cruised extensively in the West Indies and North American waters shortly after the old buccaneer empire had collapsed. At that time Kidd would have had nothing to do with piracy, for he was a sober, honest man with a reputation for great courage. He also had a wife and family in New York City.

In 1695, the governor of New York was ordered by the king of England to put down piracy in American waters. This gave some of the highest officers in the English Government an idea. They fitted out an armed ship and persuaded Kidd to be its captain. Kidd was to capture all the pirate vessels he could, and divide the booty between himself and his "employers," rather than returning the stolen goods to their original rightful owners!

Bad luck attended Kidd from the beginning. Instead of sailing to the West Indies, where the American pirates were thickest, Kidd sailed all the way to the island of Madagascar and worked out from there. He captured no pirates and eventually became a sort of half-hearted pirate himself. Even then he was unfortunate. His men mutinied and Kidd, who was enormously strong and who had of late grown very cruel, struck a sailor and killed him. To appease his maddened crew, Kidd took a few poor prizes and finally made one rich haul by looting the ship *Quedah,* which belonged to American merchants and was captained by an Englishman.

Kidd returned to New York after a cruise of more than two years. His capture of the *Quedah,* however, had caused so much stir that his own employers arrested him and some of his crew and stole all of Kidd's plunder. In 1700 Kidd was tried before a court in London, sentenced to die as a murderer and a pirate, and was eventually hanged.

There were other pirates after Kidd. There was Roberts, who is said to have sunk four hundred ships. There was Jean Lafitte, a pirate who preyed on shipping in the Gulf of Mexico and reformed long enough to help General Andrew Jackson win the Battle of New Orleans in 1814. There have also been the Chinese river pirates. But all these only echo the glory and the brutal magnificence of the buccaneers of Henry Morgan's day. Sea pirates are a thing of the past and all that they have left behind them is material for exciting stories and legends of buried treasure that is seldom if ever found.

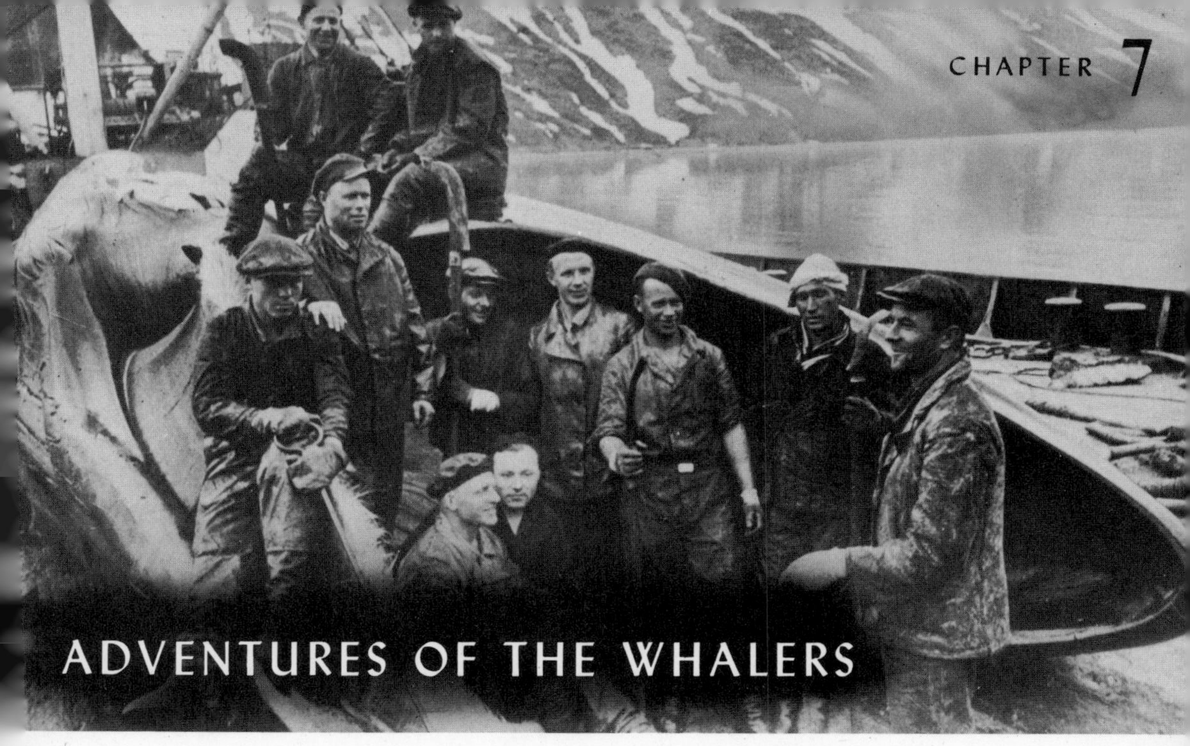

# CHAPTER 7

# ADVENTURES OF THE WHALERS

*Whaling off the shores of Kamchatka is a business of the Soviet people.*

"THERE SHE BLOWS!" No more exciting words than these have ever echoed over the waters of the seven seas. They were the words of the whalers, showing that their quarry had been sighted. They were the signal for the chase of the mightiest creature of the seas, the whale. Like the era of the clipper ships, or the days of the buccaneers, the time when American whalers pushed their way to the far corners of the globe is gone. The saga of the seas that is the story of whaling is part of the roaring seafaring past, but it is an exciting story that even today can make the pulse of modern landlubbers beat faster.

Early whale-hunting in New England was a crude affair, based more on chance than anything else. The early whale hunters worked from shore, putting out in small boats when Biscay whales, a small species of the right whale, were sighted. Many of these early whalers were American Indians, who were given many privileges because of their occupation. Between the first of November and the fifteenth of April, which represented the whaling season, the Indian whalers were free from lawsuits, arrest for debt or petty offenses, and many taxes that had to be paid by ordinary citizens, because their work as whalers was considered so important.

One day in 1712 an adventure befell a whaler named Christopher

Hussey which completely changed the history of whaling and made it an important American industry. Hussey was hunting whales not far off his native home of Nantucket, when a squall came up. It blew him far out to sea. Here, to his astonishment, he found himself in the midst of a great school of large whales. Although Hussey did not know it, they were sperm whales, quite different from the right whales which he had been hunting. However, Hussey took advantage of his opportunity, succeeded in harpooning a whale, which he towed ashore in triumph. It was quickly discovered that Hussey's sperm whale was possessed of an amazingly large quantity of valuable oil. The fisher folk of Nantucket rightly reasoned that if Hussey had achieved such good fortune by going out to sea, they could do likewise. Within a few years the whaling fleets of Nantucket were ranging far from shore. Eventually, New England whalers were seeking whales in the ice-strewn waters of the Arctic and the Antarctic, in waters off Africa, off the shores of Japan and China, off South America. They became some of the farthest roving seamen in the long history of seafaring.

Whales are remarkable creatures, for they are not fish at all, but seagoing animals. They breathe air, just as other animals, and therefore it is necessary for them to come to the surface. Hence the expression "there she blows," indicating that a whale has come to the surface to breathe. Although there are many kinds of whales, those most sought after by whalemen were the sperm whale, the right whale, the bowhead, the humpback, the sulphur bottom, and the finback. Of these the sperm and the right whales were the most valuable to the whalers, the sperm whale providing the largest quantities of oil and the right whale both oil and whalebone.

The first whaling vessels were little more than tiny sloops, but larger and larger ships came to be used, as the discovery was made that the whale oil could be extracted on shipboard and stored in casks. Since it was necessary to sail into far seas, on voyages lasting two or three years, the ships had to be very large.

Although the whaling ships themselves were not unlike other large sailing craft of the period, the whaling boats were masterpieces of boatbuilding. No boat of their size has ever equaled the seaworthiness of the Massachusetts whaleboat. Its dimensions of 30 feet in length, and 6 feet in width, and with a depth of 22 inches amidship and 37 inches at the bow and stern, might seem small, but it was constructed in a manner that permitted such a craft to ride out the heaviest seas.

The whaleboats were propelled by five huge oars, which were large enough to test the strength of any man, for they were 14 to 18 feet long. To take advantage of favorable winds, the whaleboat was also equipped with a simple spritsail.

Fully equipped, a whaleboat was the picture of neatness, for the whalers knew that everything must be where they could find it in the exciting moment of the chase and the kill. The harpoons, ready to be swiftly seized by the mate, would be located gleaming in their racks at the bow. Three hundred fathoms of rope would be neatly coiled in wooden tubs. Other equipment for emergencies would include a compass, lanterns, candles, and food, for there was no certainty that the boat would remain within sight of her mother ship. The men in each boat crew, which consisted of four oarsmen, a boat steerer (generally the bow oarsman), and a mate, knew exactly what they were to do during the chase, for each was assigned specific duties. The mate stood at the stern, from where he steered the boat with a tiller, a task taken over by the boat steerer after the kill. On approaching the whale, the

*Obsolete whaling methods are used with success by these New Zealanders.*

*Harpoons being stowed in the hold of a whaling ship.*

bow oarsman boated his oar and stood up with a harpoon. The midship oarsman was mainly concerned with pulling on his long sweeping oar. The "tub oarsman" was charged with throwing water on the rope as it paid out of the tubs, to keep it from burning as the whale raced away. The "stroke oarsman" furnished the stroke for the other men and helped in keeping the line clear and in pulling in slack and coiling the rope.

The most important weapon used in capturing the whale was the harpoon, which was a heavy instrument thrown with both hands, not with one hand as many people commonly suppose. It consisted of a steel shaft, tipped with a triangular blade, the shaft being fastened to a six-foot pole of stout oak. Attached to the steel shaft was a rope, so that when the shaft was driven into the whale the rope could be used to draw the boat close to the whale. Here a lance would be driven deep into the whale's vitals, thus killing him. Later the bomb-lance was developed. It consisted of a standard harpoon, which was thrown in the usual way, and a mechanism using gunpowder. When the lance penetrated to a certain distance, it sprung a trigger and fired a brass-tipped lance into the whale.

Although the early whalers were able seamen, the crews of nineteenth century whalers were generally a worthless and inexperienced lot. Many of them were drifters and vagrants, with no sailing experience whatsoever. Some were farmers, some factory hands, but none of them were seamen, for the men who ran the whaling cruises did not want real seamen aboard. On board ship the men were little better than slaves, for they had no way of escaping the harsh rule of the officers, who had nothing but contempt for the "bums" that made up their crew. Even when the ships put into foreign ports the men could not escape, for they were penniless. By the end of a long voyage, the men would find themselves so in debt to the whaling company, having been charged exorbitantly for even their clothes and food, that they would in all likelihood have no money coming. It is no wonder that such men rarely went back to sea again, or that regular seamen did not go on whaling voyages.

On the long voyage to the whaling grounds, it was necessary to break in these crews, so they were subjected to long grueling hours of practice under the harsh and unyielding rule of the mate. The luckless landlubbers were ordered into the rigging, even though they were terrified by the sight of the lofty trucks that swayed with every roll of the ship. If they refused to go aloft, they were driven there with curses and the sharp point of a marlinespike or the lash of a rope's end. The lot of the men of the crew was truly a hard one.

Whenever the sea was calm, the mates put their crews to rowing boats to get in practice for the hard pulls ahead. To spur them on, competitions were organized between different boat crews, and men who had never touched an oar in their lives soon came to have a keen interest in seeing how well they could row. By the time the whaling ship reached the cruising grounds, her crew would somehow have been whipped into line and would be ready for the difficult and dangerous work that lay ahead.

For a vivid picture of what whaling was like in the roaring '40's we turn to the account of Ross Browne, a whaler who set down his impressions of a whaling voyage in this manner:

> We were running down for the Aldabra Islands with a fine, steady breeze. The morning was bright and clear, and the water of that peculiar color which whalemen regard as the favorite resort for whales. I had forenoon watch below and was just congratulating myself upon getting through with my "double altitudes," when the loud, clear voice of a man at the masthead came ringing down the forecastle.

*A whaling catch is brought to a floating factory to be dismembered.*

"There she blows!" was the thrilling cry.

"That's once!" shouted the captain.

"There she blows!"

"That's twice, by jingo!"

"There she blows!"

"Three times! Where away, Tabor?"

"Off the weather bow, sir, two points."

"How far?"

"A mile and a half. There she blows!"

"Sperm whale! Call all hands!"

There was a rush on deck, each man trying to get to the scuttle first. Then came half a dozen loud knocks, and a hoarse voice shouting,

"Larboard watch ahoy! Turn out, my lads! Sperm whale in sight! Heave out! Heave out! Lash and carry! Rise and chime! Bear a hand, my lively hearties!"

Those who were "turned in" rolled out as soon as possible, and buckled on their ducks, and in less than two minutes we were all on deck, ready for orders. The tubs were put in the boats, and the main yard hauled aback. We all now perched ourselves in the rigging and kept a sharp lookout on every side for the whale's next rising. Twenty minutes elapsed since the spout was first seen; twenty-five passed, and the captain began to get into a state of nervous anxiety. We strained our eyes in all directions to "make a spout." Half an hour flew by, and no spout was seen. It began to look like a hopeless case, when Tabor, whose visual organs appeared to have the power of ubiquity, sang out,

"There she blows! There she blows!"

"Where now?" roared the captain.

"Off the weather quarter! Two large sperm whales, sir. Go it, boats!"

"Clear away the boats! Come down from the masthead, all you that don't belong there! Bear a hand! We'll take them this rising!" shouted the captain, in a fierce, sharp voice.

"All ready, sir."

"Lower away, then!"

The waist and larboard boats were instantly down, ready to "bend on." Captain A—— and some of his boat's crew being too ill to man the other boat, we struck off for the whales without them. I pulled the aft oar, as usual; and as, by this time, I was as tough and muscular as my comrades, the boat danced along the water in fine style. Although the larboard boat was much easier pulled, and had the oldest and stoutest of the whole crew, we contrived, by unusual exertions, to keep ahead of her, till the real tug of war came. Then was our mettle put to the test! One of the whales was leisurely making to windward not more than half a mile off.

"Lay back, my lads!" cried P——, pale with excitement. "Keep the larboard boat astern! Never say die! That's our whale! Oh, *do* spring—*do* spring! No noise! Steady and soft's the word."

We replied to this appeal by "piling up the agony" on the oars. Away sprang our boat, trembling and quivering as she darted through the waves. She really seemed to imbibe the general excitement as she parted the clear blue water, and dashed it foaming from her bows. Onward we flew! The larboard boat was hard upon our stern; the whale rolling lazily in the trough of the sea, a few darts ahead.

"Oh, lay back! Lay back!" whispered P——, trembling with eagerness not to be outdone by the mate. "Do spring, my boys, if you love gin! Now's your time! Now or never! Oh, see him! See him! How quiet he lies! Put the beef on your oars, every mother's son of you! Pile it on! Pile it on! That's the way to tell it! Our whale this time!"

The moment of intense excitement now arrived. We pulled as if for life or death. Not a word was spoken, and scarcely a sound was heard from our oars.

"Stand up, Tabor!" cried P——, in a low voice.

Peaking his oar, Tabor sprang to his feet and grasped a harpoon.

"Shall I give him two irons?"

"Yes; he may be wild."

Another stroke or two, and we were hard upon him. Tabor, with unerring aim, let fly his irons, and buried them to the sockets in the huge carcass of the whale.

"Stern all!" thundered P——.

"Stern all!" echoed the crew, but it was too late. Our bows were high and dry on the whale's head! Infuriated with the pain produced by the harpoons, and doubtless much astonished to find his head so roughly used, he rolled half over,

*Open whaleboats are still in use among Maori natives off the coast of New Zealand.*

lashing the sea with his flukes, and in his struggles dashing in two of the upper planks. "Boat stove! Boat stove!" was the general cry.

"Silence!" thundered the second mate, as he sprang to the bow, and exchanged places with Tabor. "All safe, my hearties! Stern hard! Stern! Stern! Before he gets his flukes to bear upon us."

"Stern all!" shouted we, and in a moment more we were out of danger. The whale now "turned flukes," and dashed off to windward with the speed of a locomotive, towing us after him at a glorious rate. We occasionally slacked line in order to give him plenty of play. A stiff breeze had sprung up, causing a rough, chopping sea; and we leaked badly in the bow planks. It fell to my lot to keep the water bailed out and the line clear as the others hauled in; a ticklish job, the last; for, as the second mate said, a single turn would whip off a shin "as slick as goose grease."

Notwithstanding the roughness of the sea, we shot ahead with incredible swiftness; and the way we "walked" past the larboard boat, whose crew were tugging and laboring with all their might, was surprising.

"Hooray for the waist boat!" burst from every lip. Three hearty cheers followed, much to the annoyance of the other boat's crew and mate. We exultingly took off our hats and waved them a polite "good-by," requesting them, if they had any news to send to the windward ports, to be quick about it, as it was inconvenient for us to stop just then. I believe Solomon says it is not good to be vainglorious. At all events, while we were skimming along so gallantly, the whale suddenly milled and pitched the boat on her beam ends. Everyone who could grasp a thwart hung on to it, and we were all fortunate enough to keep our seats. For as much as a ship's length the boat flew through the water on her gunwhale, foaming and whizzing as she dashed onward. It was a matter of doubt as to which side would turn uppermost, until Tabor slacked out the line, when she righted. To have a boat, with all her irons, lances, gear, and oars, piled on one's head in such a sea was rather a startling prospect to the best swimmer.

Meantime the whale rose to the surface to spout. The change in his course had enabled the mate's boat to come up; and we lay on our oars in order that Mr. D—— might lance him. He struck him in the "life" the first dart, as was evident from the whale's furious dying struggles; nevertheless, in order to make sure, we hauled up and churned a lance back of his head.

I cannot conceive anything more strikingly awful than the butchery of this tremendous leviathan of the deep. Foaming and breaching, he plunged from wave to wave, flinging high in the air torrents of blood and spray. The sea around was literally a sea of blood. At one moment his head was poised in the air; the next, he buried himself in the gory sea, carrying down in his vast wake a whirlpool of foam and slime. But this respite was short. He rose again, rushing furiously upon his enemies; but a slight prick of a lance drove him back with mingled fury and terror. Whichever way he turned, the barbed irons goaded him to desperation. Now and again intensity of agony would cause him to lash the waters with his huge flukes, till the very ocean appeared to heave and tremble at his power. Tossing, struggling, dashing over and over in his agony, he spouted up the last of his heart's blood. Half an hour before he was free as the wave, sporting in all the pride of gigantic strength and unrivaled power. He now lay a lifeless mass, his head toward the sun, his tremendous body heaving to the swell, and his destroyers proudly cheering over their victory!

All kinds of strange adventures were experienced by the whalers, for they sailed into the most dangerous waters of the seven seas and engaged in an occupation that had its own special dangers. The circumstances that befell the *Ann Alexander* on a whaling cruise in 1858 are typical of some of the more remarkable adventures that make up the colorful saga of whaling. One day in August, the mate's boat had been made fast to a whale, when the whale turned suddenly. His mighty jaws seized the boat and smashed it. The men succeeded in jumping overboard and were soon picked up by two other boats. When the men were put safely aboard the whaling ship, one of the boats went back to gather up the whaling gear from the crushed boat. The men in this boat caught sight of the whale, and took up the chase, but the whale sounded and was given up. As the boat approached the ship, the whale suddenly came up and lunged toward the ship itself. There was no time to maneuver the vessel out of the way, and soon there came the sound of torn planking as the whale stove a gaping hole two feet from the keel. Almost instantly the ship began to sink as the waters poured through this mortal wound. She sank a few minutes later, her crew having found time only to throw a few provisions into a boat and

*The ship that sailed on Britain's first postwar whaling expedition to the Antarctic.*

launch it. Although they were in mid-ocean, the men in the boats set out to row toward land. They had been afloat two days when they were picked up by the *Nantucket.*

Less fortunate was the fate of the whalemen aboard the *Essex,* whose story is considered one of the classics of whaling adventures. She put out from Nantucket in 1819, bound for the Pacific whaling grounds. She made a safe journey around the Horn, and late in November was far out from the South American coast when she sighted her first whale. A boat was put out, but hardly had it been made fast to the whale than the sea creature's mighty flukes smashed it. While the men were attempting to repair the damage, another giant whale appeared, and as the men in the stove-in boat watched, they saw this whale make straight for the *Essex.* There was a thunderous crash, and for a time the whale lay as if stunned, while the *Essex* started to ship water. Hardly had the pumps been started than the whale suddenly came to life and again charged the *Essex.* This time the result was fatal, for the ship began to sink. The captain ordered that her masts be cut away, in an effort to right the ship, which was listing heavily. When this was done, the *Essex*

*A whale emerging from the depths for a breathing spell.*

*"Mopey Dick," white whale of San Francisco Bay legend.*

righted herself and remained afloat. For three days the crew stood by in boats, taking from the stricken vessel everything that they could. The crew then set sail in three little boats for the coast of Peru, nearly three thousand miles away. The date was November 23, 1819.

It was a perilous journey, for the men had not been able to obtain enough food to provide for more than a few days' rations. The men took hope when, five days later, they sighted land. But it turned out to be only the barren Ducie's Island, where the only food proved to be some shellfish and a few sea birds. Worst of all, there was no water. There was nothing to do but to row on, hoping that somehow they might cover the terrible twenty-five hundred miles that still lay ahead of them. Days and weeks passed, and one by one the members of the crew died. On January 19, 1820 three wretched survivors were picked up by the brig *Indian*, and five days later two men from one of the other boats were picked up by the *Dauphin*. The third boat had disappeared, and the fate of her occupants has never been learned.

Sometimes disasters to whaling ships were caused not by attacks by whales but by the ship running into one. The records are filled with such tales, among them the story of the *Union*, bound out of Nantucket for Brazil. Proceeding under light sail at a speed of seven knots, she suddenly crashed into a solid object. At first it was thought that she had run into a rock, although none showed on any charts, but then it was realized that she must have crashed into a whale. Her sides were stove in, and sea water quickly rushed into the gap, forcing the crew of sixteen to abandon their ship, which soon sank. In two boats they started out for the Azores, six hundred miles away, which they reached after being afloat for seven days and eight nights. There have been many other cases such as that of the *Union*, in which not only whalers, but merchant ships as well, have been the victims of unexpected collisions with whales.

The greatest danger from whales was encountered by the men in the boats which hunted them down. Many times the wounded whales would turn furiously on their hunters, destroying boats with the thrashing of their enormous flukes. In many instances, the whale would actually seize the boat in his mighty jaws, crumpling it like matchwood, often killing and maiming the luckless occupants. A Captain Huntling had a strange adventure when his whale boat was seized by a bull sperm off the Rio de la Plata. He and his crew swam for safety after the boat was destroyed, but being a long way from any other boat, they actually clambered upon the back of the angered whale, where they clung until they were rescued.

These are only a few of the adventures of the Yankee sailors who ventured into the seven seas in search of the mighty whale.

*A United States Coast Guard cutter on the International Ice Patrol guards the sea lanes.*

SOMEWHERE on the ocean there is a ship in trouble practically every day of the year. There have always been ships in trouble ever since the first cave man launched a tree trunk on a lake and clung to it while he crossed that body of water. Ships get into trouble because of storms, human carelessness, or a hundred other reasons. Because ships run into disasters and are wrecked, we have some of the most thrilling of all sea stories—stories of dauntless heroism as well as stories of cowardice.

The greatest mass shipwreck of all times was probably the wreck of the Spanish Armada, that grand array of stately galleons which sailed so proudly down the Tagus River from Lisbon to seal the doom of England. It is popularly supposed that the guns of the intrepid Englishmen under the inspired leadership of Howard, Drake, and Hawkins accounted for most of the Armada. Actually it was the elements—winds, waves, jagged shoals, and cliffs—that fought for England just as the fogs and mists battled for England back in 1940 during the tragic evacuation of Dunkirk.

When the Spanish Armada put out to sea, it consisted of 129 fine fighting ships plus 20 smaller caravels and pinnaces. These ships mounted a total of over 2,400 cannons and were manned with some 30,000 soldiers, sailors, gentleman adventurers, officers, and galley slaves. The Armada engaged the English fleet on several occasions during a period covering several days. The climax of the actual fighting came in a grand-scale free-for-all on July 29, 1588. In this action, Spain lost more than 4,000 men to the English guns and by drowning.

The pride of the Spaniards was broken by that final day of battle. The Armada, during the course of the fight, had sailed up the English Channel and now was nearly into the North Sea. It could not return through the Channel to the comparative safety of the French coast without again facing the terrible guns of the English sailors. The Spaniards decided that the open sea held less danger for them than did the ships of England. So, although all the Spanish shipmasters were fully aware of the dangers that would attend them if they attempted to round the northern portion of Scotland and then sail down the west coast of Ireland in the gale that was now beginning to blow, this was the very course decided upon by the Armada's leader, the Duke of Sidonia.

Drake and Howard, with ninety English ships, sailed northward in pursuit of the Armada, meaning to close again with the Spaniards and put an end to the fleet for all time. When the Duke of Sidonia saw that the English fleet had been reduced in numbers, he considered once more the advisability of turning about and trying to battle his way through the Channel to France. A terrific storm that arose during the night, however, made up his mind for him. The Duke ordered all his ships to run before the storm and sail for the Orkney Islands.

Then began a succession of days and nights of terror and misfortune for the Spaniards. A terrible southwest gale struck the Armada; that, together with the rapidly roughening seas, broke spars, snapped masts, and caused ship after ship to leak. None of the Spanish captains had ever sailed in these treacherous waters before. This fact, plus the tempest, caused each shipmaster to press on as best he could and leave any laggards to founder in the foaming waves.

When the English captains saw that the Spaniards did not try to land somewhere on the Scottish coast, they came to the logical conclusion that the Armada was heading for Denmark. Therefore they abandoned the pursuit, put about, and headed for safety from the tempest. At this time there were still 120 ships of the 150 that had sailed so proudly from Spain just a few short months before. The English guns had taken a toll of 30, capturing or sinking these ships in the series of actions in the English Channel.

For five days the storm increased in violence. The fog and rain continued unabated; the waves piled higher and higher as the doomed Spaniards floundered away from the coast of Scotland in an attempt to round Ireland. The Spanish ships, built for cruising in the warm waters of the south and manned now by crews discouraged at losing the great naval battle and weakened by hunger and disease, fought a losing fight. For a week the ships were out of sight and so out of touch with each other. On August 9 the skies cleared for a brief spell. It was then seen that many of the huge war galleons had lost masts and yards and that practically all the sails had been split to rags by the great fury of the tempest.

That night the gale rose again and the fog returned. By August 13 the fleet was scattered far and wide. The crews were now suffering horribly from hunger and thirst. The wounded died by the hundreds. Still the Spanish captains kept on, trying to make the west coast of Ireland. They sailed through eleven more days of storm while galleon after galleon fell by the wayside.

Finally, on September 4, the Duke of Sidonia, at the head of a shattered fleet of fifty-two ships, all of which leaked badly at every seam, sailed past Blasket Sound and was safe. The Duke and every man on board were in the last stages of exhaustion from their day-and-night battle with the furious waters and dangerous reefs.

More than seventy ships of the Grand Armada, more than twice the number sunk or captured by the English, had been driven far and wide through the northern waters. There they had sunk or else been battered into driftwood on the rocky coasts, where their crews were either killed or taken prisoner and held for ransom. Many of the galleons met their fate on the cruel Irish cliffs. The ship that carried the great Spanish nobleman, Don Alonzo da Leyva and many of the young lords of Castile, struck a rock off Dunluce. Two hundred and sixty bodies were washed onto the beach.

In that one mass shipwreck, more than 8,000 Spanish soldiers, sailors, and noblemen of all degrees were lost at sea between the Giant's Causeway and Blasket Sound. On the 52 ships that eventually reached the safety of Spain, there were only 10,000 men—about one-third of the crew that had originally sailed. Those ships were worthless, battered hulks; the men racked with wounds and sickness.

Most shipwrecks are not devoid of acts of heroism, but for genuine courage and devotion to duty the wreck of the British schooner *Drake* in the early part of the last century stands as a shining example.

*A Russian freighter wrecked during a storm on the North Pacific coast.*

The *Drake*, commanded by Captain Charles Baker, was bound for Newfoundland when it struck a great rock mass just off the coast. The fog was of that density peculiar to Newfoundland, and visibility was so poor that the seamen had to work blind. Smashing waves swept continually over the helpless vessel, each new one threatening to carry officers and men overboard. Captain Baker called the crew onto the poop deck, which was the only place that afforded any shelter.

Baker calmly informed his men that their only hope of safety lay in leaving the ship and taking up their stand on the huge rock that had been the cause of the disaster. The captain, knowing that the ship would not last much longer under the intense pounding it was taking from the waves, ordered his men to climb onto the rock as quickly as they could. "I will remain aboard the *Drake* until the last man has reached safety," he told them.

For the first time since Baker had trod the deck of a ship as captain, his orders were not obeyed instantly. "We won't stir a step until you've reached the rock yourself, sir!" the men called out. It was an unusual situation in those days of hard-fisted captains, grueling work, and little pay. But this captain had so won the loyalty of his men by his competence and fair dealing that now they were willing to risk being swept into the raging ocean so that Baker could be the first to get to safety.

"My life is the least and last consideration," Captain Baker reminded his men quietly, after thanking them for their generous offer. No amount of pleading would change the shipmaster's mind. Finally the men began to abandon ship, clambering from the shattered wreck onto the jagged rock through the murky fog with as much order as if it were part of the day's drill. However, several men had become so numbed by the cold that they lost their grip and were swept to destruction in the water despite the heroic efforts of their mates to save them. Only after every man and officer had cleared the wreck did Captain Baker join his men on their precarious refuge.

Now the fog started to disperse and the dawn began to break and the crew was able to take stock of the situation. Truly, their plight was desperate. The rock on which the ship's company was so insecurely perched was isolated from the mainland by some fifty or seventy-five feet of boiling surf. It would have been no great swim in calm weather (although very few sailors in those days could swim at all) for a good swimmer, but it looked like certain death to attempt such a feat in the tempest that still raged.

But there was worse than this. Their rock rose several feet above the ocean level at that time, but as the light increased the men realized with growing horror that at high tide the rock would be completely covered with water! It seemed now that they had been rescued from a quick death only to be doomed to a slower one.

The men were exhausted with cold and fatigue; many of them had been badly gashed during their escape from the wreck and their open wounds were beginning to freeze in the icy wind and salt water that broke continually over them. Still there was no despair; men and officers were calm. These men had always fought for their lives. Now they decided to put up one more struggle before surrendering themselves completely to the sea.

Fortunately, the boatswain had taken along a length of rope when he had escaped to the rock. As he watched the tide rising higher and ever higher, he realized that if he were to carry out the wild plan that had formed in his mind, he would have to act swiftly. He knotted the line about his body, unashamedly prayed aloud to God for help, and dove into the lashing water.

The men on the rock were nearly exhausted from exposure and their injuries, but they were in an even more pitiful state now as they watched that courageous boatswain tossed about at will by the tumultuous waves, now dimly seen as he topped a crest, now lost to sight for whole minutes as he slid down into the trough of the sea. Somehow, despite the savage battering by the surf and breakers, the boatswain *did* live to reach the shore with his precious rope still unbroken.

When the sailor caught his breath, he took up his stand at the point nearest the rock and, with strength born of desperation, he hurled one end of his rope across to his friends, who caught it and held grimly to the slender line. That rope proved to be just long enough so that a man on the rock and another on the shore could hold it at arm's length!

It was a dangerous life line at best, but at sight of it the men let loose a cheer that heartened them greatly. Higher and higher raced the tide, but the men remained at the posts assigned to them until Captain Baker gave the order to start abandoning the rock. Then, as each name was called by the captain, the man stepped forward and pleaded with Baker to go ahead. Baker had but one answer to these entreaties that he save himself immediately. He had to shout the words so his faithful men could hear him above the roaring of the sea. "I will not leave this rock until every man is safe!" he shouted.

Man after man begged their stanch leader to make his bid for safety. The leader would not be moved. By his assistance, forty-four of the fifty men left in the crew slipped from the rock and, clinging grimly to the rope, made their perilous way to the shore. There were six left—and one of them a woman who had been a passenger aboard the ill-starred *Drake*. Unaccustomed to such terrible suffering and dangers, she had fainted and now lay upon the storm-swept rock as if dead.

The crew of the *Drake* never abandoned a comrade, but to take the woman through that raging waste of water seemed impossible to them. The tide rose higher and higher, periling the men on the rock as they debated what should be done. Suddenly one powerful fellow cried out, "I'll take her, sir!" He stooped, lifted that inert form in his sinewy arms, and slipped into the ocean.

Yard after yard that plucky sailor battled his way toward shore. His comrades on rock and beach held their breath and prayed that he might win his one-sided battle. The odds were too great for that. The rope, thin to start with and by now worn and strained with the passing of forty-four robust men, broke when the sailor was about halfway to safety. The man and the unconscious woman were seen for only a brief instant and then were swept away at rip-tide speed.

With them went the last means of saving Captain Baker and the remainder of the crew on the rock. Frantically the men on shore tied together every handkerchief and other articles of clothing in an effort

*Driven by a raging storm, the S.S.* Princess May *was wrecked on Sentinel Rock, Alaska.*

to replace the lost rope. It was all to no avail. Their improvised line fell far short. The tide rose higher and the surf beat against the captain and his men more hungrily as they clung to crevices and little knobs of rock, hoping against hope that their comrades on shore could yet rescue them.

Sobbing and panting, members of the crew on the beach ran up and down the barren stretch of shore, searching for help. They finally found a lone farmhouse, but while they searched for a rope, those men who had stayed behind watched as their beloved captain and three comrades were first smothered in the foam of the racing waves and then swept to their deaths. The waters were now rushing at mill-race speed between the rock and the shore and not even the strongest swimmer in the world could have stayed alive in them for a minute. When the search party returned with their rope, the tide had covered every sign of the rock and carried away the bodies of Captain Baker and his three men.

Characteristics that were the exact opposite to those shown by the survivors of the *Drake* were exhibited by the crew of the French frigate *Medusa*, which sailed for Africa in June, 1816. At that time, Napoleon was a prisoner on a lonely out-of-the-way island. Peace had been restored to Europe and France's colonial possessions which she had lost during the long war had been given back to her. On the *Medusa* sailed the man who was to be the governor of some of France's African colonies, together with his staff of ladies and gentlemen. In addition, there were on board numerous officers and veterans who had served under Napoleon. They were fierce fellows, very bitter over their general's defeat. There were men from the African colonies; fierce, truculent Spaniards; and men and women of both high and low degree.

As the *Medusa* left the French coast behind, both the governor and the ship's captain locked themselves in their separate compartments and proceeded to indulge themselves in a prolonged revel. Management of the ship was left in the hands of a sailor who knew absolutely nothing about navigation and even less about the coast of Africa. Thus it came about that the *Medusa* sailed full tilt onto the Arguin bank, a reef that is plainly marked on every sailing map.

There were some four hundred people aboard the stranded frigate. When it became evident even to the befuddled, incompetent officers and seamen that their ship could not be rescued from the rocks, orders were given to abandon ship. There were only five lifeboats aboard. Into one of these the governor and his company of ladies and gentlemen were carefully lowered, together with plenty of provisions. The captain and his friends took another boat. Other dignitaries and high officers filled the other three boats.

There were still one hundred and fifty people of all descriptions left to seek safety somehow. A clumsy raft, made of boxes and barrels, shattered masts and broken spars, was hastily thrown together. The resulting craft was a disgrace to the poorest sailor who ever fouled a line. Nevertheless, all but seventeen of the remaining people were herded onto that raft. The men in the lifeboats promised to tow it to safety with towing lines. The seventeen who stayed aboard the stranded *Medusa* were too frightened to exchange the comparatively firm deck under their feet for what seemed to them to be certain destruction aboard the frail raft.

The lifeboats pushed off in good order, towing the makeshift raft and its ill-assorted cargo behind them. They had not gone five miles from the wreck, however, when one after another the crews of the lifeboats cast off the towing lines! Later, all these men swore that the ropes had broken. This was not the truth, for if the lines had merely parted they could have been spliced in a hurry. At least the lifeboats could have stayed as a convoy for the raft. Instead, the boats abandoned the raft and rowed ahead at full speed toward safety.

By this time the badly overloaded raft had settled into the sea to a depth of three and one-half feet. The people were jammed together so tightly that they could scarcely move, and breathing was difficult. Most of them were up to their waists in the salt water. When the castaways finally realized that they had been heartlessly abandoned, they nearly went insane with fear and rage. Only with the utmost difficulty did some of the officers manage to restore a little semblance of order and discipline. There was neither chart nor anchor aboard; there was only one tattered sail; and their only compass was soon washed overboard.

To add to their terrors, the officers now discovered that the only food on the entire raft consisted of twenty-five pounds of ship's biscuits and several kegs of wine. The biscuits were broken up and some of the wine added to form a thick paste. There was just enough of this dubious concoction for each of the refugees to receive one spoonful! Night came on and brought with it a strengthening of the waves. This caused the crude raft to spread apart. A number of the people fell between the spars and other timbers of which the raft was constructed and were unable to get out again. There they stayed, some of them with their heads barely above water, screaming in pain as the timbers shifted back and forth breaking their legs and crushing their ribs.

*Victim of a U-boat, a United Nations tanker sinks slowly by the stern in the North Atlantic.*

When morning came, it was found that twenty members of the crew had been washed overboard during the hours of darkness. Somehow the long, blisteringly hot day passed, but the night that now descended on them was even worse. In their terror at another interminable stretch of darkness, the people crowded toward the center of the vessel. Several of them were smothered and trampled to death this way.

Then it was that the ex-soldiers banded together with the sailors from the *Medusa* and broached a number of the wine kegs. They swilled all the liquor they could hold and, as the alcohol began to react on their empty stomachs, they went fighting mad. They tried to hack apart the cables that held the raft together; they seized what weapons they could and fell upon other members of the party; and some of the more drink-crazed destroyed the rickety sail and mast.

The officers and passengers now banded together and attacked the mutineers fiercely. There in the dark, waist-deep in water, a terrible battle was waged. Men fought with knives, swords, axes, and their bare hands. Men were hurled into the sea, in spite of their pleas. Eventually order was restored, but again the mutiny broke out. This time the slaughter was even worse. When the fight finally died down near dawn, it was found that seventy of the refugees had perished during that frightful night.

The next day the enfeebled men let the raft drift. Hunger became so great that many of them gnawed the leather belts and cartridge boxes

*The* S.S. Delhi, *wrecked at Sumner Island, Alaska.*

they still wore. Others tried to devour their shirts and their hats. The third night passed peacefully, that is, as peacefully as it could with most of the survivors wounded and suffering from salt water boils that stripped big patches of skin from their flesh.

Fighting broke out anew on the fourth night and was so fierce that when the sun rose again there were but twenty-eight refugees alive, and thirteen of them appeared to be so far gone as to have no chance of survival. In order to conserve their food supply—a little wine and some miserable fish they had caught—the fifteen able-bodied people threw the other thirteen overboard!

Six days later the surviving fifteen people were picked up by a small brig. They were so far gone from starvation, wounds, and exposure that six died within a few days. It is claimed that all but one of the others went insane. This one man, the only one who could have testified about the abandonment of the raft, was shot in the back before the story could be brought to court.

What about the seventeen men left aboard the *Medusa*? Eventually the frigate's captain, who, together with the crews of the other five lifeboats had gotten ashore without too much privation, decided to have a look at his vessel. Fifty-two days after he had abandoned it, he approached it in another ship. A crew boarded the *Medusa*, which was still held fast on the reef. They found two men still alive, but they too were insane from hunger and fear.

No wonder the wreck of the *Medusa* is sometimes referred to as "history's most frightful shipwreck."

With the coming of iron ships propelled by powerful engines—ships that no longer had to depend upon the vagaries of the wind for locomotion—the number of wrecks caused by ships being blown onto rocks and other such typical causes of sailing ship disasters naturally decreased. On the other hand, as ships grew larger and could accommodate more people, the number of lives lost in one wreck increased. Thus it was that when the *Titanic* went down, ripped wide open by an iceberg, she carried with her more than 1,500 people.

The eyes of the world were on the *Titanic* as she set sail from Southampton on April 10, 1912 for her maiden voyage across the Atlantic. She was a magnificent craft, the world's finest liner. She was nearly nine hundred feet long, and her powerful engines could drive her at a speed of twenty-two knots. Her builders boasted proudly that at last they had built an unsinkable liner. To avoid the hazard that might result from collision with another ship, she was built with a double bottom. If somehow water did manage to get in, it would be confined within the separate bulkheads, sealed off from each other by water-tight doors. If fire broke out, there were special tubes leading to each compartment that could be used to pipe inert gas ($CO_2$) for extinguishing purposes. No pains or expense had been spared to guard against the known hazards of the sea. The 2,208 persons aboard the *Titanic* had every reason to believe, and rightfully so, that they were embarking on a safe voyage.

Up on his bridge Captain E. V. Smith was not unmindful of the danger that he knew lurked as a hidden assassin in the sea lanes of the North Atlantic. He well knew that there was danger of encountering ice, and he had posted special lookouts at all points, men trained in spotting the deadly "ice blink," the strange ghostly sheen that shows even through fog to indicate the presence of an iceberg. In the engine room there were devices that would indicate any drop in the temperature of the water outside, betokening the fact that ice was near.

What the captain had not foreseen was something just as deadly as an iceberg. An iceberg can be easily seen because of its great size, but floe ice, which is less massive, is not readily observed, but is every bit as menacing to a passing ship as a great rock. The officers of the *Titanic* believed that they were far south of the region in which floe ice was found. There was no case on record of a ship having come to disaster because of this kind of ice in the latitude in which lay the *Titanic's* course. Yet whatever the human calculations, there was floe ice under the surface on the clear sunny day of Sunday, April 15. Floating cakes of it gave some evidence of its presence, but they were taken to be only the remnants of larger floes that had broken up into small and harmless pieces. Wireless messages came in from other ships reporting ice. As night fell, the captain's orders were the same. "Full speed ahead." The *Titanic* was out to make a swift crossing.

Disaster came swiftly. In the crow's nest the lookout rang the bell three times, calling for attention.

"Something ahead, sir," he spoke quietly into the telephone.

"What is it?" Chief Officer Murdoch on the bridge demanded impatiently.

"I—can't make—out." The lookout was straining his eyes into the blackness. "It's ice, sir!" Now he was certain, and the officer below wasted no time.

*Torn in two by a German torpedo, this tanker remained afloat although it lost its forward section.*

"Starboard your helm!" he commanded the man at the wheel. In a matter of seconds the great ship began to swing slowly to port, starting the huge arc that would turn her to safety. It was too late. For one moment the *Titanic* shuddered, a slight, shivering tremor running through her. That was all the evidence there was that all the precautions taken by her builders to make her unsinkable had been undone at a single stroke. The ice she hit literally sliced the craft open, cutting a three hundred-foot gash along the bilge at the exact point where the plates of her protecting double bottom were joined.

"Close all water-tight doors" was the order swiftly given, but the compartments were useless, because a number of them had been laid open to the inrushing waters of the Atlantic. The nature of the injury was not known immediately, of course.

About midnight the two radio operators were astonished when Captain Smith walked into the radio room and calmly said: "We have struck an iceberg, and I am having an inspection made to tell us what to do about it. Be prepared to send out a call for assistance, but do not send it until I tell you to." John Phillips, the chief radio operator, and Harold Bride, his assistant, looked at each other in amazement. After the captain was gone, they began to laugh, for it seemed to them that it must be a joke. Assistance for the unsinkable liner on this calm and peaceful night when she had merely scratched ice?

Ten minutes later Captain Smith came back. This time his face was grim, though he seemed completely calm.

"Send out the call for assistance," he said sharply.

"Which call?" Phillips asked, still not believing in the full seriousness of the situation.

"The regular international call for help," Smith answered as he rushed away.

Soon the air waves were crackling with a distress signal no one in the world ever expected to hear from the *Titanic*. "C D Q. . . . C D Q. . . ." Six times Phillips hammered out the signal.

"You might try S O S too," Bride suggested. This was the signal that had been internationally adopted four years earlier, but had not yet replaced C D Q as a distress signal from British ships.

Captain Smith came back for a moment, listening silently to the signal. Bride tried to joke.

"Better make that signal good," he told Phillips. "It may be your last chance to send an S O S." Captain Smith joined in their laughter. None of them knew what an accurate prophecy it would turn out to be.

Added to his distress signal, Phillips also sent a longer message.

"Have struck iceberg. We are badly damaged. *Titanic* latitude 41:46 N. Longitude 50:14 W."

What happened then might have been avoided if the officers of the *Californian,* a liner which was at that moment only twenty miles away, had known that the airways were crackling with the *Titanic's* distress signal. They could not know it because their radio operator had gone off duty, as was the custom on some ships in days when continuous wireless operation was not a legal requirement. On the chance that some liner might be near, the *Titanic* sent up distress rockets. Strangely enough, they were seen by the watch on the *Californian,* but the lookout could not picture the possibilities of disaster on such a calm night and decided that they must be signals sent up by fishermen on the banks.

The nearest ship that did pick up the distress signals was fifty-eight miles away. She was the Cunard liner *Carpathia*. When her radio operator, H. T. Cottam, rushed in to tell her captain, Arthur Rostron, of the amazing distress signal, the captain could not believe it.

"Are you sure it's the *Titanic?*" he demanded.

"Yes, sir!" Cottam could not doubt the clear signals he had received.

Still the captain was unconvinced. "Are you absolutely certain?"

*The floating stern of a doomed tanker is blown up by the Coast Guard to clear the sea lanes.*

Again the radio operator expressed his certainty.

"All right, tell them we're coming," Rostron said.

The liner was supposed to do a normal fourteen knots, but now she was forced up to over seventeen, the absolute danger point, and she shook from stem to stern. It was a wild and risky race against time, for the rescue liner had to make her way through the very ice-strewn waters that had already brought the mighty *Titanic* to disaster.

While the *Carpathia* made her historic dash through the night, the terrible tragedy of the *Titanic* was moving to a climax. By 12:20 A.M. the work of lowering the lifeboats had started. Astonishing as it may seem to the reader today, there were only sixteen lifeboats available—not enough boats for even half the people on board this giant liner. There was no panic as the boats were loaded.

The ship remained brightly lighted to the very end, because engineers were using emergency dynamos located above the water line. These courageous engineers were working far below the water line, fighting desperately to keep the pumps going up to the last minute.

The *Titanic* sank slowly at first, one row of lighted portholes after another disappearing below the water. By 2:00 A.M., two hours after her encounter with the hidden ice, her bow had tilted down and was underwater. Hundreds of people clung to stanchions and handrails. Efforts to find objects that could be made to serve as rafts had been futile. The lights went out, finally, and then flashed on again for a moment just as the ship finally went completely under water. There was a tremendous roaring sound as machinery inside the sinking craft broke loose. With the internal balance upset, the *Titanic* stood on end and then slid slowly downward. The hundreds of people floating in the water could now see only the black cold sea.

When the *Carpathia* arrived, 3½ hours after receiving the *Titanic's* distress signal, she managed to rescue 504 passengers and 201 of the crew. The loss of life was 815 passengers and 688 of the crew.

Another wreck, almost as famous as that of the *Titanic,* was that of the *Lusitania*. There were plenty of lifeboats along the *Lusitania's* decks, enough to carry comfortably 2,605 people. In addition, the vessel carried 2,400 life jackets and 35 special life buoys. She was not a big ship by the standards set by later ocean liners, but in her day her 755-foot length and beam of 88 feet seemed very large. She was trimly built, intended for great speed, and her engines could produce 68,000 horse power, capable of giving the ship a speed of 25 knots.

She used little of that speed in her crossing of May, 1915, however,

*Torpedoed by a German submarine, the* Lusitania *sank on May 5, 1915.*

for there was a terrible danger lurking beneath the surface of the Atlantic—the German U-boat. Everyone knew that the danger was there, for a few days before the sailing this notice had appeared in the New York newspapers:

> Travelers intending to embark for an Atlantic voyage are reminded that a state of war exists between Germany and her Allies and Great Britain and her Allies; that the zone of war includes the waters adjacent to the British Isles; that in accordance with the formal notice given by the Imperial German Government, vessels flying the flag of Great Britain or her Allies are liable to destruction in these waters; and that travelers sailing in the war zone in ships of Great Britain and/or any of her Allies do so at their own risk.
>
> *Imperial German Embassy*
> *Washington, D.C., April 22.*

As the *Lusitania* neared the Irish coast, she was prepared for trouble. Captain Turner doubled all lookouts and had the lifeboats lowered to rail level. All water-tight doors were secured except those which had to be used. Because it is frequently possible to outmaneuver a torpedo, the captain ordered that a full head of steam be kept in the boilers because he knew that there might be sudden need for great speed. He gave instructions that if the telephone rang in the engine room, that would be the signal for the chief engineer to throw the throttle wide open instantly.

With all these precautions, the *Lusitania* began her zigzag run toward safety. She was close to shore, for Old Head of Kinsale was only ten miles away from her.

At 2:15 came the dreaded cry of, "Torpedo coming, sir!"

Captain Turner saw the deadly white wake coming swiftly toward them amidships. It was already too close for any kind of dodging action on the part of the ship. A moment later there was a prodigious explosion. Water rose in a great black column and the air was filled with flying pieces of steel. Again that deadly white wake slashed toward the wounded liner; this time the explosion struck the vessel a mortal blow. The engines stopped with a scream of torn machinery. The ship began to list heavily. There was so little time between the launching of the first and the second torpedoes that the theory was advanced that two U-boats participated in the attack.

It was clear to all the officers that the *Lusitania* could not stay afloat much longer, with those gigantic holes that had been torn in her side.

"Lower out all boats!" was the command quickly given.

The *Lusitania's* speed, which had been designed to protect her from just such a catastrophe, became a danger. With her engines shattered, there was no way to check her speed. Yet it is extremely difficult to lower lifeboats safely when a ship is in motion. They are equipped with quick-release devices that cause the tackles to let go as soon as the boat is in the water. In this case the swift movement of the *Lusitania* caused a rush of water which capsized some of the lifeboats along her sides.

Meanwhile, another problem presented itself. The *Lusitania* was listing heavily to starboard, which meant that on her port side her sides had become an almost horizontal expanse of steel over which it was impossible to launch a lifeboat! On the starboard side the situation was not much better. Here the angle of the ship was so sharp that boats, when lowered over the rail, completely disappeared from the sight of those lowering them, so that launching became very difficult. Reserve boats could not be launched at all.

Only twenty minutes after the first torpedo struck, the great *Lusitania* slid down beneath the still, calm waters only ten miles away from land. Her S O S had been picked up and near-by ships were steaming full speed ahead toward the scene of the wreck. But they arrived too late to save the lives of 1,198 people who had not been able to find lifeboats and who had not been able to keep swimming until rescue arrived.

Yes, there have always been wrecks on the ocean, but thanks to such scientific achievements as radar and Loran, they are becoming fewer. And such new developments are sorely needed, for as long as men "go down to the sea in ships" those ships will probably continue to get into trouble whether it be from negligence, storm, tide, collisions, reefs, or any of the many other things that overwhelm gallant ships and brave men.

CHAPTER 9

# SHIPS TO THE RESCUE

*A battered cargo ship gratefully accepts a line from a Coast Guard cutter.*

THAT frantic cry for help, "S O S! S O S!" flashing over the air waves brings to a sudden stop every ship within hundreds of miles. Lurching seas and violent weather cannot stop the brave men who speed to the rescue when a stricken ship struggles helplessly in the ocean. It takes expert seamanship and superb courage, but the traditional gallantry of sea rescues meets the challenge wherever it is laid down.

Before radio was invented, ships had to depend upon rockets to signal their distress, hoping that another ship was near enough to see the bursting flares. The perils of the sea—storm and fog, fire and collision, icebergs and derelicts—claimed many a crew then. However, the thrilling stories of rescues made under incredible conditions are written deep in the log of seafaring history, and upon them is built the fearless reputation of America's merchant marine.

The Dutch ship *Veendam*, steaming out of Rotterdam in the winter of 1898 with 212 people aboard, was three days out of port when the sky clouded over. A fierce gale lashing out of the southwest whipped the angry, yellow waters into towering waves that slammed across the decks at breakneck speed. The mighty breakers lifted the sturdy ship to dizzying heights, then plunged her deep into the trough of the waves. The captain stood on the pitching bridge and eyed the sullen sky uneasily, hoping that the gale would soon blow itself out. But all signs pointed to a long siege.

The *Veendam* had weathered many a storm, and Captain Stenger was confident that the stanch little ship could ride out the rough weather, but he had not counted on meeting one of the most dreaded perils of the sea. As the *Veendam* slid down a mountainous wave, there was an ugly, cracking noise. With a lurch that hurled its passengers abruptly to the floor, the ship staggered and reeled and began to settle by the stern. The dreaded peril was a derelict.

The impact had ripped off the propeller, and foaming water gushed into a gaping hole in the stern. The crew peered out into the murky, gray darkness, hoping desperately to sight another ship, but there was none. The crippled *Veendam* lay floundering in an empty, seething ocean, with land four hundred miles away.

The keen-eyed captain was everywhere at once—driving, encouraging, demanding. The exhausted, grease-spattered men, up to their waists in freezing water, toiled at the pumps, but the water level crept higher and higher. Suddenly hissing clouds of steam rose from the engine room. The sea had found the fires below deck and put them out. That would have finished the pumps and dynamos if it had not been for the auxiliary "donkey boiler," high above the flooded decks.

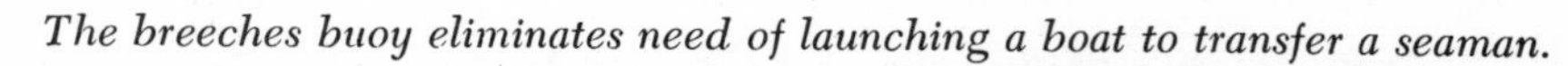

*The breeches buoy eliminates need of launching a boat to transfer a seaman.*

*The yacht* Uvira *taken in tow during a northwest gale by the cutter* Ponchartrain.

In spite of the frenzied efforts of the laboring men at the pumps, the stern wallowed in the sea. A towering mass of green water had swept away a section of lifeboats. Instead of wearing itself out, the fury of the storm increased. The captain realized that the *Veendam* could not stay afloat much longer. He commanded his crew to start firing rockets, hoping desperately that some ship would be close enough to see them. Flare after flare burst in the gray sky. No answering light showed on the horizon. Then came the order to abandon ship. The small, fragile lifeboats could not possibly live in that foaming, turbulent sea, but to stay on the sinking ship was certain death. As the drenched, shivering passengers climbed into the boats, the crew fired the last rocket and scanned the darkness for any sign of a light. Then one of the men shouted and pointed to the northeast. A faint glow shone for a moment, then another, and another. Far out, a ship was answering their signals!

It was the American liner *St. Louis,* speeding to the rescue. All hands were on deck, ready to risk their lives to save the helpless people aboard the *Veendam.* Cutting head-on into the wild sea at twenty knots,

*Standard equipment of life rafts.*

the *St. Louis* drew closer and closer to the fast-sinking ship. The captain of the rescuing ship ordered the lifeboats cleared and called for volunteers to man them. Every member of the crew stepped forward, although they all knew that the tiny boats had one chance in a thousand of staying afloat in that churning ocean.

The ship's doctor threw up cots, gathered blankets, and set up emergency quarters for whatever survivors the boats could manage to pick up.

The *Veendam* was sinking rapidly under the terrific punishment she had taken from storm and sea. It was a matter of minutes now before the gallant ship plunged beneath the waves. At last the *St. Louis* was near enough. Captain Randle shouted to his crew to lower the boats. Down went the first one, looking like a toy beside the giant swells. Time and time again the angry ocean threatened to swamp it, but brawny backs bent over the oars and miraculously righted the boat whenever it tipped dangerously. In spite of the icy weather, the men sweated as they rowed. It took all their strength to gain any headway in those violent waters.

As the second boat hit the frothing sea, a mighty wave smashed it to splinters. The wet, spluttering men clambered back over the side. Instead of reaching for hot coffee and blankets, they grabbed the next lifeboat and swung it out! The anxious captain watched it touch the water; this time they were successful. A third boat went over the side.

A stupendous effort brought the boats within reach of the *Veendam*. Carefully the Dutch crew swung the women and children down to the waiting boats. All but one of the *Veendam's* lifeboats had been battered into wreckage, and the only whole one tossed alongside the three from the *St. Louis*. The heavily laden boats made it back to the American ship, transferred their human burden to ready hands, and turned back again to the *Veendam*. The sea grew rougher, and more than once the sturdy little lifeboats almost capsized. Every minute was precious now; the decks of the Dutch ship were almost level with the surface of the water. As the rescuers fought back and forth through the lashing ocean, the officers of the *Veendam* waited for them to take off the last passengers. At last Captain Stenger was the only one left. He touched a flaming torch to the superstructure of his ship and stepped into the waiting lifeboat. Ten minutes later the *Veendam* turned on her side with a mighty crash and slid down beneath the waters.

In the short space of three hours the *St. Louis'* men had saved 212 people from the clutches of the sea. Regardless of their own lives these courageous American sailors had cheerfully answered the call of their comrades in distress. Their heroism is an epic in seafaring history.

The most spectacular advance in rescue tactics came soon after the sinking of the *Veendam*. Wireless radio, the greatest lifesaver of all, came into use, and insistent messages flashed over the sea from radio-equipped ships. Some uniform distress signal was needed; so an international conference in 1906 decided upon S O S.

With the catastrophic sinkings of the *Titanic* and the *Lusitania* and the frightful loss of life, people began to realize the value of equipping ships with radio. In 1925 the tremendous importance of wireless was vividly stressed.

An S O S from the *Ignazio Florio* streaked out to all ships. The United States liner *President Harding* picked up the message and steamed full

*Coast Guard cutter* Cayuga *towing the disabled trawler* Loon *off George Bank, Maine.*

speed to the disabled Italian ship. She went straight into the teeth of the ferocious gale, against the battering of fifty-foot waves.

The *Florio* kept constant radio communication with the *Harding*. Piece by piece over the telegraph came the dramatic account of what had happened. The ship had left Montreal with a heavy load of grain bound for England and had run into heavy weather on the way. Snarling water twisted over the decks, ripping up everything in its path, and leaked down into the hold. The wet grain began to swell and shift, making the ship list. This was dangerous enough, but the sea had just begun its damage. It snapped the rudder chains like a thread and sent the steering gear hurtling into the sea. The unfastened rudder banged against the ship's side. At any moment it would gouge out a yawning hole, and the *Florio* would be lost. There was no time to lose. The alert, courageous mate caught up two mattresses and, with a rope around his waist, went over the side to try to wedge the rudder. No sooner was he halfway down, out of sight of the men holding the rope, than he looked up, terrified, to see the huge rudder swinging straight at him. No one could hear his shouts above the screeching of the gale. Faster and faster it sped, threatening to crush him completely. Frantically he jerked at the rope. The puzzled men above, who could not see him, began to haul in the line. They got him up almost in time, but the rudder caught his foot. The wounded mate had been unsuccessful in his brave struggle to fasten the steering gear, and the ominous crashing went on.

Water was everywhere in the unlucky ship, even the coal in the engine room was floating. Every lifeboat lay in splinters. Mighty booms came crashing down on the decks.

For twelve hours the gallant *President Harding* had been bucking the storm and was halfway to the scene. By the use of their radio direction finder, they knew at all times the position of the Italian ship. Captain Grening knew he was risking the lives of his three hundred passengers and crew by this daring race through a fierce sea to save twenty-eight men.

*Coast Guardsmen bring an injured seaman ashore from a freighter stranded by a storm.*

*Endless boat drills train a crew in quick methods of launching lifeboats.*

He was not even sure he would get there before the *Florio* went under, and even if he did, the storm might easily keep him from rescuing the men. But it was a chance he had to take, for the call of a ship in distress is the most important signal of the sea.

Dawn turned the darkness gray. All over the *Harding* men were trying to sight the *Florio*. Nine hours passed while crew and passengers strained their eyes for a glimpse of the stricken ship. Suddenly the *Florio* loomed dead ahead out of the fog. Captain Grening determined to try every means of rescue before lowering boats. He ordered oil poured onto the waters, hoping to calm the sea, but it was a vain hope. The waves snarled defiantly and rose as high as before.

Then a Lyle gun was fired, sending out a strong line fastened to a black projectile. But the line could not reach the *Florio*. The captain dared not wait any longer. He called out a lifeboat. All eyes followed it as it neared the foundering ship. Just as success was within its grasp, it disappeared! Searching the sea for it, the crew sighted it a half mile away, capsized. The attempt had failed, and darkness was closing in. It was impossible to launch a lifeboat in that sea.

The Italian captain signaled the *Harding* that he could stay afloat until morning. Captain Grening kept his searchlight on the *Florio* all

*Survivors of a shipwreck eagerly seize the lines dropped on their raft by their rescuers.*

night, ready to make a desperate rescue attempt if she should start to sink.

At seven o'clock in the morning the wind ceased abruptly! For a moment the men of the *Harding* were too stunned to move. Then, exultant, they realized that this sudden lull was their chance for a successful rescue. Quickly they lowered a boat and rowed to the *Florio*. One by one the weary Italian sailors dove into the water and climbed aboard. They were rushed back to the American ship, where doctors treated them for shock and exposure.

Cheering crowds and brass bands met the *President Harding* when she docked in New York. Everyone knew the exciting story of her daring race across one hundred and fifty miles of churning water to save twenty-eight men clinging perilously to a sinking ship. This dramatic rescue drew a vivid picture of the vital necessity for equipping every liner with radio. No longer did battered ships and weary, drenched men have to depend on the feeble glare of rockets to tell of their distress. Now the magic of wireless could get the message through to ships far out of sight.

The *President Harding* was not the only ship that answered the call of the *Ignazio Florio*. The Norwegian tramp steamer *Elven* arrived at the scene just in time to see the *Harding* lower its boats and make the rescue. The lull in the storm ceased as quickly as it had started. For three days the tiny *Elven* stood up under the battering of the gale. Then she began to wallow. Rising water licked at the fires in the engine room and slapped threateningly in the holds. Rough, foaming waves spun the lifeboats across the decks and smashed great, gaping holes in them.

Quickly the Norwegian radioman tapped out the signal—"S O S! S O S!" One hundred and seventy-five miles to the south the *American Trader* lay on the edge of the hurricane, riding out the storm. The moment the message came through, Captain Fish sailed into the storm he had been trying to avoid. The biting October wind piled the water up into waves of incredible height, towering green masses sixty feet high. But the stanch *American Trader* was answering the call of a ship in distress, and she fought her way through the sea with no thought of danger.

A murky, gray fog clouded the night when the *Trader* neared the *Elven*. The two ships were within a few yards of each other, but the visibility was so poor that they could not see each other.

The *Elven* clattered out urgent, frantic messages. The flooded engines could not work the pumps, the after bulwarks were gone. They could not hold out much longer. At six the next morning the *Trader* sighted the *Elven*, so low in the water that Captain Fish called out the lifeboats immediately. The boats struggled back and forth three times through the stormy waters, in constant danger of being sucked under if the Norwegian ship should sink. But the *Trader* had not made the long, perilous trip in vain. She took off every one of the thirty-two men aboard the *Elven*.

So the *American Trader's* gallant heroism wrote another chapter in the long saga of courage at sea. Such daring rescues as these are the sturdy foundation for the mighty reputation of America's brave merchant marine.

*Escape ladder and life line from the bridge of a tanker.*

*To save the life of a stricken seaman, this doctor went from one ship to another by breeches buoy.*

In the winter of 1926, one of the worst gales of the century swept over the North Atlantic Ocean. Fierce winds whirled thick, blinding clouds of snow through the air. In the middle of this seething blizzard at sea, a British ship called the *Antinoe* had been sailing by dead reckoning for ten days. Suddenly a savage gust of wind rocked the ship, slicing off half the bridge and twisting the steering rods so sharply that the rudder was jammed. Water soaked her cargo of five thousand tons of wheat, and the swollen grain burst the hatches of the hold. Sailors fastened them down with weights, but the writhing, expanding wheat ripped them open again, letting in great quantities of water.

The *Antinoe's* radioman sent a distress call ringing down the seas, to be picked up by the *President Roosevelt,* sister ship of the *President Harding.* The Yankee ship raced across the seething ocean to the rescue. When he reached the scene, Captain Fried barked out the order for oil and more oil. Tons of ugly, black slime gushed from every waste pipe, spreading a greasy blanket over the angry waters. Slowly the waves stopped foaming, and soon the listing *Antinoe* rode easier. Encouraged by the slacking, her captain decided to try repairs. The *Roosevelt* stood by. That night the full force of the blizzard howled down upon them. Great, rough chunks of hail stung the faces of the anxious, watchful Americans. Suddenly the *Antinoe's* radio did not answer! Frantically the *Roosevelt's* key tapped, but no reply came through. Searchlights cut the darkness, swinging back and forth to try to locate the wounded ship. The man at the Direction Finder shook his head—no contact.

The storm grew more and more furious. Captain Fried saw the violently heaving *Roosevelt* slam its passengers against walls and litter the decks with smashed dishes and chairs. Gaunt men, fearful now for the *Roosevelt's* own safety, watched the dawn break. Daylight showed no sign of the *Antinoe*. No one doubted that she had sunk, but Captain Fried refused to give up hope. He had not seen the *Antinoe* sink. While there was any chance that she was still afloat, he was determined to keep searching. All that day the *Roosevelt* combed the ocean, unmindful of her own danger. Late in the afternoon a shout from the lookout brought all hands racing to the deck. There, to starboard, the *Antinoe* lay on her side, barely afloat and in desperate need of help. Her crew was launching the one remaining lifeboat, already smashed in the bow, when a rising swell whipped it out of their hands and crushed it to bits. Just then the freezing, exhausted men saw the *Roosevelt* loom up out of the swirling snow. Cheering, they watched a lifeboat swing down the side and pull toward them. When they were halfway there, warning shouts reached the men in the lifeboat. A sudden gust of wind pushed a biting barrage of hail directly at them, snapping the boat over. All but two of the brave little crew got back through the icy water to the American ship.

*Coast Guardsmen give blood plasma to a boy injured on a fishing boat.*

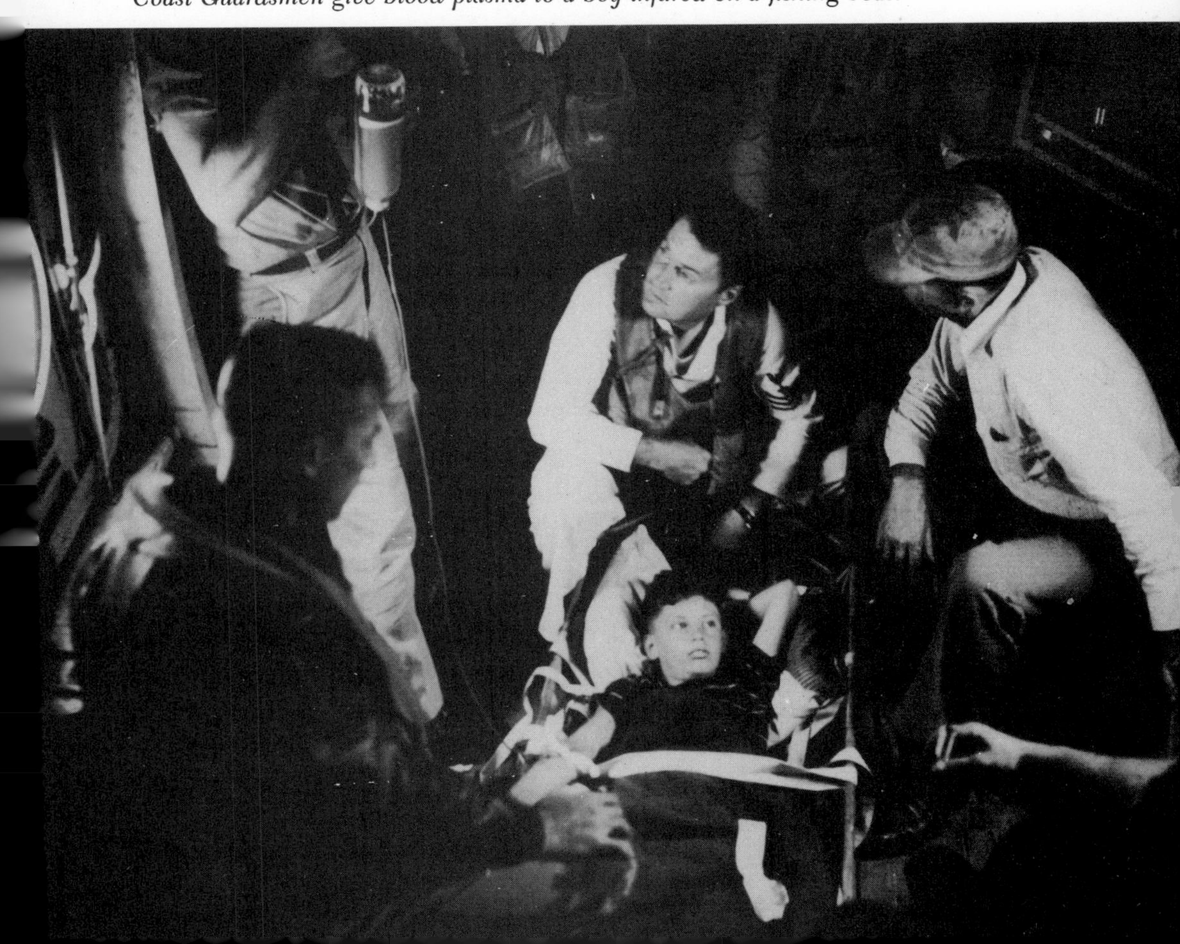

*A trawler disabled in a storm is taken in tow by the cutter* Cayuga.

At three o'clock the next morning the fast-sinking *Antinoe* radioed frantically for immediate help. The Yankee sailors dragged out the Lyle gun. Again and again they fired it, but each shot fell short. All day long through the raging gale the *Roosevelt* circled the *Antinoe,* praying that she could stay afloat a little longer, until they could make a successful rescue. Only the greasy oil slick on the water kept the towering waves from smashing the *Antinoe* to bits.

In the middle of the night Captain Fried tried a daring new plan. He tied one end of a strong line to a lifeboat and the other to a block on the ship. Then, towing the boat in a circle, he tried to foul the line on the *Antinoe,* so they could haul in the boat. But the plan did not work; the line would not snag on the British ship.

The black projectile from the Lyle gun shot out over the water again, each time just missing its goal. Now the *Roosevelt's* crew was showing signs of exhaustion. The rough sea had left injuries and broken bones in its wake.

Three tons of oil poured from the rescue ship's pipe lines every hour. The water-logged *Antinoe* barely showed above the water. It was now or never. Once again Captain Fried gave the order to lower a boat. Over the side it went and out into the darkness. Ten minutes went by, then twenty. Each minute was an eternity to the anxious American spectators. How could the tiny boat hope to escape disaster in that brutal sea?

Soon the searchlight beam shone on the returned boat, packed with the English survivors. Cheers went up, and willing hands pulled the men over the rail. The American merchant marine had added another thrilling rescue to its honored record.

Vast numbers of people and tons of freight crossed the oceans every year. This fast-growing traffic, which crowded the steamship lanes and increased hazards, needed uniform standards for equipment and safety. So, in 1929, representatives of eighteen nations met in London for a safety conference to lay down certain requirements for all companies to follow. Now every ship that puts out to sea can get insurance coverage only if it has met rigid government building specifications and is inspected regularly for seaworthiness.

Central controls on the bridge operate every safety device. Double-bottomed liners are made up of sections with water-tight bulkheads in between. The man on the bridge can tell where the ship is taking water. By snapping a switch, he cuts off the flooded part to keep the water from spreading to another section. The bridge controls the electric gyrostabilizers that lessen the ship's pitching in rough seas and the automatic pilot that can guide the ship with no one at the wheel.

The officer on watch can tell from the panels in front of him whether fire has broken out in any part of the ship, and where. He can set an automatic fire-fighting system going with a flick of his finger. Distress calls come through to him when there is no operator at the radio transmitter.

These safety precautions and ingenious devices for protection have cut sea disasters to a minimum. Now passengers can travel aboard the smooth-riding ocean liners with much more assurance of safety than was formerly possible.

Three years after his rescue of the *Antinoe,* Captain Fried was again racing over a snow-swept ocean to aid another foundering ship with a damaged rudder. Part of the crew of the Italian ship, the *Florida,* had been seriously injured by a sea anchor, her lifeboats lay in splinters, and she was listing so badly that her captain was afraid to stop the engines. She was zigzagging wildly over the ocean, but the *America,* commanded by Captain Fried, found her in the blizzard and hove to, lowering a boat.

Bending low over the oars, the men strained all their efforts to push

*Lifeboat of the S.S.* American Merchant *approaches the crippled British ship* Exeter City.

the boat ahead through the foaming seas. Their only guide was the *America's* searchlight, splitting a path through the darkness. Snow blinded the men, and stinging hail left red bruises on their arms. Their muscles ached from the long tough pull, but these hardy sailors had lives to save and every sweep of the oars brought them closer to the battered ship. When they neared her, one of the Americans tossed a line and shouted to the Italians to hitch it fast. The injured men started to come over on the line. Five, ten, twelve, fourteen. Suddenly the taut line snapped. Another one spun through the air to the deck of the stricken ship. Down swung the rest of the crew, thirty-two in all. All this time the gale had been growing stronger. A piercing wind scooped the water up into gigantic waves that threatened to overturn the boat. For two hours the Yankee sailors had been struggling with wind and snow, hail and water. The lights of the *America* seemed miles away, and they wondered if they had enough strength for the long, hard pull back. Their breath came in heaving sobs, and sweat dripped down their faces. But they would not give up the fight. Bit by bit the distance closed. At last the *America* loomed up beside them in the darkness. Then began the slow process of getting the wounded men on board the liner. One by one they went up in the breeches buoys, followed by the American crew.

Expert seamanship and gallant heroism had again saved life at sea.

The *American Merchant* made one of the most amazing rescues in seafaring history during the hurricane of 1933. A freak sea had caught the English *Exeter City*, which was carrying a cargo of china clay to Maine, and ripped a jagged hole in her. The frothing water had wrenched away the bridge, wheelhouse and chart room, and swept the captain and three men overboard. A great pile of wreckage littered the deck. Out of the debris the crew salvaged parts of what had been the radio, and by the next day they had it in working order again. A weak signal flashed out, which was answered by the *American Merchant*. With the chart room gone, there was only one way the *Exeter City* could find her position. Chief Officer Rowen "shot" the sun with a sextant and radioed his findings to the *Merchant's* navigator, who made a rough estimate of the damaged ship's position. Ten miles separated the two ships—ten miles that would mean life or death to twenty-two men.

The deeply laden freighter was in serious trouble now. It was shipping water with every toss of the sea, and her engineer realized that once the engines ceased and the ship stopped moving the impact of one mighty wave would roll her over. Clay choked the pumping machinery. The British ship and her desperate crew, settling deeper and deeper by the bow, waited for a glimpse of the *Merchant*.

All power on the ship had failed and the patched-up radio went dead. Long before the Yankee liner neared the *Exeter City*, all her rescue equipment lay tested and ready. Thousands of yards of three-inch line was coiled on the deck. Sailors hauled the Lyle gun out and rolled up cargo nets. There were only two ways to make the rescue in that heavy storm. Captain Stedman could either use the breeches buoy, which would take

*Lifeboats and safety equipment on the deck of a freighter plowing through heavy seas.*

hours to rig, or he could try to float a boat across. Time was invaluable; so the captain decided on the shorter way.

The *Merchant* circled the *Exeter City* and covered the foaming water with an oil slick that kept the waves from breaking. The *Merchant* stopped its engines four hundred yards from the English ship. The Lyle gun boomed, and a white line snaked across the sea to land on the deck of the *Exeter City*. American sailors tied their end of the line to one end of a lifeboat, and another line to the other end, so that they could haul it back. This way Captain Stedman could send over an unmanned boat and not risk the lives of his crew.

Captain Stedman won in this gamble with the waves, because the boat made it safely across the stretch of oil-slicked water. Every man aboard the *Exeter City* was eventually hauled to safety.

Our civilization has no finer example of good sportsmanship than the high code of honor that sends ships to the rescue of stricken vessels. So long as storms lash the seas, and ships are in danger, this rule of the high seas will be at work to protect passengers and sailors who venture to cross the oceans.

CHAPTER 10

# CALLING THE COASTGUARD

*Coast Guard motor boat comes to the rescue of a sailboat capsized by the wake of a flying boat.*

THE GREAT armada sailed through the straits of Gibraltar and on into the Mediterranean. This gigantic striking force, driving the first wedge of invasion against the port of Oran, a Vichy-French stronghold, held back its fire power and concealed its movements, waiting for reports from two small ex-Coast Guard cutters, manned by British naval personnel, that had preceded them.

Far from their traditional homeland coasts, men of the Coast Guard were once again spearheading a drive that might be likened to Stephen Decatur and his conquest of Barbary pirates.

The mission of these two cutters was to blow the big boom that barred the way for the invasion troops carried by the eight hundred and fifty warships, transports, tankers, and freighters that stood out to sea behind the two dauntless cutters. Under the very muzzles of the big guns in the forts ashore, the crew slipped up alongside the chain-rigged boom and carefully laid their charges.

Then the signal! Hundreds of pounds of explosives detonating at the same time. A man-made lightning rent the air with a fiery flash. That was the signal. The immense armada moved in for the kill, the way opened by the men of the Coast Guard.

What of the dauntless crews of these two cutters that spearheaded this opening of the second front in World War II? Under the guns of the forts, and in the light made by their own explosions, they went down with their guns blazing, in the traditional manner of the United States Coast Guard.

In war and in peace the heroic men of the Coast Guard, the men who go down to the sea in small ships, have written their immortality in deeds that rank high in the stories of seamen's valor. No more fitting motto than its watchword, *Semper Paratus,* "Always Prepared," could have been chosen by the Coast Guard. It serves in so many ways that there is not a day in the year that the Coast Guard does not see some sort of exciting action.

The biggest task of the Coast Guard is to save human lives. With its lightships, cutters, lighthouses, lifeboats, beach patrols, and flying boats, it works night and day at this task. In action, the Coast Guard presents a thrilling picture of individual bravery and fortitude, combined with teamwork. The heroism of John Midgett, Coast Guard surfboatman, a few years ago, is a good illustration of the kind of courage that is commonplace among Coast Guardsmen.

Three times the rumbling, roaring surf had pushed them back. On the fourth try, after righting their surfboat, the Coast Guardsmen stood poised, each man in his place on either side of the boat, waiting for a sea that would launch them or throw them back. Then it came—a surging line of foam-flecked, swirling, green-laced water.

"All together!" shouted Keeper John Midgett, the warrant officer in command.

Muscles strained, necks corded, and weathered faces grew taut, then the boat was afloat. They pushed the surfboat out until water came up to their hips. Then each man jumped and was in his proper position. The motor started with a rumbling roar and the surfboat headed for the next breaker. She took it easily because it was nearly spent. Then they caught the full force of the following comber. The boat reared its head, its motors slowing with the effort; it stood on end, then fell with a crash that threatened its stout timbers. It raced off into a trough with express-train speed, its motor humming. The battle had a certain regularity, but certainly not a monotonous one. The Chicamacomico Coast Guard Station personnel were off to investigate the source of a heavy smoke pall reported as a burning ship, lying off Cape Hatteras, that turbulent stretch of Atlantic where quiet waters are unknown. Even a moderate sea causes frenzied tumbling waters because of the stretch of shoals. Running the breakers at this point holds a thrill for even the most hardened veteran of Chicamacomico. Running this stretch of water is dangerous, spine-tingling work; work that requires every ounce of strength, skill, and ingenuity, and something besides—that inner fire that makes men risk their lives for their fellow men.

Outside the treacherous reefs the Coast Guard boat met a lifeboat coming from the burning vessel, which now could be plainly seen. They learned that the burning ship was the British tanker *Mirlo,* which had been torpedoed. Midgett persuaded the master of the *Mirlo,* who was in the lifeboat, not to attempt to run the stretch of water into the beach because of the dangers for one not familiar with that part of the coast. The captain of the *Mirlo* agreed, and the lifeboat set out a sea anchor. The valiant little crew of Guardsmen continued on toward the stricken vessel. It was a terrifying sight. It seemed that for an area of approximately two miles the entire ocean flamed. Great billows of brownish-black smoke poured upward, and an occasional pocket of gas exploded with a dull swoosh. The fire ran this way and that with the heavy seas. It formed a gigantic crescent, the points of which alternately opened and closed as the turbulent sea boiled with fury. The crew tensely scanned the inferno as the Coast Guard boat approached the opening.

Suddenly Midgett stiffened, his keen eyes cutting into the smoke and fire. Open water beyond a wall of flame revealed a drifting, capsized lifeboat from the *Mirlo.* Figures clung to the lifeboat!

"Wet down everything," ordered Midgett. "We're going through." The surfboat was dampened down. Midgett gave the order. The boat moved directly for the flame, which

*Taking care of lighthouses is just one of the Coast Guard's many tasks.*

*The keeper of Owl's Head Lighthouse, Maine, cleans an emergency kerosene lamp kept in the tower.*

slowly parted as the seas receded. An opening! But only for an instant! The motor roared and then the boat was through, even though stifling smoke blanketed it. Water coming over the gunwales smelled of oil. Everywhere about the men was flame and smoke, and an incessant terrifying roar and crackle. After coming through the opening they found they were still separated from the capsized lifeboat. Midgett put the little surfboat through the flames and picked up the six tired men who were clinging to it. Then they found they were completely surrounded by flaming oil. Slowly they cruised inside the wall of flames, looking desperately for an opening. They found none, and Midgett decided to take the boat through the fire.

Pulling his sou'wester over his head, Midgett ordered the crew to do likewise. Then he put the boat straight at the wall of crackling, sputtering fire. The smoke was blinding and the heat blistering. The men gasped for breath, and Midgett coughed smoke from his lungs. The motor missed, spat, missed again. Every man held his breath. The lack of oxygen in the burning area had deprived the carburetor of the necessary air to function. Then they were out. The motor resumed its steady beat. The men bailed frantically to splash water on the smoldering boat and on their parched faces. All thoughts of a moment's relaxation vanished as another boat from the *Mirlo* was sighted. It contained a group of panic-stricken men without a leader. Oars stood aloft at all angles and the boat drifted helplessly toward the flames. Midgett put the surfboat alongside and took the lifeboat in tow and pulled the men a safe distance from the fire zone while rescuers and rescued rested in exhaustion. That is, all rested except Midgett. His mind was alive with the possibilities of getting the crew from the *Mirlo* safely ashore through the stretch of murderous surf. The wind was rising now, and the seas running heavily.

Darkness was falling as Midgett brought the surfboat alongside the lifeboat that contained the captain of the *Mirlo*. He took three men aboard and then, as he unshipped his tiller to replace it with the great steering oar, he assured the remainder of the *Mirlo* crew that he would return for them.

At a word of command the boat was turned toward the beach. The surfboat picked up a comber and, racing along at a spine-tingling pace, they rode it out like a surf board. Then in a trough they waited for another. It came, lifting them high, thrusting them along, and each man in the boat felt the power and relentlessness of the Atlantic on a rampage.

This sort of work requires great strength and skill on the part of the steersman; a skill and strength possessed by Midgett. The last great breaker rolled the boat into the beach. Station personnel had placed flares on the sands out of reach of the roaring surf. These same men now removed the crew members of the *Mirlo* from the surfboat, and Midgett and his crew turned back. Darkness was on them, and they still had many trips to make.

Four more trips were made, and dawn was just breaking as the last crew member from the *Mirlo* was placed ashore. The surfboat was pushed on the waiting carriage and the tired men trundled it to its shelter. This, then, is part of the work of the United States Coast Guard, the only organization of its kind in the world today. No other country maintains a service in any way like it, although numerous countries contribute financially to certain phases of its operation. The Coast Guard is essentially a peacetime force and is a division of the Treasury Department, but in time of war it is placed under the Secretary of the

Navy and acts as a part of the Navy. During World War II the Coast Guard built an enviable record in combat as it has in all our wars since we became a nation.

After the War of Independence, Congress disbanded the Continental forces and set to work to cement the several states into a unified nation. At that time the country was chiefly agricultural and most of the manufactured articles had to be imported. The struggling Federal Government imposed customs duties on these imports in order to raise enough revenue to meet Federal expenses. Trouble started at once because many people resented this tariff. Smuggling began on a large scale. To protect the Government's chief source of revenue, Alexander Hamilton had a bill passed establishing the Revenue Cutter Service to enforce customs laws. Ships were obtained, and before long the coast was being successfully patrolled. Many other duties were gradually added to the Revenue Cutter Service. In 1915 it was combined with the Life-Saving Service, and in 1939 the Lighthouse Service was added. Much of the Lighthouse Service equipment and personnel was used to establish our present-day system of Civil Airways. Even today at some of the Airway Radio Stations there will be a piece of equipment marked "U.S. Lighthouse Service," so it can be seen that the Coast Guard indirectly had some part in our present-day Federal Airways System.

The Coast Guard patrols the entire American seacoast and the Great Lakes, warning shipping of storms and dangers to navigation. Laws against smuggling and other laws governing the operation of marine craft are enforced. The Coast Guard gives examinations for all seamen papers, such as masters, mates, and pilots. When a ship is in distress, the Coast Guard immediately sends a vessel to its aid. Every year thousands of lives and millions of dollars' worth of ships and cargo are saved. The Coast Guard gives medical and dental aid to the sick and injured on ships and fishing boats and gives shore aid to the victims of shipwrecks.

Sometimes the Coast Guard serves on inland waters, fighting the menace of flooded rivers. A few years ago the flood crest on the Mississippi passed Natchez and the levees were breached. Water poured from a dozen breaks in cascading torrents, flooding an already inundated countryside with swirling, muddy water that rose higher and higher, in the streets, over highways, railroads, fields, and homes. Cries for help went humming out over communication lines still up. A long string of flatcars, loaded with Coast Guard surfboats, backed slowly on submerged rails. Brackish water rose higher and higher around the flatcars. Each boat was provisioned, stocked with medicine and first-aid supplies. Crews stood by in complete readiness. Soon the train had backed the flatcars into such deep water that the boats floated off their racks. Manned by Coast Guard personnel, the boats fanned out, seeking to aid all those in distress. Overhead, planes of the Coast Guard flew at low altitudes, the observers scanning the flooded areas looking for people in distress. When such a case was found, the plane circled until the attention of the seeking boats was attracted and then headed for rescue. After a boat reached the indicated spot, the plane flew off to continue the search. Thus the Coast Guard responded to the worst Mississippi flood in history. From Memphis to New Orleans, cutters, river boats, and powered surfboats plied the backwaters, rescuing stranded families, moving cattle and livestock, acting as messengers and couriers, transporting workers and supplies from one point to another, moving sick and injured people to hospitalization centers. Frequently the radio transmitters and receivers, manned by experienced radio operators of the Coast Guard, were the only means of communication with the outside world. After this flood crisis had passed and there was time for accounting, it was found that the Coast Guard had rescued sixty thousand people and moved eleven thousand head of cattle to places of safety. Some of the boats had covered more than five thousand miles.

Another job of the Coast Guard is to locate floating derelicts and submerged wrecks that are a great menace to ships. The Guard has regular patrols of ships and airplanes along the shipping lanes to look for these floating dangers. Whenever possible, they sink the derelicts by gunfire or blow them up with explosives. When this cannot be done, the patrols issue warn-

*A radio beacon buoy that transmits signals that can be picked up by navigators of an approaching ship.*

*A student Coast Guardsman learns how to make repairs on a light buoy.*

ing to all near-by ships. These warnings are also broadcast by the Navy Hydrographic Office through all Naval Radio Shore Stations. More than two hundred floating derelicts were removed from the shipping lanes in one typical year.

One of the great services of the Coast Guard is the North Atlantic Ice Patrol, which protects modern shipping against the perils of icebergs. Ships plying the cold sea lanes of the North Atlantic have always faced the danger of colliding with these great white ghosts that challenge the right of ships to pass.

Icebergs are really broken pieces of big Greenland glaciers. They make their way slowly southward, carried by strong sea currents. In the spring they drift down as far as the Grand Banks, where they often go aground. Here they create a new menace, because the evaporating moisture from the melting bergs creates dense fogs. Some of the bergs are of tremendous size. Flat-topped bergs have been sighted which are more than two miles in length and tower more than three hundred feet in the air. The part of a berg showing above the water represents about one-eighth of its bulk, and the real danger to shipping lies in the hidden part of the berg. Some bergs have practically no visible peak above the water, and these are extremely dangerous to shipping because they are so hard to see. Sometimes a different kind of ice, field or floe ice, drifts far south into the shipping lanes. At times huge floating ice fields have been found to be over one hundred miles in length. On one occasion a steamer reported that it had traveled through such an ice floe for three days and nights.

Modern science has found many ways to overcome the danger of icebergs, the latest being instruments based on radar which return a radio "echo" if icebergs are near. The work of the United States Coast Guard in keeping track of icebergs and of warning shipping has done much to enable all ships to avoid these white killers of the sea lanes.

Before the Coast Guard took over, there were many disasters brought about by encounters with icebergs. Just how many ships have been lost by collisions with icebergs is unknown, for many ships have simply disappeared at sea. Among them was the *City of Glasgow,* a crack liner of her day. She left Liverpool in 1854 with 450 persons aboard. She was never heard of again. During the years that followed there was a steady procession of lost ships, presumed to have met destruction by hitting icebergs. The *Tempest,* lost in 1857 with 150 passengers; the *United Kingdom* in 1868; the *City of Boston* in 1870; the *City of Limerick* in 1881; the *Erin* in 1889 are just a few of the ships that disappeared completely on the ice-strewn northern sea lanes.

Many narrow escapes were reported. In 1879 the liner *Arizona* was plowing through the Atlantic when suddenly, with the full force of her eighteen knots, she slammed into a huge berg. Her bow crumpled, and tons of ice fell onto the forward deck with a crunching roar. Frightened passengers rushed from their berths but the captain managed to overcome their panic by assuring them that the vessel was safe and would not sink. With great skill he succeeded in backing his ship off the berg. The forward bulkhead held and, although the bow was a crumpled wreck and huge pieces of ice still covered her decks, the *Arizona* made her way safely to St. John's, Newfoundland.

Many other ships met destruction through collisions with icebergs in the years up to 1912. Then came the greatest disaster of all, the sinking of the great *Titanic,* the story of which is told in Chapter 8. Something had to be done, and in 1914 an agreement was reached between various countries to maintain an ice patrol and observation service in the North Atlantic for the benefit of all shipping. Each nation was to bear part of the expense, and the United States was to carry out the actual work. This duty was assumed by the Coast Guard. The record speaks for itself—since that time not a single life has been lost because of icebergs. The danger period usually lasts from March until July, during which time the Coast Guard cutters locate the bergs. The Ice Patrol warns shipping as to the location, size, and drift.

The regular Winter Patrol is another Coast Guard task. Every year during the period from December to the end of March, when coastal storms are most severe, the stout little cutters cruise up and down the coastal waters, aiding distressed vessels and carrying on the regular routine of law enforcement, taking sick and wounded men off fishing

*This lighted bell buoy off the Aleutian Islands has a radio mechanism that turns it on and off automatically.*

boats, giving medical aid, destroying derelicts, and so on. These boats, and the men on them, work regardless of storms or bad weather. Sometimes patrol boats come off duty completely caked with ice, their crews wet to the skin and blue with cold. The men get accustomed to two-week tours of duty in which lack of sleep, seasickness, missed meals, and cold, stormy watches are the order of the day and night.

The story of the *Talapoosa* is typical. As she cruised through the North Atlantic, the lifting mist revealed an appalling sight. As far as the eye could see, there was a jumbled reach of jagged ice kept in motion by heavy seas. Captain James F. Hottel, U. S. Coast Guard, commanding the cutter *Talapoosa,* for once was thankful for half-gale winds. They kept the ice from solidifying. Once the seas and wind subsided, the ice pack would close around the gallant little *Talapoosa* and she would be stuck fast in the ice for months to come. Furthermore, the men they were en route to rescue would die. The radiogram that had started Captain Hottel on this journey had stated that the crew of the wrecked fishing schooner *Arkona,* numbering nine men, were in imminent danger of starvation. The radiogram had ordered: "Proceed at once to Jobs Room, Forteau Bay, Labrador, and pick up crew of *Arkona.*" It did not mention that the Straits of Belle Isle, entrance to Forteau Bay, were considered closed to navigation at this time of the year. There was no mention of the violent winds and strong tides and currents, or that the *Talapoosa* was not designed for bucking heavy ice.

Nevertheless, the dauntless cutter pushed on, and Greenly Island was picked up in record time. A radio message from Point Armour reported the Straits of Belle Isle jammed with heavy ice. A similar report from Flower Cove on the Newfoundland coast just abreast of

Forteau Bay did not deter the captain of the *Talapoosa.* He pushed his ship on, although barometer and temperature were falling. After cautiously feeling its way through the Straits, the intrepid cutter pushed into miraculously open water at Jobs Room. But Captain Hottel knew it couldn't last. With feverish haste, medicine and supplies were unloaded for the starved natives who must remain; the crew of the wrecked *Arkona* were taken aboard and the return trip began.

Trying to ram through the ice would have been fatal. The *Talapoosa* was not an ice breaker, and to try forcing it through would have been similar to running into the rocky mainland coast. It was necessary to weave back and forth, cautiously seeking an opening, forging ahead little by little. To make matters worse, a full gale was now blowing. The extreme cold was slowly transforming the brave little ship into the likeness of an iceberg. Wind moaned through the rigging of the *Talapoosa,* and the icy coating grew steadily as the cutter butted cautiously along through the gale-whipped waters. Spray, flying across the ship, froze instantly, and even the mist froze as it touched mast, rails, and halyards. The captain had the crew turn to with chipping hammers, wrenches, and anything that would serve to keep the ship free of ice. Captain Hottel was afraid ice would accumulate to such an extent that the ship would become top-heavy and swamp. The men were aware of this danger, but even though they were blue with cold, their clothes frozen stiff, they worked to save their ship and their lives. For thirty-six hours, without let-up, the men worked, labored, froze, becoming mechanical men that chipped the ice automatically; falling from sheer exhaustion but rising again to resume their work. At last the gale subsided, and the *Talapoosa* limped into port, still covered with ice, but safe.

The Northern Patrol is another task of the far-ranging Coast Guard. This is conducted each year by several cutters in the Northern Pacific, the Bering Sea, and Alaskan waters. This patrol was established in 1911 as the result of an agreement among several nations. It was designed to protect and conserve the wild life of the North, which includes the fur seal and the otter. Also, as in other phases of their work, they are continually on the alert for people in distress. They carry mail to isolated ports and give dental and medical aid to the natives and to seafarers. They administer oaths, hold courts of justice, perform autopsies, examine vessels, carry food and supplies to distressed communities and, in general, play an important part in the life of this primitive region.

It was on a patrol such as this that the cutter *Tahoma* was lost; one of the rare instances when chance and elements combined to rout the Coast Guard. The *Tahoma* was built especially for the rigors of the Arctic Patrol. She was a two-thousand-ton vessel, well-built, stanch and strong. She went down on uncharted reefs near Boldir Island, under the command of Captain Crisp. Only superb seamanship on the part of Captain Crisp and his officers brought the crew out of this catastrophe.

The Coast Guard Beach Patrol is another service that is little known. But in peace and in war, like the rest of the organization, it serves well.

A lone man was pacing his midnight patrol along a six-mile stretch of Amagansett Beach, Long Island. Suddenly, through the fog, he spotted three men, two in bathing suits and one in civilian clothes. When he approached them, they refused to answer his queries until he grabbed for his flash light to throw a beam of light on their faces. Evidently the three men thought he was grabbing for a gun, for they began to talk.

"We're a couple of fishermen from Southampton," said one, "who have run aground."

Then, after threatening him, the Nazi spies, for that is what they were, offered the Coast Guardsman, John C. Cullen, one hundred dollars to "forget the whole thing."

When Cullen refused, the spies offered him three hundred dollars. Cagily he accepted it, and turned to leave.

"Just a minute," said one, and he ordered Cullen to "look him in the eyes."

Reluctantly Cullen obeyed, afraid that the man meant to hypnotize him, but instead the man snarled out: "You won't recognize me again, will you?"

Cullen assured the man that he wouldn't and casually walked away. As soon as he was covered by the fog, he raced to the Coast Guard Station. The alarm was given and within a few minutes several men were armed and ordered to search the beach for any further signs of the invaders. No signs were found, however, until fifteen minutes afterwards, when Chief Boatswain's Mate Barnes saw "a long, thin object, about 70 feet long, about 150 feet offshore."

The men were ordered to take shelter in the sand dunes in case of a landing, but the submarine disappeared in the fog. The men searched all night, with reinforcements from near-by Army and Navy stations.

Around dawn, four wooden boxes, with a tin case enclosed in each, were found in the sand. One of the tins contained a large number of pen and pencil sets. Another box was filled with loose powder and glass tubes. Material for incendiary bombs!

From that point FBI men under J. Edgar Hoover took up the chase until the group of men who had landed off Amagansett Beach and also a group who landed in Florida were caught.

That was how the Beach Patrol was instrumental in the capture of German spies landed by submarine on American coasts during World War II. But capturing spies and saboteurs is not the usual rôle played by the Beach Patrol. Because they are constantly on the alert for ships that go ahead off the coast, the men have earned the lifetime gratitude of all mariners for their dangerous and thrilling rescues of wrecks reported by surf men.

Although the Coast Guard is a distinctive service, many of its traditions and customs are patterned after that of the United States Navy. Naval discipline is maintained aboard ships and at shore stations. The

*Coast Guardsmen pull for their lives after setting dynamite in an iceberg to destroy it.*

uniform is the same except for the Coast Guard's identifying shield. Pay grades are the same as those of the Navy, and the Commandant of the Coast Guard ranks with an Admiral in the Navy and a Major General in the Army.

During peacetime the Coast Guard usually consists of about 19,500 officers and men. In addition to their numerous other duties, they care for more than 10,000 lighted aids to shipping, 1,500 visual and day marks, about the same number of foghorns and whistling buoys, about 4,000 cutters and surfboats, numerous amphibians, and even a few destroyers.

If Stephen Decatur should come aboard a Coast Guard cutter today, the first difficulty would be to convince Decatur that this was really a ship. The doughty old sea dog would look for the cannonades, the bulwarks, the sails. Perhaps the chime of the ship's bell, or the pipe of the bos'n whistle would convince him—or the spirit of the Guard, which has not changed. Nor has the motto, *Semper Paratus,* the term that so well describes the United States Coast Guard.

# CHAPTER 11

# FLOATING LIGHTHOUSES

*Off Cornfield Point, Connecticut, the lightship of that name stands guard over the shipping lanes.*

GRAY, swirling fog, thick with the sense of hidden danger, shrouded the lightship *Nantucket* as she lay at anchor in her appointed place. The twelve men aboard the lightship knew there were many ships feeling their way blindly through that thick blanket. At any moment one of them might come plunging out into the dim circle of radiance cast by the powerful lights of the *Nantucket*, which in clear weather could be seen for miles. It was a terrifying experience to see a ship come looming out of the gray shroud, seem to tower above the lightship, and then race by so close that the wash from powerful screws set the small craft to rocking. These men knew, for they had seen it. Just a few weeks before this October night in 1934, a big liner, the *Washington*, had come thundering down upon the *Nantucket*, carrying away part of her superstructure. Somehow the little ship had survived, but the men knew that they had been lucky. The big liner could have struck the lightship squarely amidships. Since that experience the men had been tense every time a ship came close. However, they were not worried when they heard the hoarse bellow

*A seaman makes repairs to the foghorn of a lightship.*

of a foghorn at a distance of what they judged to be several miles. It was coming closer, but that was not unusual.

The *Nantucket* was well equipped with devices to indicate her presence. From her powerful diaphone foghorn came four roaring blasts a minute, blasts that could be heard at a distance of at least fourteen miles. From her radio beacon came the warning signals, over and over again. An underwater warning was emitted continually by her submarine bell. Seemingly, she was well protected, and seamen on approaching vessels had ample opportunity to learn their exact distance from the lightship. Her foghorn was synchronized with the last beat of her radio beacon. Since radio waves travel 186,000 miles a second, and sound waves only about 1,100 feet a second, men on approaching ships could readily measure the distance by measuring the time interval between the radio signal and the foghorn sound. To determine the number of miles, all they had to do was to divide the seconds of interval by five, which would give the distance in miles. Sometimes it can happen, however, that the foghorn cannot be heard at all, even by the best of sea-trained ears. Differences in air temperature are the cause of fogs; these same differences, unfortunately, can also distort sound waves and cause them to bounce upward. Later these same waves may be sent bouncing back to sea level by a higher layer of cold air. Thus it can happen that a ship five or six miles from a lighthouse or lightship may hear a signal clearly while a ship much closer cannot hear it at all. Other strange things can happen to the sound of a foghorn. It may be deflected by the edge of a fog bank; it may be distorted by the wind to such an extent that it seems to come from almost the opposite direction from its real source.

The submarine bell is designed to overcome this distortion. It sends out underwater waves that travel at a speed of about forty-eight hundred feet a second. Many big ships are equipped with special receiving devices in the hull that pick up these signals. Since the speed is uniform, it is possible to calculate easily the distance from the source of the signal wave.

Because the men of the lightship *Nantucket* were protected with these devices, which were the best of their kind before the days of radar, they might well have felt secure when the lookout man reported: "Ship on port quarter!"

The men could tell she was a big craft, and traveling fast, because her signal came closer at an alarming rate. Although they still could not see the hidden monster in the fog, they suddenly heard the thundering roar of the bow wave. For a moment the captain stared anxiously, trying to pierce the fog. Should he call the men who were below? Then, before he could move, he saw it—a looming wall leaping out of the fog. The captain sprang to the doorway and shouted to the crew: "All hands—on deck—lively!"

The crew members gripped the rail tensely and looked up at the frightening structure that was rushing down upon them. She was a big ship, and at last they could make out the letters O-L-Y-M-P-I-C, far above. A moment later came the crash of crumpling metal and shattering wood. The crushed lightship was carried along for some distance like a chip caught against the bow of the great liner. Then the *Nantucket* anchor chain held and in a moment jerked her free of the liner. That jerk tore the gaping hole in her side still wider. While some of her men, including her captain, lay stunned in the shambles of fallen superstructure, the *Nantucket* went down. The boats put overboard by the *Olympic* as soon as she succeeded in cutting her speed found no trace of the ship. They picked up seven men of her crew, who were floundering in the water. Just how a modern liner like the *Olympic*, equipped with every possible device to receive the lightship's signals, could have crashed into the source of those signals is one of the curious mysteries of the sea that has not been solved. This incident well illustrates the

*The main reason for a lightship is the beam of light from its beacon.*

dangerous life faced by all the men who go out to sea in lightships to protect other ships on the high seas.

Being run down is a danger that confronts the lightship crews not only in foggy weather but even when the weather is perfectly clear. Proof of this strange experience is found in the accident that befell the lightship *Hedge Fence* as she lay off Massachusetts on a calm and starlit night.

In a routine manner the lookout reported sighting a ship heading in the general direction of the *Hedge Fence*. Certainly there was nothing in this fact to alarm members of the crew. Ships often appeared to be heading toward the lightship, and then, at the last moment, they would swerve off and pass by. But the lookout grew a little uneasy as he saw the ship looming larger and larger. She was getting too close. The captain and the crew lined up along the rail, staring at this strange sight of a ship bearing down on them through the calm sea. In the brilliant rays of the lightship's lamps, it was seen that she was a sizable freighter.

*The Swiftsure shoals off the coast of Oregon are marked by this Coast Guard lightship.*

The men shouted, but their warning was unheard above the throb of engines. There was a terrific crash as the freighter plunged headlong into the lightship, striking her near the pilot house and slashing a huge, gaping hole in her side. The crew managed to get a lifeboat launched barely in time, for in a matter of a few minutes the wounded lightship sank. The lightship crewmen were as angry as they were frightened, for there seemed no possible reason why a steamer should run them down under such perfect weather conditions. They were no less angry when they heard the explanation in the hearing that was held later. It seemed that the captain of the freighter had left the bridge, giving a new helmsman a course to steer by. The helmsman stuck to instructions, continuing doggedly on the course given him, even though he knew that a collision was going to result. It was an unusual case of blind and unreasoning obedience.

The lightship is literally a floating lighthouse, which can be located in positions offshore where it would be impossible to build a regular lighthouse. The maintenance of lightships is not new in American history, although today it is one of the Coast Guard's many tasks. The first lightship was an old but seaworthy wooden schooner that was anchored in the Chesapeake in 1820. Today's lightships are specially designed for their job, with high prows and bulging sides that enable them to ride high seas on a fairly even keel. Unlike the lightships used by other countries, which are usually simply floating platforms with no means of propulsion, American lightships are equipped with powerful engines that enable them to beat their way back to their stations if they should be blown away. The lightship anchor weighs nearly four tons, but sometimes it is not sufficient to hold the ship during a severe storm.

High seas are the most deadly enemy of the lightship, and there are countless stirring tales of epic battles with raging waves. One of the exciting stories told is of one of the many ships that have borne the name *Nantucket.* One dark January morning she was fighting against gigantic waves that seemed to tower above her. She strained at her big anchor cable until it was drawn taut many times. Perhaps she might have ridden out this January storm, as she had many another, had she not been struck by a huge wave. It seemed to hover for a moment above the lightship, then crashed down with the tremendous force of tons of water. It carried away parts of the superstructure, smashed the lifeboats, and came cascading into the ship through shattered skylights.

*Lightships are small but rugged and are built to stand rough seas.*

The *Nantucket* was carried along with the crest of the wave. For a moment the vessel jerked back, then there was a loud snap, heard even above the roaring fury of the waves. The unfortunate ship had parted its cable!

Hastily the men stopped the signals going out from the ship, for now that she had left her fixed position they would give false directions that might lure ships to destruction. Then the captain considered the unhappy position of his ship. She was rapidly being driven by the gale toward the shoals that lay closer to shore. It was against the dangers of these very shoals that the *Nantucket* was intended to warn vessels. Now she herself was in danger of being wrecked by them. Although she was built to ride out heavy seas at anchor, the *Nantucket* was hardly the right kind of craft to fight seas of the kind that were carrying her toward destruction. She rolled and pitched. Her bows dug deep into the waves and came up with tons of water roaring across her decks. To make matters worse, there was a heavy fog, and it was impossible for the captain to see where they were going. The lightship was driven through the fog for hours. Finally, as dawn approached, the captain managed to find her location by radio bearings. To his astonishment he learned that she had been carried over thirty miles from her proper position.

As the morning wore on, the storm abated somewhat and the captain gave orders that the great chain should be heaved in. Then the ship's engine began to make some headway. Slowly they were able to pull away from the menacing shoals. It was painfully slow progress, but by one o'clock the following morning, twenty hours after she had broken away from her anchor, the *Nantucket* had managed to fight her way back to within fifteen miles of her regular position. Then, ominously, the barometer began to fall, a warning that was soon followed by another furious attack by the elements. In the violent gale that swept down on her again, the helpless lightship was tossed about like a cork, her crew clinging desperately to whatever was handy. The chain that had been so laboriously drawn up from the sea was paid out again to provide some drag. The chain and the ship's racing engines succeeded in holding the *Nantucket* in an all-day battle to keep from being swept into the shoals. All day and night the *Nantucket* continued the terrible struggle to hold her own and managed to make some progress during lulls in the storm. At midnight of the third day of her wild journey to nowhere, she had fought her way back to within six miles of her station, and again her signals were sent through sea and air to guide ships on their way.

*Boat crew of lightship* Blunts Reef *off the California coast prepare to lower a lifeboat.*

The Master of the *Nantucket* then wrote this modest report of what had occurred:

*Nantucket Shoals Lightship, January 27, 1933*

SUPERINTENDENT OF LIGHTHOUSES, Chelsea, Massachusetts.

*Subject:* Lightship No. 117 parting her mooring.

*January 27, 1933.* This day begins with strong gale and heavy breaking seas. Fog and radio signals going O.K. Ship laboring heavily and straining on cable; shipping lots of heavy spray over pilot house.

5:20 A.M. Very heavy comber boarded ship forward of amidships on port side without any warning, shaking ship all over with a loud report like the firing of a cannon. It washed the port lifeboat out of the chocks and put her out of commission, making three holes in starboard and bottom side and one in forward bow. The ship seems to have taken in water everywhere.

7:00 A.M. Fog lifting. Commenced to look for marking buoy. Mr. Logan, 2nd Mate, and myself, came to the conclusion that the ship was dragging off station.

7:05 A.M. Stopped all signals.

7:15 A.M. Found by bearings that ship was 32 miles to the WSW of station. Ordered broadcast that the lightship was off station.

8:10 A.M. Commenced to heave in chain. Found chain parted 75 fathoms from mushroom anchor; a clean break in the forward end of the third link from shackle.

9:35 A.M. Radio put ship 39 miles off station. Underway, steering NE or trying to. Very heavy sea, strong gale, and rain squalls.

Noon. Ship 42 miles from station, strong gale, and heavy breaking seas running. Moderating. Ship making headway.

Midnight. Ship 16 miles from station.

*January 28.* 4:21 A.M. Heavy gale and seas getting heavier.

Noon. Heavy gale and heavier squalls with rain. Ship holding her own. Wind NW and sea NE. 30 miles 242 degrees from station.

8:00 P.M. Paid out all chain, 105 fathoms, for drag; 40 fathoms water. Engine going various speeds to hold our own, and keep ship head to sea. Ship behaving fine but rolling and pitching heavily.

*January 29.* Noon. 28 miles off station laying to drag.

4:30 P.M. Moderating. Took in chain drag. Steering northeasterly or trying to; making from three to five points leeway. Making about 1½ knots per hour.

Midnight. Moderating, but heavy cross sea. Trying to steer NE. Got within six miles of buoy.

*January 30.* 3:30 A.M. About two miles from station, running ESE. Found it hard to keep any kind of position. Everybody getting played out. Station buoy NNW. Paid out chain without anchor as a drag and let her lay until daylight. At 4:45 A.M. chain all out, buoy bearing NW, two miles.

7:30 A.M. Commenced heaving in.

8:10 A.M. Chain in. Proceeded to station.

9:15 A.M. Started heaving out chain.

9:45 A.M. Chain out to keep ship in position. Moderate gale and heavy seas running. Set watch. Sent out broadcast—ship on station. Also message to superintendent. Hove in main chain and commenced to cut out broken link.

G. BRAITHWAITE, *Master, Lightship, No. 117.*

The four-day battle of the *Nantucket* was not considered anything unusually heroic by lightship men. It is the kind of thing that happens all too often, for the lightship must defy the gales that send bigger and safer ships to port. There are many stories of the battle of lightships to ride the storm. Although no lightship is located in a very safe place, the *Diamond Shoal* lightship rides in one of the most dangerous spots of all, some thirteen miles southeasterly from storm-ridden Cape Hatteras. This location puts her in the track of hurricanes roaring up from the West Indies. On September 15, 1933 the *Diamond Shoal* lightship was involved in a hurricane adventure, which has been described thus by her Master, C. C. Austin:

> On the morning of the fifteenth the weather showed indication of a hurricane. At 8:00 A.M. wind E between forty and forty-five miles per hour, increasing barometer falling. I got engine under way and began to work ahead slowly. From noon to 4:00 P.M. wind ENE between fifty and sixty miles per hour, increasing, barometer falling. Seas getting rough and washing ship badly.

*The* Umatilla, *on duty in the Pacific off the coast of Washington State, bears the number "88."*

*Lightship 81, stationed off the port of Boston, sends its beacon's beams into the darkness.*

At about 2:00 P.M. station buoy sighted for the last time as the weather was thick with rain and spray. I judge the ship began to drag anchor at about 4:00 P.M., wind increasing to about seventy miles per hour. I began to increase the speed of the engine from forty to sixty revolutions per minute. From 8:00 P.M. to midnight, wind ENE, between seventy and eighty-five miles per hour, barometer falling. Seas were getting mountainous high and washing the ship terribly. Engine speed increased to ninety revolutions per minute.

September 16, between midnight and 1:00 A.M. ship went into breakers on SW point of Outer Diamond Shoals (having dragged the fifty-five-hundred-pound anchor and twenty-four thousand pounds of chain the five miles from her station). Wind about one hundred and twenty miles per hour. The first breaker which came aboard broke an air port in the pilot house which struck me (Master) in the face and around the neck and on arm, cutting face and neck badly. This same breaker carried away one ventilator close to the pilot house. Mate S. F. Dowdy tried to get a stopper in the hole in the deck and was washed against a davit and broke some ribs. He was almost washed overboard. From 4:00 to 5:00 A.M. wind decreasing to about fifty miles per hour, barometer falling to 28.19 (lowest point).

We laid in the breakers from 12 midnight until 6:30 A.M., breakers coming aboard, breaking up everything on upper deck, washing boats, ventilators, awning stretchers away, bending awning stanchions inboard. Taking water in around umbrella of smokestack and through ventilators to such an extent that the water was rising at times above the fire-room floor with all pumps working, and we were using every means we had to keep the water out of the ship.

At 5:30 A.M. day began to break, so I could see the condition outside. I could see an opening about SSW from the ship that looked like a chance to get away. Breakers coming over at intervals, and I decided that it was the only chance out. I told the mate to get ready to slip the mooring, as we had to get out of that place, for when the wind came from the west it would carry her into the breakers and finish her up. I slipped the mooring at 6:40 A.M. and got the ship outside the breakers at about 7:15 A.M., being in the center of the hurricane. I had just got the breakers behind me when the wind struck from the west at about ninety miles per hour. I ran the ship SE until I was sure I was all clear and then ran NE, thinking the hurricane would pass. I ran this course for a while, and it did not get any better. I considered it was moving very slowly (the barometer was rising fast) so I changed my course to S and ran this course until I ran out of the hurricane.

September 17, 5:00 A.M. Wind NW, strong gale, but decreasing. At 6:00 A.M. I called the mate and told him to get the crew out and see if he could get the wireless antenna fixed up so that we could establish communication. (There had been no radio communication since Friday evening.) About 9:00 A.M. I got radio-compass bearings, which put the ship approximately sixty miles ENE from Cape Hatteras Lighthouse; at 4:00 P.M. radio bearing placed the ship about one hundred and ten miles ESE from Cape Henry. All the crew were at hand at all times and ready to do everything they could to help save the ship, both deck and engine force. During the storm one of the fusible plugs in the boiler blew. They let all steam from the boiler and opened up the furnace, went inside and took out the fusible plug that had blown and put in a new one, and closed the furnace and got steam on the boiler in the strength of the hurricane. I consider this a brave deed, and M. W. Lewis and J. J. Krass, firemen, and A. D. Ameyette, seaman, are due all credit for accomplishing this job. I consider each and every man of the crew did all in his power, and through their bravery, energy, and will power we brought the ship through the hurricane and safely into port. The vessel I consider a most excellent seaworthy ship to come through such a severe hurricane with such comparatively light damage as was sustained; so much water came aboard that at times there was three feet of water in the engine room bilges.

The lightships are not the only ships that play an important part in making sea travel safer by providing navigational aids. The lighthouse tenders have the task of carrying supplies to lighthouses and placing and keeping track of buoys. They have been described as "a fleet of vessels whose duty is to go where no other vessels are allowed to go, and who, through storm, darkness, and sunshine, do their work for humanity."

Some of the tenders are very large craft, as much as two hundred feet long, with a beam of about thirty feet. They have equipment that

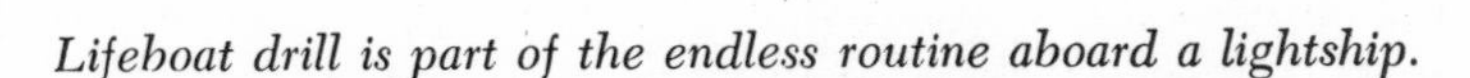

*Lifeboat drill is part of the endless routine aboard a lightship.*

*An "oil can jockey" lubricating the engines of the lightship* Columbia River.

permits them to lift heavy buoys and they carry large stores aboard. They are, regardless of size, sturdy craft designed to take terrible punishment from the sea.

The lighthouse tenders spend much of their time servicing and placing the buoys that dot navigable waters in and around the United States. Altogether there are 1,700 lighted and whistling buoys and 12,700 unlighted buoys. The tenders are constantly at work inspecting buoys, bringing back buoys that have broken loose from their moorings and floated away, bringing buoys in for their annual overhaul, and replacing acetylene gas tanks. Some of the buoys are giants that are forty feet long, weigh twelve tons, and cost nearly ten thousand dollars. These are the huge whistling buoys, many of which are also equipped with lights to make them visible at night. The solemn, penetrating sound or moan of a whistling buoy is produced from a tube in the buoy, closed at the upper end by a steel diaphragm, an inlet, and exhaust pipes, with a whistle attached to the latter. As the buoy rises on the waves, water in the tube falls and enters through the inlet valve. While the buoy sinks, the air is forced through the whistle and sound ensues.

There are many different kinds of buoys, each one numbered according to its purpose. Eight types are in common use—can, spar, nun, bell, whistle, lighted bell, lighted, and lighted whistle. The buoys are the highway markers of the sea lanes. Red buoys mark the right side of channels entering from the seaward, and black buoys mark the left side. Black and red horizontally banded buoys mark obstruction, or the junction of one channel with another. White buoys mark an anchorage. Yellow buoys mark a quarantine anchorage.

In spite of the fact that buoys are well anchored, they sometimes break loose and float away and are not always easy for the tenders to find. After the Florida hurricane of 1926 the big buoy that marks the entrance to the Straits of Florida was reported missing. Then reports began to come in that a strange buoy was floating off the coast far to the north. The lighthouse tender *Cypress* went in pursuit of it and at last found this runaway hundreds of miles away from its station. Somehow it had dragged its moorings into deep water; chain, anchor and all, was floating along with a weight of about thirteen thousand pounds!

When a wreck occurs off the coast on any important waterway, a tender hurries out at once to place buoys to mark it as a warning to shipping. A red bell buoy with a red light is placed at one end, and a black whistle buoy with a green light is placed at the other. Vessels frequently run down buoys, and these must be replaced by the tenders.

Wherever they operate, whether in the oceans or on the Great Lakes, the tenders must perform their duty in weather that is unfit for navigation.

Some of the difficulties of their work may be judged from this report filed by the Master of the tender *Marigold,* operating in Lake Superior:

SUPERINTENDENT OF LIGHTHOUSES, Detroit, Michigan.

Sir: Referring to the severe weather conditions this fall in connection with the relief of the Keepers on Lake Superior, at the close of navigation, would state in my thirty-three years in this service this was the stormiest trip I have experienced.

*November 29:* Tender left Marquette bound for Point Abbaye to relieve the buoys. Just before we reached there a severe northeast snowstorm set in. Ran to Huron Bay for shelter. At 8:00 P.M. the barometer registered 27.98, the lowest in my experience.

*November 30 to December 3:* Sheltered in Huron Bay, moving tender occasionally to prevent freezing in.

Nothing further noteworthy until—

*December 7:* En route to Portage Lake Ship Canal, to recover gas tanks and remove steel tower. When within one hour's run of the canal a severe southwest snowstorm set in. It was considered too dangerous to try to make the entrance in a snowstorm and the wind blowing right on; so the only thing to do was to head for the open lake and ride it out at slow speed. The weather was getting worse all the time, very heavy southwest sea and northwest cross sea running, very low temperature, and tender icing up rapidly, tender riding the heavy seas splendidly under slow speed.

*December 8:* Riding out storm heading for north shore. 11:30 changed course for Apostle Islands. 5:00 P.M. anchored near Bear Island for the night.

*December 9:* At 5:00 A.M. underway, discovered Raspberry Island displaying distress signal, sent second officer and crew ashore over ice, brought keeper and assistants on board tender, and transported them to Bayfield. Crew removing ice from tender, estimated weight about twenty-five tons.

*December 10:* Breaking through ice from Bayfield to Oak Island, an all-day job.

*December 11:* Underway at 7:00 A.M. searching for York Island Shoal Gas Buoy without success. Lake covered with ice for miles. Relieved San Island keepers and started for Rock of Ages, a heavy southwester set in, had to turn back to Apostle Islands, relieved keepers from Outer Island, and sheltered under Presque Isle for the night.

*December 12:* Weather clear, wind NW light, at 2:00 A.M. en route to Rock of Ages, after running two hours on this course a northeast gale with snow set in and a very low temperature, causing tender to ice up for the second time. In making this passage there was nothing visible and nothing audible, and the seas were the largest that I have ever had to contend with in my experience. It was very difficult to estimate speed and location at any time. When the sea moderated, soundings were taken from the starboard gangway, as no person could stand on deck on account of ice and weather; the cold was so penetrating that it was necessary for the officers and quartermaster to wear heavy overcoats, while two radiators were going full blast in the pilot house. Soundings were frequently taken and when bottom was reached at seven fathoms, anchor was cast for the night off Rain Bow Cove.

*December 13:* Heavy vapor, nothing visible. By careful navigation was able to shelter in Grace Harbor. Remained here storm-bound until 1:00 P.M. the 16th; arrived at Rock of Ages at 3:00 P.M., relieved keepers and started on run to Duluth. Two of the assistant keepers were frostbitten while coming out to the tender, but our hard-boiled seamen stood the hardship all right. (Tender then proceeded to Duluth, where it arrived on December 17, with only a limited amount of fuel on board.)

This is just one of the many stories of calm courage that can be found in the records of the lightship service. The gallant men who man the lightships deserve a high place in the story of man's never-ending battle to make the seas safe for travel.

*Heavy clouds of smoke billow up from this tanker torpedoed in the Atlantic.*

FIRE AT SEA! Through the ages those words have always had a special terror for sailors. No menace of the sea—fog, storm, or ice—has been as frightening as the fearful necessity of fighting the fury of fire aboard a ship. The modern metal ships of today, as well as the wooden ships of the past, have had fires rivaling the biggest blazes ashore. The stories of some of these fires provide a fascinating chapter in the annals of the sea.

Of all the stories of fire at sea, one of the grimmest is the account of the fate of the flame-swept *Amazon* in 1852. In her day she was a great ship, the largest of the wooden steamships sailing from England. By modern standards she was hardly a steamship at all, for her eighty-horse-power engines were used only as an auxiliary when favorable winds were not blowing. Her builders intended her to be driven mostly by winds against billowing canvas. Bound for the West Indies, the *Amazon* set sail from Southampton on January 2, 1852 with a valuable cargo, a crew of 110 officers and men, and 50 passengers. She was not long out of port when she encountered a strong head wind, and Captain

*Clad in asbestos suits, these Navy specialists are expert at snuffing out fires at close range.*

Symons gave orders that the canvas be taken in and the engines started. Her westward progress would have been discouragingly slow if she had depended on sails. It proved even hard enough for the laboring engines to force her against the wind. The passengers soon began to hear disquieting reports as firemen came off duty. The bearings of the new engines were getting so hot that it was necessary to keep a stream of water played on them. Even then it became necessary to make repeated stops to permit the bearings to cool.

For thirty-six hours the *Amazon* forged her sluggish way through the Bay of Biscay. Although various passengers protested, the captain insisted on keeping the engines going, pointing to the fact that the ship was making some progress and that they would soon run into a region of favorable winds. Then, on a pitch black night, the ship was suddenly lighted up by flames as the engine crew came stumbling out of a flaming engine room. Somehow the extreme heat had ignited the ship's store of oil and tallow.

"Fire stations!" the captain roared from the bridge.

Men rushed to drag the fire hoses toward the flames. To do this they had to move along a lower deck, and the clouds of vile choking smoke soon drove them up to the promenade deck. The captain gave orders that the now thoroughly frightened and panic-stricken passengers be kept in the saloon, and stewards rushed to lock the doors. The captain did not want passengers getting in the way of the grim business of fighting the flames. Minute by minute the conflagration grew as new barrels of oil exploded and hurled their flaming contents against tinder-dry decks and bulkheads. The strong wind created a fierce draft that increased the fury of the fire. Officers trying to use fire hoses on the upper deck found that the canvas hose quickly burned through. In desperation, bucket brigades were organized, but it was soon clear that there was no chance of winning against the fire by this crude means.

The captain ordered the ship turned to lie before the wind so that the flames would be kept forward. For a time this relieved the situation slightly. The flames leaped higher, but at least they were blown away from the aft positions where most of the crew and passengers had sought refuge. What happened then was something that the captain had not foreseen. Although there was no canvas aloft, the violent wind caught hold of the masts and spars, and the ship leaped before the wind. In addition, her engines were still working at full speed. Now the flaming craft went plunging through the high, rolling seas at a breakneck pace. Although parts of the ship had burned through so completely that her naked oak spars were visible, she roared through the waters, an uncontrollable runaway. No seafarers have ever found themselves in a more frightening predicament than the passengers and crew of the *Amazon*. So long as the craft maintained her mad pace, there was no chance of launching the lifeboats safely. Yet to stay aboard meant certain death.

For a time the officers hoped that the water in the boilers would run out and the engines stop. With their limited knowledge of steam, they did not know that such an event would have resulted in an explosion. However, there was little danger of that, because the engineer had turned on the valves that kept the boilers replenished from the tanks. Not knowing this, the captain gave orders that the lifeboats should not be lowered. He still had hopes that somehow the ship would lose her headway and stop her forward plunge.

As the minutes went by, and the flames crept under the decks, even the lifeboats that were farthest forward caught fire. Reluctantly Captain Symons at last permitted them to be lowered. Quickly there was a fight for the boats as panic-stricken passengers scrambled for what seemed like safety. The boats themselves were death traps, for they were fastened in such a manner that in the efforts to get them launched they spilled their

*A United States Marine of the Pearl Harbor Fire Department learns how to climb down a line.*

helpless passengers into the sea. Somehow five boats were successfully launched in the raging seas after being crammed with people. Captain Symons staggered to the wheel and told the steersman to seek safety. Grimly the captain continued to steer the ship, as the flames gradually enveloped the whole ship.

The fifty-eight occupants of the boats floated helplessly in the flickering light of the fiery *Amazon*. Their hopes rose when another ship, a barque, passed slowly a few hundred yards away. Strangely, she did not stop, but kept steadily on her way, ignoring the tragedy of the *Amazon* and the signal rockets of the survivors in the boats. The name of the ship was not determined, but her callous action in ignoring the distress of another vessel has few parallels in the annals of sea disasters. Many more lives might have been saved if she had stopped to try to save some of the people who had leaped overboard. As it was, those in the boats had a hard time weathering the seas, until they were picked up by various ships the next day.

There are few more dramatic episodes in the long history of fire at

*Putting out a fire on an Army transport in the harbor of Naples.*

*Crew members of this tanker were able to bring the fire under control.*

sea than the burning of the *Volturno*. Although not a large ship, the *Volturno* carried 564 passengers and a crew of 93 when she sailed from Rotterdam on October 2, 1913, bound for Halifax and New York. She was 1,260 miles at sea, almost in mid-ocean, when fire was discovered at 6:55 the morning of October 9. Her captain, F. J. D. Inch, took one look at the flaming hold and instantly ordered that the S O S be sent. He had too many human beings aboard and too inflammable a cargo to take chances with a fire in mid-ocean. That cargo, which included various oils, straw bottle covers, burlap, and chemicals like barium oxide, made perfect fuel for a fire.

While the S O S was flashing out over the air waves, Captain Inch and Second Officer Lloyd ventured to cut a hole through the hatch covers so that they could use a fire hose against the flames in the hold. A tremendous explosion blew them away from the opened hatches; so this plan was given up. Half-blinded, and suffering intensely from severe burns, Captain Inch calmly discussed the problem with the chief engineer. Could the forward holds be flooded as a means of putting out the fire? It was quickly decided that this might stop the fire, but it would probably sink the ship. Thereupon the captain ordered the

*Navy firemen learn how to put out fires at sea.*

lifeboats to be made ready, and life belts were given to the now frightened passengers.

Now the full fury of the fire showed itself. There was another explosion that wrecked the steering gear. Great flames licked up fifty feet into the air and whipped back toward the bridge in the strong wind that was blowing. The rope stays that held the antenna aloft were burned away, and it began to sag, endangering the radio signals that were spreading the *Volturno's* call for help. Courageously, Second Officer Lloyd scrambled up into the shrouds and managed to tie the antenna to the mast. On his way down he was overcome by the clouds of smoke and fell twelve feet to the deck, where he lay unconscious.

As the morning advanced, the *Volturno* still lay flaming, helpless and alone on the seas, for no rescue ship had arrived. Captain Inch made various efforts to launch lifeboats, for the advance of the fire led him to believe that the end for his ship might not be far away. When the Number 2 boat was lowered, it capsized and spilled its twenty-two unfortunate passengers into the sea. A few of them clambered back in when the boat righted itself, and it went racing away in the gale. Number 6 boat was safely launched, and it too plunged away in the storm and was never seen again. Number 7 was safely launched, but before it could pull away from the ship, the *Volturno's* stern, lifted high by the seas, came crashing down on it.

"Hold all lifeboats," the captain ordered, for he could well see that there was no hope that the other boats could be more safely launched than those which had already met destruction in the seas. His orders were disobeyed by some members of the crew and some passengers, who tried to launch one boat. One end of it swung downward and spilled all its occupants into the sea.

Meanwhile, the nearest ship, the *Carmania,* which was fifty-eight miles away at the time she received the distress call, was nearing the scene. From miles away she could see the column of smoke that showed the presence of the fire aboard the *Volturno.* Captain Barr of the *Carmania* had been informed by radio that the *Volturno's* efforts to launch boats had been unsuccessful, but when he saw the condition of the flaming ship, he decided that an effort should be made to reach her. Oil was poured on the waters while a boat was launched. After fighting its way through the raging seas for two hours, the crew gave up and came back to report that it was impossible to reach the stricken *Volturno.*

Would it be possible to run a line from the two ships and pull a boat along it? Captain Barr decided that this plan was hopeless. No line could be maintained between the two ships being tossed about on the high seas. He did try another scheme, that of dropping some of the *Carmania's* boats overboard in the hope that they might float in close enough to be picked up by the *Volturno.* Instead, they simply drifted

*Annapolis midshipmen learn fire-fighting as part of their naval training.*

*Every large naval ship has a special crew of fire fighters.*

by, a short distance from the bow of the burning ship. Efforts to drift a buoy downwind to the *Volturno* also failed.

As these efforts were being made, other rescue ships appeared on the scene, making up a veritable international fleet. The first comer after the *Carmania* was the German freighter *Seydlitz.* Soon afterward came the Belgian *Kroonland,* the American *Minneapolis,* the French *La Touraine,* and the Russian *Czar.* Altogether, there were soon eleven ships clustered there on the high seas. The tragedy was that they could only lie there helplessly, unable to help the ship they had come to save. They could see the raging fury of the flames increasing by the moment. Naked girders showed, twisted into grotesque shapes as the flames ate their way aft toward the huddled mass of passengers.

Captain Inch sent out a despairing radio message: "Come at once. We may go down at any minute. She is buckling."

Two hours later, at 6:30 in the evening, he sent another call urging the waiting, watching ships to do something. Captain Inch himself had been suffering a terrible ordeal. His shoes were burned off, his uniform burned and torn to shreds, his hair and eyebrows burned off.

Finally, as the hours went by and the danger increased, Second Officer Lloyd, who had already risked his life many times, decided to try to launch a boat. He believed that if he could do it safely, it would show the other ships that it was possible to launch boats. He succeeded in getting a lifeboat launched and started the two-mile journey to the German ship *Kurfuerst*. As he and his men reached her, the lifeboat was sinking, for it had been filled with water as it made its way through the breaking waves. Lloyd's heroic example spurred the captain of the German ship to give orders that a boat be put out and an effort at rescue be made that night.

At 9:30 there was a fresh burst of flame on the *Volturno* as the fire reached the mid-section and roared up around the bridge, where rockets and signal bombs were kept.

Again Captain Inch flashed a message: "For God's sake, send us some boats. Do something."

It seemed that the end could not be far away.

Then into the circle of radiance from the fire came a boat from the *Kurfuerst*. The crew shouted up, urging passengers to jump. No one made a move. They preferred the smoking decks to the fury of the sea. Finally the boat returned empty to its ship. Boats from the *Devonian* and the *Minneapolis* likewise battled their way through the waves only to find that no one would jump.

By daybreak the weather took a turn for the better, and the sea became much calmer. The waves were further smoothed by quantities of oil pumped onto them by the tanker *Narragansett*, which had come up during the night. Across this slick of oil came boats from the many vessels, and soon boatloads of women and children

*A student fireman learns how to smother an oil fire with chemical foam.*

were being carried to various rescue ships. The loading of the boats was orderly to the last, as Captain Inch maintained discipline. At last everyone else had been taken off. Only Captain Inch was left; he had stayed with his ship to the last through twenty-four hours of such frightful terror as has seldom been the lot of any sea captain. He took a last look at his craft, now an inferno almost from stem to stern, tucked the ship's papers under his arms, and stepped quietly into a boat. His work was a credit to the high tradition of ship's officers. He was properly honored on his return to England, where he was given the Freedom of the City of London in recognition of his services.

Years after the spectacular burning of the *Volturno* in mid-ocean, there was another great fire that ranked with this disaster. Strangely, it occurred within sight of shore. Much progress had been made in ocean-going fire fighting equipment since the *Volturno's* disaster, but modern precautions were not enough to save the *Morro Castle*. Her destruction was as fearful as that aboard the old *Amazon*, for human failings can undo all mechanical precautions. The *Morro Castle* was a

*Putting out a dock fire that endangered a near-by ship.*

sturdy and handsome ship. She had been built in 1930 and plied the waters between New York and Cuba. Aboard her were countless devices to fight fire. She had an excellent automatic fire-detecting system, with a smothering system that was supposed to release automatically clouds of carbon-dioxide foam in case of fire. Her deck houses were constructed of steel. Scattered about her were no less than forty-two fire hydrants and seventy-three portable fire extinguishers.

How, then, did she burn?

That question was the subject of one of the longest investigations in the history of sea disasters, and some parts of the answer were never settled, but briefly the story seems to run something like this:

The *Morro Castle* had made an uneventful voyage from Havana, expecting to dock in New York on the morning of Saturday, September 8, 1934. First of the events that were to give rise to strange tales of sinister deeds aboard occurred when Chief Officer William Warms went to the captain's stateroom Friday evening. He found Captain Robert Wilmott unconscious. Hurriedly Warms summoned the ship's physician, who pronounced the captain dead, indicating heart failure as the cause. There were those who afterwards said that the captain had been murdered, but there was no proof, and the physician died in the fire. In any case, Chief Officer Warms was now in command of the ship, and it was to prove a most unhappy command.

At 1:55 the *Morro Castle* passed Barnegat Light and her course was laid for Ambrose Light, outside New York Harbor. Just before 3:00 A.M. Assistant Beverage Steward Daniel Campbell was passing the writing room on the port side of the promenade deck when he smelled smoke. It seemed to be coming from under the door of a locker room; so the steward rushed over and opened the door. When he did, flames leaped out at him, and he could see that the entire locker was afire. Campbell rushed to advise the captain, who had already been informed by a watchman who had observed smoke coming out of a ventilator. Within a few minutes the fire had spread and was roaring forward through the promenade deck. There

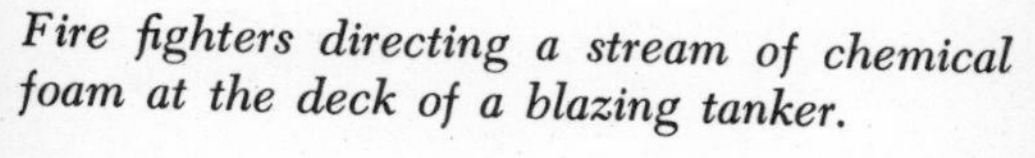

*Fire fighters directing a stream of chemical foam at the deck of a blazing tanker.*

seems to have been wild confusion and lack of any proper effort to use the fire extinguishing equipment. To make matters worse, the ship's speed was maintained at twenty knots. Not until later, when the fire was hopelessly out of control, was her course changed and the vessel slowed down so that the flames would not be fanned by her speed and the heavy twenty-mile wind that was blowing. The fact that she had many doors and ventilating systems suitable for a ship in tropical trade accounted for the ease with which the flames spread, although there were many who believed that some sort of incendiarism had helped them to gain their incredibly rapid headway.

It is clear that a wise captain would have changed his course at once and slowed down. It would seem also that any captain, seeing the swift spread of flames, would think of the safety of his passengers and send out the call for help. Yet there was a strange delay before the S O S signal was sent. Charles Maki, the Second Assistant Radio Operator, rushed to awaken his superior, Chief Operator George Rogers. Just before 3:00 A.M. Maki shook Rogers, shouting, "Chief, there's a fire!" Rogers and the First Assistant Operator, George Algana, rushed into the radio room. Outside, men were rushing by dragging hoses, and there was a confusion of shouts; the ship was already lighted by flames. Algana went out on deck and made his way to the bridge. He found Captain Warms and asked if there were any orders. To his astonishment, Warms said there were none; so Algana rushed back to the radio shack to report to Rogers and Maki. Wisps of smoke were curling up inside the radio room and Rogers had his face wrapped up in a towel. The three radio operators felt completely helpless. There they sat, hearing the crackle of flames, the screams of passengers, all the con-

*The* Morro Castle *afire off the coast of New Jersey.*

fused sounds of a vessel in mortal danger, yet they could not send out an S O S until they had orders from the captain. Rogers did take one step without orders. He sent out the general C Q, an order to clear the air for an S O S.

Soon after the C Q had gone out over the air waves the radio room lights blinked out, as did the lights all over the ship. The power had failed. Algana and Rogers quickly changed over to the emergency battery-operated set, working by flashlight. After that Algana made repeated trips to the bridge, each time asking Warms if there were any orders. Always the answer was no. Finally, on the fourth time up, Algana informed the captain that conditions in the radio room were becoming unbearable.

"All right, send an S O S," Warms finally said, like a man in a daze.

Having received the order, Algana began the perilous trip back to the radio shack, but found himself completely cut off by a thick wall of smoke that he knew he could not get through. He hurried back to the bridge and asked for use of the telephone, but soon found that it was dead. Frantically, Algana tried again to get through the smoke and again found it impossible. He scrambled down a ladder to a lower deck and found the air somewhat fresher, but not for long. Soon he was in smoke even worse than that above; so he went back to the upper deck, where he found that a slight change in wind direction had cleared the air to some extent. Somehow he fumbled his way forward until he came to the radio room and staggered in to cry out: "Send the S O S. Twenty miles south of Scotland Light."

Algana hurried back to the bridge again to inform the captain that the S O S had been sent and then again hurried back to the radio room. Just before he got there Rogers had gasped out the words, "Can't hold out . . . longer . . . fire under radio room."

Algana found him only half-conscious. Fumes from sulphuric acid poured on the hot floor from bursting batteries had created a poison gas.

"Chief—come on. . . . Get out of here!" Algana shouted.

"No—have to stand by," the half-conscious operator muttered.

Algana was able to drag him away from his post only when he was convinced that the orders had come from the bridge for him to leave.

Now rescue ships quickly appeared as the near-by *City of Savannah, Monarch of Bermuda,* and *Andrea F. Luckenbach* rushed the few miles that separated them from the *Morro Castle.* Meanwhile, before the rescue ships arrived, passengers were jumping into the sea to escape the searing heat. A few succeeded in swimming ashore to the New Jersey coast, six miles away. Others were drowned, and still others burned to death. Some members of the crew made off with partially filled lifeboats, ignoring the captain's orders and the frantic screams of the victims. Most members of the crew, however, stayed with their ship.

Lifeboats from the rescuing ships found many passengers who kept afloat by holding hands in groups. The sea was filled with floating survivors who had jumped from the stern of the *Morro Castle* or who had let themselves into the water with ropes. Altogether, rescuing vessels saved 228 of the 318 passengers.

Captain Warms, still dazed, refused to leave the ship that he had commanded for such a brief and disastrous time. He asked for volunteers to stay aboard, and all but two men promptly agreed to stay on the fiery hulk of the *Morro Castle*. She was taken in tow by the Coast Guard Cutter, *Tampa,* with the idea that she could be towed to New York Harbor, where the New York City fire boats could put out the blaze. The flames continued to advance, although the men left threw overboard all inflammable material they could move to slow the fire. By mid-afternoon the captain of the *Tampa* advised them that a storm was coming up and that they would have to leave the ship. After they were taken aboard the *Tampa,* they saw the entire forecastle, which they had recently occupied, burst into flames. A little later the hawser parted and the *Tampa* narrowly escaped being crushed against the burning ship. Finally the *Morro Castle* drifted ashore, where her black and smoking hulk lay beached at Asbury Park, New Jersey, a mute testimony to the terrors of fire at sea.

CHAPTER 13

# DEEP-SEA ADVENTURE

*Diver-tending barges, such as this, transport divers and supply them with air under water.*

NOT ALL the great adventures of the sea have befallen the men who sail its surface in ships. When ships sink, when there is salvage work to be done under the sea, then the deep-sea diver comes into his own. Clad in a grotesque suit he ventures bravely into an underwater world filled with hidden dangers, many of them more frightening than the perils of storm, fire, and collision that face the surface mariner.

Deep-sea diving has a long history. The ancient Greek poet, Homer, in his *Iliad,* mentions the action of a diver diving for oysters. Thucydides, the Athenian historian, who lived during the fifth century B.C., tells of the use of divers during the siege of Syracuse to saw down the barriers that had been built below the surface of the water to obstruct and damage any Grecian vessels trying to enter the harbor. At the siege of Tyre, Alexander the Great ordered divers to destroy the submarine defenses of the besieged. Livy, the early Roman historian, writes that during the reign of Perseus much treasure was recovered by divers from the sea.

Aristotle, Greek philosopher of the fourth century B.C., was the first writer to mention any appliance for aiding divers. Divers, he wrote,

*Clinging to his guide rope, a diver descends.*

were sometimes supplied with instruments for drawing air from above the water so that they could remain under the sea a long time. He said divers breathed by means of a metallic vessel that did not get filled with water but retained the air in it. Alexander the Great was recorded to have descended into the sea in a machine called a colimpha, which kept a man dry and admitted light. The Roman Pliny wrote of divers engaged in war who drew air through a tube, one end of which was in their mouths, while the other floated on the surface of the water.

Roger Bacon is said to have invented, in 1240, a device that enabled men to work under water. Books published in the sixteenth century show engravings of a diver wearing a tight-fitting helmet, with a long leather tube leading to the surface, where it was kept afloat by a buoy. In the years that followed, other experiments were made with underwater suits, but it was not until 1830 that Augustus Siebe invented the diving suit that was to become the ancestor of today's modern diving garb. Siebe's helmet was fitted with air inlet and regulating outlet valves. Since Siebe's death in 1872 many important improvements have been made; nevertheless, it is his basic principle that is the foundation of the deep-sea diving gear of today. His invention, with its improvements, opened up the whole modern era of efficient underwater work and has been the means of effecting rescues and salvaging cargo.

The modern version of Siebe's diving dress is a clumsy one-piece suit of two layers of duck canvas with a layer of pure rubber cemented between them. It is made in only three sizes and is not designed for fashionable fit, because the three sizes are intended to cover men of different heights. Since men less than five feet six inches tall and men much over six feet are not accepted as divers, the three sizes are loosely adequate.

The outer or breastplate collar of the suit is of thick tough rubber and curves down onto the breast and the back and in on the shoulders.

The inner collar or bib extends higher than the outer collar to keep out any water that should get in behind the outer collar. The suit is reënforced with patches at the knees, ankles, crotch, and elbows. Extra flaps are sewed on the legs to be laced together to bring the suit close to the diver's legs and keep air out of the lower part of the suit. This decreases the hazard of capsizing, as well as the peril of an inflated suit becoming punctured. The sleeves end with rubber cuffs that clasp the wrists of the diver tightly. To make them water-tight, sections of rubber tubing like an inner tube are inserted. These "snappers," as they are called, are so tight that if they are worn for long above water they make a man's hands turn blue. Under water they are comfortable, for outside pressure equalizes inner pressure. In cold water divers wear gloves. These have two fingers and a thumb and are made in a position like a half-opened fist. Replacing the cuffs, they are cemented on the ends of the sleeves.

Twelve small holes are punched through the rubber breastplate collar of the suit. The breastplate is worn underneath this collar and the studs on the edge of the breastplate come up through these holes. A curved metal strap in four sections is next donned, and the studs come out through corresponding holes in the strap. Nuts are then fastened onto the studs, squeezing down the strap on the collar to make a water-tight joint between the suit and the breastplate.

The top of the breastplate is a perfect circle threaded so that the helmet can be screwed down onto it. A lock-nut at the back of the helmet secures it to the breastplate. Helmet and breastplate are made of copper, with gray over-tinning.

The helmet is the diver's control office for air supply, telephone communication, and observation. The air inlet is back of his head. To a coupling on the back of the helmet, out of the way, comes his air hose. The safety valve, a non-return valve, is just outside the helmet. This keeps air from going back up the hose, in case of an

*This odd-looking suit is an early French contribution to the art of deep-sea diving.*

*A diver climbs laboriously up a ladder after inspecting the bottom of a battleship.*

accident. Close to the diver's hand, three feet away from the helmet, is the air-control valve on the air hose.

Both the air hose and the life line are made fast with short pieces of line to metal rings on the front of the breastplate and are then carried back, one under the right arm and the other under the left, to their connections with the helmet. The head-set receivers are clamped securely over the diver's ears, connecting through little plugs with the right side of the helmet. The telephone transmitter is part of the inside wall of the helmet to the left of the faceplate.

The escape valve for used air is on the right side of the helmet. The valve, with a spring in it, opens only when the pressure reaches a certain height within the helmet, but the diver can turn a handle outside to increase this pressure point to retain his air, or he can lower it and let his air escape faster. He can also turn his head and press his chin against a button at the end of the valve stem to open the valve to release some air, in case he cannot spare a hand.

A relief valve is on the front of the helmet to the left of the faceplate. By opening it with a small handle outside, the diver can blow out any water that may have seeped between his breastplate and bib. The air is spread into the helmet through a three-branched tube. The used air is circled around the helmet through an outside tube and is released into the water near the back so that bubbles won't block the diver's view.

The diver can see in four directions. In front of his eyes is the faceplate, which, hinged to the helmet, can be swung open when the diver is out of the water. His other windows of glass, protected by gun-metal gratings, are the right and left side-lights and the top-light.

The diver wears over the suit a harness of leather that holds a belt in place even when the diver is upside down. Lead weights are fastened to this belt all the way around. The weights vary from sixty to one hundred pounds, depending on the depth of the dive. The deeper the dive, the greater the water pressure. The greater the water pressure, the greater the air pressure and consequent buoyancy, which requires greater weight to keep the diver down. The helmet and breastplate weigh about sixty pounds; the shoes, thirty-two; the suit, eighteen. With the weighted belt, the diver wears some two hundred pounds of apparel.

On the belt in a sheath the diver carries his keen-bladed knife, the back of which is fitted with saw teeth for more difficult work. Working overalls of canvas, with pockets in which tools may be carried, are sometimes worn over the suit. Immense shoes with lead soles are finally buckled on the diver; the weight will help to keep him right side up.

Underneath the diving suit, divers usually wear three suits of diving underwear, heavy woolen suits, and two pairs of socks, and sometimes a canvas underjacket with rubber gloves as well. Some divers also wear a "doughnut," a cushion with a hole in it, around the neck and over the shoulders as a support for the breastplate.

The life line contains a telephone, but telephones will not always work; so the diver must learn to use it as a signal rope as well. One pull at the line signals "more

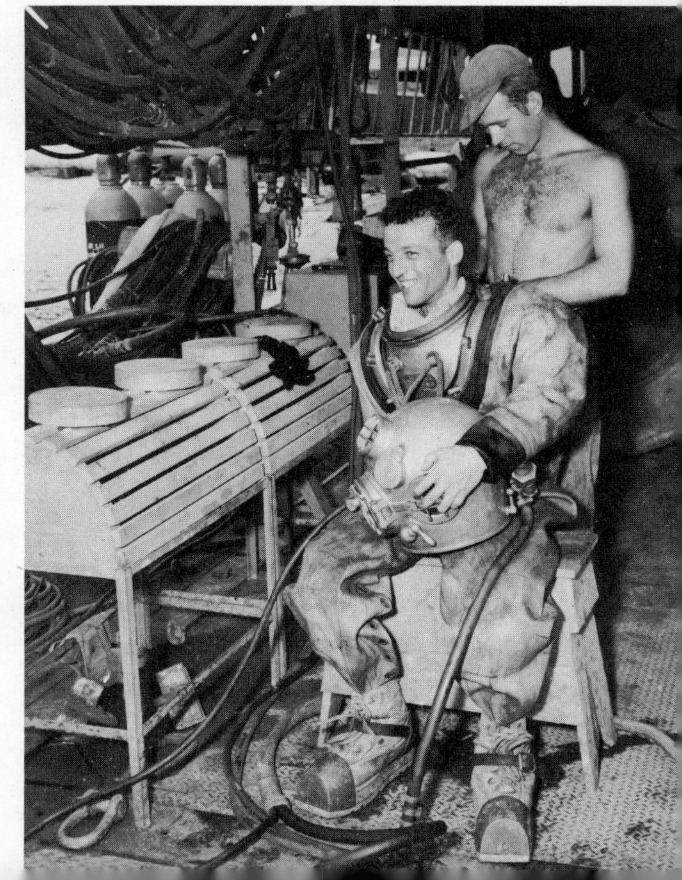

*The assistant, or "tender," is always on hand to help the diver out of his heavy suit.*

air"; two pulls, "give me slack" or "lower me"; two pulls repeated many times, "send down another diver; I am foul and can't get loose"; three pulls, "coming up"; four pulls, "haul me up"; five pulls, "send down a line."

The air hose is made of five layers of linen and rubber alternately, with rubber for the outside and inside layers. It will stand a pressure of five hundred pounds per square inch for ten minutes, when it is new. The upper end of the air hose is attached to an air pump, which is always kept on the deck of the vessel from which the diver operates. When a diver descends, the pump is immediately started and kept going all the time the diver is below the surface.

A diver could not get into his cumbersome diving suit by himself. He has dressers, called "bears," to help him. After he is inside the suit, the bears secure the breastplate, lace up the leg straps, and buckle on the heavy shoes. The telephone is tested and the bears connect the air hose to the inlet on the back of the helmet. When the telephone wires are plugged in, the bears put the helmet over the diver's head and fasten it to the breastplate with a twist.

When the diver is ready his lines are cast off from their coils on the deck. The bears help him to walk over to the stage, a flat grating on which he is let down into the water. Several hands steady the stage as the diver is swung out into the air and then lowered slowly into the choppy water. As the diver descends, he adjusts the control valve for a little more air, inflating his suit a little. Once the diver is totally under water, the stage stops. Then the diver checks his equipment—telephone, valves, suit. As he steps off the stage into the deep water, he inflates his suit to lighten his weight. He wraps one leg around his descending line as he slides down.

The diver's job is a salvage job. Some of the great stories of salvage are told in Chapter 14, but there are many others. One of the tough salvage jobs was that of raising the submarine *S-51* from her ocean bed. On September 25, 1925 the *S-51* was sent to the bottom when she was hit accidentally by the steamship *City of Rome*.

The *S-51* was lying on clay, coarse sand, and fine gravel. It was decided to raise her by making her buoyant enough to rise. This was to be done by placing pontoons along her sides, chaining them to her, then filling the pontoons with compressed air. The only catch to this scheme was that the submarine lay deep in the sand and there was no room for the pontoons. The only thing to do was to dig out channels or tunnels along her sides. Twenty-one divers worked on the salvage of the *S-51*. Commander Edward Ellsberg has given us an excellent account of the dive of one of them, Francis Smith:

We were still two feet from the keel on the port side. Francis Smith was in the tunnel, burrowing his way along. Imagine his situation. In the ice cold water, utter blackness, total solitude, he was buried one hundred and thirty-five feet below the surface of the sea. No sight, no sound, no sense of direction except the feel of the iron hull of the *S-51* against his back, as he lay stretched out flat in a narrow hole, scarcely larger than his body, not big enough for him to turn around in. Ahead in his outstretched arms he grasped the nozzle, burrowing his way deeper, while around him coursed backward a black stream of freezing water laden with mud and clay.

He had been working about twenty minutes, when on the *Falcon* the man at the telephone got a call from Smith. He could not understand and passed the telephone set to me.

"Hello, Smith!"

In an agonized voice came the reply:

"I'm in a very bad position, Mr. Ellsberg. Send some one to help!"

Joe Eiben was working aft on the other side of the submarine. I dropped Smith's phone, seized Eiben's, ordered Joe to stop whatever he was doing, climb over the

*A diver of the Royal British Navy goes below the waters of Cherbourg Harbor.*

boat to the tunnel and help Smith. Eiben acknowledged the message, started forward.

Meanwhile I tried to figure out what had happened. The fire hose leading over the rail was throbbing violently. Perhaps the nozzle had torn itself from Smith's grasp, was thrashing him to death.

I took Smith's phone again, called down:

"Shall I turn off the water?"

Almost a scream came the answer:

"No! For God's sake keep it going! The tunnel has caved in behind me!"

I felt faint. Hastily we coupled up another fire hose, slid it down the descending line for Eiben's use. But it had taken two weeks to drive the tunnel to where Smith lay! On deck we looked at each other helplessly. Over the telephone, I could hear Smith's labored breathing as he struggled in the darkness.

No further messages came. The sailors stood silently around the deck, waiting for Eiben to arrive at the tunnel, wondering what good he could do when he got there.

Eiben reached the descending line at the gun, cut loose the new hose, dragged it forward with him, and dropped over the port side to the bottom. Finally, after what seemed an age, he reported himself at the tunnel mouth and said he was trying to enter.

I waited; then over Smith's telephone, I heard Smith say to Eiben:

"I'm all right now, Joe. Had a little accident. You better go on back to your own job."

Though he could not turn round, Smith had managed to pass the nozzle back

*Navy divers awaiting word to go below to salvage a Navy plane that crashed and sank at Patuxent River, Maryland.*

between his legs, and guiding it with his feet, he had washed his way out backward through the cave-in!

Eiben left. Smith sat down on the ocean floor a few minutes to rest, then picked up his hose, crawled back into the tunnel, and for half an hour more continued to wash his way toward the keel.

No deed ever performed in the heat of battle with the enemy where thousands cheer you on, can compare with Francis Smith's bravery, when in the silent depths of the ocean beneath the hulk of the *S-51* he washed his way out of what well might have been his grave, then deliberately turned round, went back into the black hole from which he had by the grace of God escaped, and worked his way deeper and deeper into it.

The story of that epic dive shows one of the dangers which confront the deep-sea diver. There are many others. The most ever-present is the pressure of the water in which the diver works. Water weighs sixty-four pounds per cubic foot. For every foot a diver descends he has to add a further pressure of sixty-four pounds on each square foot of his body. At a depth of twenty-two fathoms, or 132 feet, a diver is under pressure of four and one-quarter tons per square foot, a total load of five atmospheres—five times as much as man was designed to stand. Air must be supplied the diver at a slightly greater pressure than that of the water surrounding him to prevent his chest from being crushed by the colossal load of deep water. If through any accident the diver loses the air pressure in his suit, the weight of the sea crushes him.

Breathing under such unnatural conditions leads to the worst hazard a diver meets, that of "the bends." When deep-sea diving was just beginning, divers found that if they went much below a depth of sixty feet and stayed down much more than an hour, they were subject to a strange illness on returning to the surface. The diver suffered terribly and doubled up in strange convulsions. Because of contorted movements, the malady was called the bends.

Often the bends took a more serious form. The victim was paralyzed for life or else died quickly after emerging from the sea. Sandhogs working under air pressure, such as when constructing tunnels under rivers or providing deep foundations along river banks for huge bridges, also incurred the same disease. In 1878 a French scientist, Paul Bert, demonstrated that the disease was caused by bubbles of nitrogen gas which got into the blood and tissues of a diver emerging from the sea. Bert concluded from his experiments that if the diver were to rise to the surface slowly but steadily, the nitrogen dissolved in his body would slowly come out of solution in amounts insufficient to cause sizable bubbles and would escape continuously through the lungs. This process is known today as decompression.

In 1906 J. S. Haldane, a British scientist, found it was safer to decompress in stages, coming up sharply part way to cut the pressure on the diver in half, permitting considerable nitrogen to escape, but with pressure still sufficient to prevent the formation of any large bubbles. Again and again the pressure was to be halved until the diver had returned to normal atmospheric pressure. Professor Haldane worked out a series of tables for times of decompression for different depths, tables that have proved invaluable.

Another hazard of deep-sea diving is oxygen intoxication. At about one hundred and sixty feet down, for instance, a diver breathes five times as much oxygen as he does normally. A diver susceptible to this intoxication is completely helpless reeling below the sea. Such divers have to be stricken from the lists for their own safety. Other divers show the effects of oxygen intoxication only upon returning to the surface, when they laugh and sing gaily.

The "squeeze" is another danger. The diving rig must be supplied with air pressure to counteract the sea pressure. But only the helmet and a little space in the suit just below the breastplate actually contain any air, to avoid too much buoyancy. The pressure of the air in the lungs of the diver, transmitted to every part of his body, inflates him to balance off the sea pressure. But a slight decrease in the pressure of his helmet results in a strange sensation of being hugged chokingly by the sea. With more air released, the embrace of the sea forces the blood out of the legs and then out of the lower abdomen, a condition at once painful and dangerous.

A real squeeze, however, is fatal. Usually it is caused by a fall under water to a much greater depth where the pressure increases on the diver before he can get additional air into his helmet to withstand it. The pressure then forces the blood from limbs and body into the chest cavity and rams the diver up into his helmet.

"Blowing up" is another peril that makes diving a most dangerous occupation. On reaching sea bottom, a diver regulates the amount of air so as to keep himself heavy enough to remain at the depth but not too heavy to move comfortably. He is taught, however, never to lighten himself to a point at which he begins to float. If inadvertently he adjusts his inlet and exhaust valves to retain a little more than the necessary air in his suit, he at once starts floating upward. Because of underseas conditions, he is not always certain to notice this occurrence. As he goes up, the water pressure decreases and the air in his suit expands still more, thus increasing the rapidity of his ascent.

There is still time for him to shut off the incoming air and to open the exhaust valve by striking it with his chin, thus deflating his suit and enabling him to sink. If, however, he fails to do this in the first fathoms of his ascent, it is too late. The expanding air fills out his suit until it becomes stiff as iron and he can no longer bend his sleeves to reach the air valve on his breastplate.

After a slight further ascent, his suit balloons out and he begins to race to the surface like a torpedo. If he rises under the diving ship, he would break his head against it. Should he avoid the ship, he would break through the surface and shoot up into the air like a huge flying fish, fall back into the water, and then be pulled in by his tender. If he has stayed long at depth, he will get the bends unless he can be rushed into the decompression chamber. Of course, if his suit burst under the internal pressure, he at once plummets down again and is promptly squeezed to death.

Often a diver faces one of these dangers; it is rare that he comes face to face with all of them. Tom Eadie came close to it on one of his dives from the *Falcon* during the salvage of the *S-51*. Eadie was working in one of the tunnels along the submarine's sides, perhaps the same tunnel that caved in on diver Smith. Again we shall let Commander Ellsberg tell the story:

> Eiben and Eadie, who had been working, one in the port tunnel, the other in the starboard one, met at the gun on the submarine's forecastle, climbed on the stage at the ninety-foot mark, and, according to ritual, began their sitting-up exercises while decompressing.
>
> On the quarterdeck, we turned attention to the next diver, who, except for his helmet, was ready to go over. He was testing his telephone.

*A boatswain's mate helps a diver put on his diving suit.*

*The life of the diver depends on the specialist who keeps his equipment in order.*

A voice came from the superstructure.

"Tom Eadie said something, but I couldn't make it out. I can't get him now!"

Hartley tried; I tried; Gunner Tibbals tried. None of us could understand, although it did sound as if Eadie were shouting something. Eiben was on the stage down there with Eadie. I took Eiben's telephone.

"Hello, Joe! Ask Tom what he wants!"

A pause, then Eiben replied:

"Tom's not here! What did you pull him up for?"

Surprised, I looked at Eadie's tender. He had not pulled Eadie up.

"Where's Tom?" I asked him.

"He's still down there, sir. I'm trying to signal him. I've given him 'One' on his line, two or three times, but he doesn't answer."

A shout over the telephone from Eiben.

"Eadie just fell back on the stage. His suit's nearly torn in half, and he's full of water. Take him up quick!"

Half a dozen bears grabbed Eadie's lines and heaved hard. The weight was tremendous, evidently Eadie's suit was wholly water-logged. Others grasped the lines wherever they could lay hands on them, and we heaved rapidly. Over the side went another stage, two men on it, dropped into the water up to their waists. Hand over hand Eadie's lines came in, then at last Eadie's helmet. The men on the stage seized it, dragged his limp form on the stage; the winchman jerked the stage up, swung it in on deck.

Eadie's suit was nearly completely torn in two just below the breastplate, the leather straps over his shoulders were broken, his lead belt was hanging round his ankles. No need to take off his helmet. We cut loose his shoes, dragged him out of the suit through the hole around his breast.

Eadie was very pale, bleeding badly from the mouth and nose, but apparently still conscious. We did not wait to investigate. The tenders who pulled him out of the suit dragged him hurriedly to the decompression tank, thrust him in, together with Surgeon Flotte who hastily ran the pressure up to fifty pounds.

Hours later, after Eiben had come up, and Eadie was below, wrapped in blankets in his bunk, with Eiben resting in the next berth, I asked them what had happened. Eadie told me.

"Joe and I were on the stage at ninety feet, I was jumping up and down to decompress myself and I guess Joe was doing knee stoops.

"All of a sudden my exhaust valve jammed shut and my suit started to swell out. I tried to reach my control valve and turn off the air, but before I could swing my arm around, my suit stiffened out from the pressure inside, and it spread-eagled me. Both my sleeves shot out straight sideways, and I couldn't bend my elbows to get my hand in on the control valve.

"By that time I was so light I started to float up off the stage and I yelled in the telephone to the man on deck to turn the air off on my hose. I guess he didn't understand me."

I interrupted Eadie and turned to Eiben.

"Say, Joe, didn't you notice it when Eadie started up?"

Eiben looked at us sheepishly.

"Yes, I sort of saw him go, out of the corner of my faceplate, but I just thought he was taking an extra-high jump, and I went right on exercising. I wasn't thinking about Tom and I didn't look around again for him till you called me from the deck."

Eadie went on:

"As I started to float up, I thought fast. Of course, I knew if I 'blew up' without any decompression I'd probably get 'the bends,' but that wasn't what worried me most. We were hanging from the *Falcon*, and if I came up from the bottom with all that buoyancy, I'd be going as if I'd been fired from a gun by the time I hit her hull. My copper helmet would flatten out like a pancake and that would be my finish right there.

"As I shot up I saw the top of the steel bails from which the stage was hanging flash down past my faceplate. I couldn't do anything with my hands, but as I went by I shoved out the toes of both my shoes, and I managed to hook the brass toe caps on my diving shoes into the triangle where the balls join. That stopped me with a jerk, and there I was, hanging onto the balls with my toes and just praying that the caps wouldn't tear off the shoes!

"I tried again to pull my hands in but I couldn't. My suit swelled out some more in a hurry and burst the shoulder straps holding my belt up and my helmet down. The lead belt dropped around my feet, and my helmet flew up over my head. As it went by, the breastplate hit me a lick under the chin that nearly broke my jaw, and my suit then stretched out so the helmet was nearly two feet over my head. When the straps let go and the suit stretched, that gave me still more buoyancy, and the pull on my toes was awful.

"I tried to yell in the telephone to you to have Joe climb up to me, shut off my air, and open the pet cock on my helmet so as to let some air out of my suit, but the telephone transmitter was up in the helmet and that was two feet over my head and I couldn't make you understand.

"Then the pressure increased with a rush and nearly broke my ears, and I started to bleed from my mouth and nose. The strain on my toes was fierce, and I was wondering how much longer I could hang on, when all at once my suit tore apart under all that pressure, let out all the air, and I nearly burst as the extra pressure suddenly disappeared. My helmet sort of dropped back, my suit all filled up with water, and I fell down again on the stage.

"I felt you starting to pull me up. I tried to hold my breath, because there was no more air in the suit. Then I remembered that the lines you were hauling me with were only secured to my helmet, and I could feel that my suit was nearly torn in two just below the breastplate. I was down in the rest of the suit and I could feel my heavy shoes and that lead belt hanging round my ankles. I was afraid that what was left of the suit wouldn't stand the strain, and it would tear all of the way across. Then you'd pull up the helmet and I'd sink with those lead-soled shoes and the lead belt as anchors. I thought how surprised you'd be when my helmet came up empty. I tried to kick the belt free from round my feet. No use, I couldn't get it off; so I just held my breath and prayed that the suit wouldn't rip any more. I tried hard not to swallow any water, and the next thing I knew they were dragging me onto the stage."

A terrible experience. In less than a minute's time, Eadie had seen death in four different horrible forms, successively staring him in the face—"the bends," concussion against the *Falcon*, sudden heavy pressure, and drowning had each in turn seemed about to kill him. He came through, saved by his quick thinking, weak and wounded, but with unshaken nerves. A wonderful diver, Tom Eadie. All the world learned what we already knew, when he later won the Medal of Honor on the S-4.

A strange, dangerous job is this business of deep-sea diving. Although efforts are constantly being made to make it a safer occupation, the deep-sea diver must still be a brave man, with courage to face the sea alone.

*Salvage crew raises the bow of the U.S.S.* Pittsburgh *ripped off in a Pacific typhoon.*

TWO STORIES from the exciting history of salvage deserve to be told more fully. They are the accounts of the great undersea treasure hunts that brought to the surface the sunken riches of the *Laurentic* and the *Egypt*.

Of all the treasure ships that have gone to sea, none was more heavily laden with riches than was the British liner *Laurentic* when she set sail in a January gale during the war year of 1917. She carried in her hold the fabulous sum of £5,000,000 ($25,000,000) in the form of 3,211 gold ingots, a total of forty-three tons of gold. This great sum was being shipped to America to provide for the purchase of desperately needed war goods. The British Admiralty was well aware of the dangers that faced the *Laurentic,* for German submarines were roving the waters of the Atlantic like hungry sharks, taking a terrible toll of British shipping. To get the liner to America safely, a special course was worked out that would take the ship north of Ireland, where the stormy weather

*An American submarine moves down the Mississippi in a floating dry dock.*

made it difficult for U-boats to operate. The *Laurentic* was a fast vessel, capable of outrunning submarines in the open sea, and she was well enough armed to fend off an attack. As she passed north of Ireland and turned westward toward the open Atlantic, her captain must have congratulated himself at having passed through the most dangerous waters. Then came a terrific explosion caused not by a torpedo but by a mine. It did terrible damage, and the liner began to sink swiftly. In the icy water and high seas the crews did their best to get the lifeboats manned, but the liner listed so heavily that their efforts were unsuccessful. Over half the crew perished in those cold Irish waters.

The news of the loss of the gold was a crushing blow to England, and the Lords of the Admiralty determined at once that whatever the hazards they must somehow attempt to salvage the *Laurentic*. Commander G. C. C. Damant, Britain's leading diving authority, was hastily called and given the difficult assignment. Damant resolutely set out on his task. It was found that the liner lay in 132 feet of water in a very exposed position off Lough Swilly. Here the winds would sweep with unabated fury; there would be no protection whatsoever for the salvage ships from the northerly and westerly Atlantic gales. Even worse, there were strong tides continually sweeping back and forth along the coast, creating currents that the divers would have to fight. The icy cold water would numb the divers and form freezing spray on the decks to make work there slippery and dangerous. To add to all these difficulties, there was the danger of German submarines. As soon as the Germans discovered that they had sunk the *Laurentic* and that attempts were being made to salvage her, they would certainly make an effort to stop the salvage operations.

Damant was not deterred by these considerations. There was a job to be done, and his country desperately needed that gold. The situation looked even worse under the water. When the first divers went down they discovered that the *Laurentic* was heeled over at a fifty-degree angle, making it impossible for a diver to walk on her decks. The divers clung by their fingers, getting a grip where they could as they explored the sunken hulk. Soon they discovered a menacing situation as they sought the entry port. As one of the divers clung precariously to the slanting deck, something swished by his head a short distance from his faceplate. In the shadowy darkness he turned to see what it was. He was horrified to discover that the boat falls from the boats that had been lowered were hanging free, the heavy blocks at the end of the falls swinging back and forth like deadly pendulums, ready to strike down the divers. There was nothing to do but to take the time to cut every one of the falls free before the search could be continued.

Midwinter gales buffeted the salvage craft and made it practically impossible to keep her in a fixed position. The chill waters made it hard for divers to stay down long. Work was, therefore, painfully slow, and it took weeks to accomplish work that under favorable conditions might have been accomplished in days. However, by the time two weeks had passed, the gate at the entry port had been removed, and the passageway to the strong room had

*The chief diver of the Italian salvage company that recovered the S.S.* Egypt's *gold cargo.*

been cleared. To break into the strong room itself, Damant sent down a diver for whom he had high regard, E. C. Miller, who was considered one of England's best divers. Armed with a sledge hammer and chisel, Miller groped his way through the dark passageway, carefully paying out his lines to make sure they did not catch on any sharp obstruction. It was treacherous going on the slippery, slanting deck, but at last Miller stood before the steel door of the strong room. Powerful blows of his hammer drove the chisel through the door, and he was soon inside the room.

A muffled exclamation of excitement came to the men listening to Miller's telephone. He was inside the strong room, and spread out before him were the piles of boxes containing the 3,211 gold bars. Gold! Seldom in history has one man stood on such a vast treasure as lay beneath Miller's leaden feet.

"It's all here!" Miller reported, hardly able to contain himself for excitement. Miller had already spent too much time below, for he had expended an hour of his precious time in getting to the door of the treasure he had discovered. He lifted one of the boxes, small in size, but weighing one hundred and forty pounds. With this heavy load, he struggled out through the dark, sloping passage, pushing the box ahead

*An ocean-going tug alongside the* S.S. Elihu Thompson, *which it towed to the beach of Noumea Harbor.*

*Using pneumatic chisels, these workers are chipping the old paint off a ship's hull.*

of him or wrestling with it in his arms. Damant and the crew of the salvage vessel eagerly gathered around to examine the five gold bars in the box when Miller was hoisted aboard.

The weather looked bad when dawn broke the next day. Heavy gray seas were running and the barometer was falling. Damant was afraid they would have to run from the forthcoming storm, but he decided that it would be possible for Miller to make one dive. This time Miller knew his way into the strong room and succeeded in sending up three boxes of gold before he had to ascend. The gale was rising when he ended his decompression periods on the landing stage, and the ship made for the safety of Lough Swilly. So far all had gone well, and the men could not know what a heartbreaking development lay ahead.

The work was resumed after the storm. The first diver sent up a shocking report. Something had happened to the *Laurentic* during the storm. Under the pressure of the sea and the violent action of the waves, her plates had buckled, and she was crushed together like an accordion. The passage through which Miller had made his way was now closed. Damant gave orders to place T.N.T. and to try to force the plates apart.

*Painting a ship's bottom can be done only in a dry dock.*

This was done, and the passage was shored up foot by foot, to make a tunnel through which it was possible for a diver to crawl. Damant, himself a diver, was a strong leader who inspired his men to carry out this difficult task. It was terrifying to crawl through that dark, shaky, sloping passage with the feeling that at any minute the five decks above might give way. When the passageway was finally completed, Miller successfully reached the bullion room. He felt about in the darkness for the little boxes of gold. His fingers found nothing! The bullion was gone and the strong room was completely empty. The weight of the gold had been too much in the storm, and the plates had given way, spilling it somewhere into the dark depths of the shattered ship below.

This new development was enough to make less stubborn men give up, but Damant was determined to recover the gold for his country. He decided that the only thing to do was literally to tear the *Laurentic* to pieces there where she lay on the bottom of the sea. Thus the divers could work their way down to the spot where it seemed reasonable to believe the gold would be found. Explosives were set under the plates of the collapsed ship. Then it was found that explosives did not destroy the plates that were hanging loose. The force of the explosion would simply make the plate wave back and forth in the water, but would not cut through it. Damant then had the plates drawn taut by seizing each with a clamp attached to lines on the salvage ship. When the plates were thus drawn tight, the explosive was effective. It was slow work, but it was the only way.

Getting the charges placed under the plates was dangerous work, as is well illustrated by what happened to diver Blachford. On all fours he crawled under a plate that was being held up by a clamp already placed by another diver. Carefully Blachford rammed the charge of guncotton between the plate and the wreckage. Above him the plate wavered with the motion of the waves. With gentle, sure motions the diver made certain that the firing wires that would conduct the electrical charge from above were not tangled. Then something happened. The men on board the salvage ship saw the wire that held the plate up suddenly leap clear, writhing on the surface of the sea. That must mean that the plate was free, that its ton weight had fallen on Blachford!

Frantically Damant called the diver on the telephone. For a moment there was silence, then Blachford's strained voice gasped: "Give . . . me . . . air . . ."

Damant gave the order that sent more air pressure surging down the air line.

"More! More air!" came the words from Blachford. "Get . . . diver . . . down . . ."

Swiftly a diver who had just come up rushed to get back into his suit, and was lowered overside to make a swift descent to the spot where Blachford was trapped. Meanwhile, Blachford was calling for still more air, and Damant was faced with a terrible decision. If he sent down

*Plywood forms are used as guides in cutting new steel plates for damaged ships.*

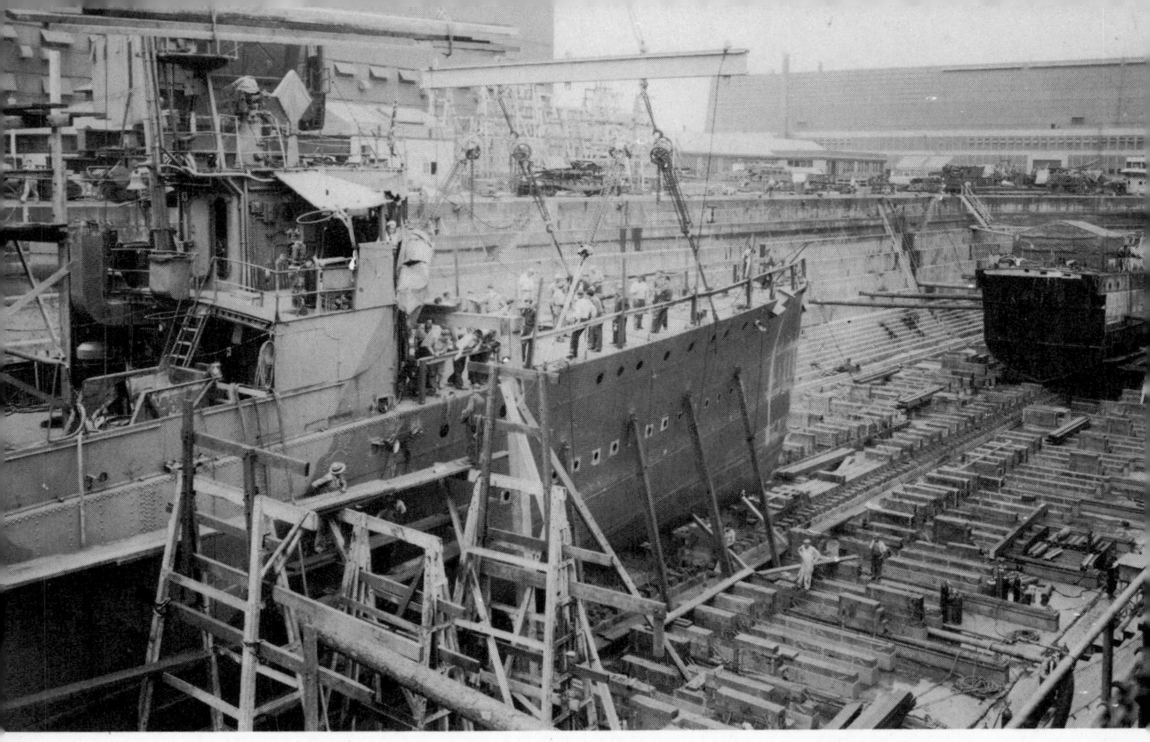

*The bow of the damaged destroyer* Taylor (right) *was welded to the unfinished U.S.S.* Blakely.

more air, there was grave danger that Blachford's suit, already undergoing too much pressure, would burst. Yet Damant knew that the extra air pressure, ballooning out the suit, was the only thing that was keeping the diver from being crushed by the great weight of the steel plate. Damant made his choice, and decided against more air.

The rescue diver could see a stream of air bubbles rising from under the plate as he hastily worked a new clamp onto one corner of the plate under which Blachford lay. It crossed the mind of the diver that not only was Blachford under that plate, but also a tricky charge of guncotton that might go off at any moment. He worked carefully, got the clamp attached, and then gave orders over his telephone for the crews above to heave away at the plate. Slowly it lifted, and Blachford's form came into view. He was rising with the plate, as if he were fastened to it, for the extreme buoyancy of his suit made it impossible for him to stay down. Now the rescuing diver saw a new danger for Blachford. If he should slip around the plate, he would shoot up to the surface to almost certain death because of the sudden change of pressure. Carefully the diver moved toward Blachford and found his exhaust valve. A stream of hissing bubbles shot upward as Blachford's ballooning suit shrunk, and in a few minutes both divers were brought up to safety.

Week after week the work went on as the blasting tore the *Laurentic* apart. Again it fell to Miller to make the discovery that gave the crews new heart. While he was digging in the wreckage he caught the gleam of an ingot. He kept on digging and found more, and extracted ten bars altogether. That time he stayed down ninety minutes and paid for his overlong stay on the bottom with a bad case of the bends when he got to the deck. Commander Damant hastily descended to the location where Miller had found the gold and spent an hour examining it, in an effort to calculate where the rest of the treasure might be. When he came up, he too was suffering from the bends. There was only one decompression chamber on board, and it was occupied by Miller. There was no way to enter it without reducing the air pressure. Looking out through the glass window in the chamber Miller saw the distress of his commander, and courageously reduced the air pressure and let Damant in. The drop in the pressure gave Miller another severe and painful attack of the bends and, although Damant felt better, Miller began to feel worse. The unfortunate diver had to spend the entire night in the cold, uncomfortable tank.

During the remainder of 1917 the divers managed to salvage 542 bars of gold, worth $4,000,000, before the winter storms drove them away. Not until the spring of 1919 did they come back to renew the task. Then they discovered that they had to work under the shadow of the shaky superstructures, which were leaning toward each other. The divers could not be sure that they would not collapse at any minute. To make matters worse, it was also found that the gold ingots were becoming scarcer. Soon the disappointed divers were reporting that there were no more to be found. It seemed plain that the gold must have divided into two parts when the strong room collapsed. One part had now been salvaged, but where was the rest of it?

The divers came back in 1920 to find out. The year passed while they cleared away the wreckage of the superstructures, which had finally collapsed. But they found no gold. In 1921 they came back again and spent a long summer of hard work, with no results except a few stray bars of gold. Storms had battered the hulk of the *Laurentic*, and sand and rocks, sweeping over her, had become packed in between the metal plates. The sand created a difficult problem of salvage, because it did not respond to explosives. Powerful pumps were unable to suck it up because it was so tightly packed. It was impossible to use grabs, because the salvage ship could not stay still enough on the rolling surface of the sea. The only method that did work was to play streams of water on the sand to loosen it and then load it into sacks that were hoisted up. It was discouraging, because it often seemed that the sea brought in more sand faster than the men could take it out. To speed up the work Damant turned the sand-gathering into an athletic contest. He offered prizes to the diver who could dig out the most sand during his dive. During the thirty minutes that each diver could stay down, he was allowed twelve minutes with the hose to wash the sand, thirteen minutes to pack the sand into the bags, five minutes to get the sand over to the hoist. Competition was keen, and the amount of sand dug out increased.

It was 1922 when the divers finally struck gold again. It lay beneath the crushed deck plates, and it became necessary for the divers to crawl between the plates, digging for the gold bars. The sea had pressed deep corrugations into the plates, and these had filled with sand. In these corrugations the bars had become embedded. The men could not wear gloves, because gloves would deaden their sense of feeling; so they dug in the packed sand with their bare hands. It was painful, dangerous work, for when pressed between the plates, the divers' feet would be higher than their heads. Sometimes the air would balloon up into the legs of their suits, and then they would have to force themselves out backward to let the air return to the helmet. Despite these difficult circumstances the work went on. By the end of 1922 the salvage totalled $7,500,000. They came back again in 1923 and 1924. When the search ended that year, they had accomplished the astonishing feat of finding all but 25 bars of the 3,211. To do it, they had made over 5,000 dives, yet not a single life had been lost nor one diver seriously injured.

Two years before the *Laurentic's* treasure was finally salvaged, the British S. S. *Egypt* met her fate on the bottom of the sea. It was a calm May night in 1922, and heavy fog lay over the sea off Brest, France, as the *Egypt* plowed her way southward. She sounded her fog warning frequently, and the captain had reduced her speed as he peered uneasily into the thick gray mist. Then suddenly there came the sound of a steamer whistle, blasting a hoarse warning from somewhere alarmingly close to the port side. Hardly had this whistle died away, to the captain's relief, than there loomed out of the fog the bow of another ship. There was no time to maneuver the *Egypt*. In a matter of seconds there came the grinding crash of metal on metal, and a great gaping hole was torn in the side of the *Egypt*. The mysterious steamer swept on into the fog and disappeared.

*The clamshell bucket of this 2,000-ton dredge can take twenty tons of mud in a single bite.*

"S O S–S O S–S O S. Position 48° 10′ North, 5° 30′ West. *Egypt*," flashed the frantic message as the stricken ship heeled heavily to port and started to go down. In just twenty minutes the ill-fated steamer had disappeared beneath the surface. The steamer *Seine*, which had struck her, reappeared to save some of the crew.

When the *Egypt* went down she took with her not only seventeen unfortunate passengers, and seventy-one of the crew, but 5½ tons of gold and 43 tons of silver, insured by Lloyd's of London for $5,000,000. This was a treasure worth recovering, and Lloyd's set out to find some-one to attempt the job of salvage. It presented many problems, the major ones being to find the wreck in the first place, and after that to work at the tremendous depth at which she almost certainly lay. Various attempts were made to locate the *Egypt*, but they all failed. At last, in 1928, there appeared on the scene an Italian, Commendatore Gioganni Quaglia who headed the Societa Ricuperi Marittimi, the Society for Maritime Recovery, an organization with a very remarkable record of successful salvage in Italian waters. Sorima, as the organization was called for short, signed a contract with Lloyd's that would give it fifty per cent of whatever it recovered from the *Egypt*.

Early in the summer of 1929 the work was started. First there was the baffling problem of locating the wreck. It was true that the captain of the *Egypt* had radioed his position as the ship was sinking. However, there was every reason to believe that this position, hastily taken in the fog, in waters known for their swift currents, was not accurate. Two radio compass stations in France had taken directional bearings on the *Egypt* at the time, and calculations based on these showed that the ship was at 48° 6′ North and 5° 29′ West, a location a mile east and four miles south of the position indicated by her captain. Hedback, the captain of a Swedish ship that hunted for the wreck in 1923, reported that his drags had struck an obstruction that he believed to be the *Egypt* at a spot close to that indicated by the bearings established by the radio compass stations.

With this choice of locations, Quaglia laid down buoys around an area six miles wide and ten miles long. Under this sixty square miles of ocean surface he proposed to drag the ocean floor inch by inch until the *Egypt* was found. To accomplish this incredibly difficult task, he used two ships, the *Artiglio* and the *Rostro*. Between these two craft was paid out a mile-long wire, held down by weights. The plan was that if the wire struck an obstruction as big as the wreck they were seeking, there would be a jerk that would indicate the strike to the men above. As the work began, the salvage crews ran into their first difficulty. The cable caught, but not on the wreck. The crews discovered that, instead of being smooth sand, the floor of the ocean was covered with jagged rocks thirty feet high. Yet each time they hit one of these rocks, they had to send a diver down to see if by any chance the obstruction might be the *Egypt*. Slowly they inched forward. Weeks, then months went by, and still they did not find the missing ship. As the world watched with interest and skepticism, various scientists came to join the quest, bringing electromagnetic devices that were supposed to locate masses of metal. But the summer of 1929 drew to a close, with the stormy winter ahead, and there were no results whatsoever to show for the months of hard work.

The salvage crews came back in the summer of 1930 with a different kind of drag, one which would go high enough above the rocks to avoid catching on them and still remain low enough to catch on the *Egypt*.

The months slipped away again, with no results. Then one day late in August the drag caught on something, a mile west of the spot where Captain Hedback had reported a strike. A diver was sent down, and from a depth of 360 feet there came the exciting words: "It's the *Egypt!*"

Men on the decks above shouted and hugged each other, joyous at the success that had come to them after nearly two years of apparently fruitless searching.

Now their problems were only beginning. The *Egypt* lay at such a depth that divers in ordinary diving suits could not possibly work aboard her. The record dive at that time was 306 feet, and even this was considered too deep for ordinary diving operations. Of course, Quaglia had expected this, and the observations already made had been accomplished with a grotesque diving suit called the Neufeldt & Kuhnke diving armor. It was a massive metal monster, weighing so much that a diver inside could hardly move. It was equipped with claws that were operated by the diver's hands, but in this suit no diver would ever be able to move around enough to accomplish anything.

*A merchant ship with a damaged bow is towed into a shipyard to have its "nose" repaired.*

*After the water is drained out of a graving dock, the ship settles down on supporting blocks.*

The clumsy device was useful only to permit the diver to make observations at depths where he would be crushed in an ordinary suit.

Since the suit could be used only for observation, and since the depth was too great for divers to work in, the directors of Sorima decided to dispense with divers altogether. They proposed to attempt the salvage of the *Egypt's* treasure trove by "fishing" from above. They constructed a cylindrical steel shell, a type of bathysphere, with five glass ports. In it, an observer could be lowered, and over the telephone he could direct the work of the men using the grappling hooks from above.

Their first task was to prove that the wreck they discovered was indeed the *Egypt*. In the dim depths of the sea, it looked like the craft they sought, but they had to be sure. They used grappling hooks to tear off the roof of the captain's cabin, and the observation shell was dropped inside it. Peering through the glass ports into the semidarkness, the observer gave directions that guided the clutching steel jaws of a grappling device to fasten over the captain's safe. The safe was taken to Brest, and burned open by acetylene torches while dignitaries from Lloyd's looked on. When the papers were removed from the safe, they proved to be those of the *Egypt*.

That ended the salvage work for 1930. Two years of hard work had still yielded no treasure. While working on another salvage job during the winter, the *Artiglio* was destroyed by an explosion of a shipload of T.N.T. Many of her crew and Quaglia's best divers were killed. Nevertheless, Quaglia came doggedly back to work on the *Egypt* the next year with a new ship and a hastily assembled crew. The job ahead was a tremendous one, for the bullion room was so situated that it would be necessary to tear away the *Egypt's* superstructure down to her main deck and then to blast through the heavy plates of her steel hull. The work of tearing off the superstructure was accomplished with comparative ease. Giant claws picked it up and threw it free of the ship. But the task of getting through the steel plates was a delicate one. Heavy charges of blasting powder could not be used because there was grave danger that the floor of the bullion room might give way if the *Egypt* were too badly shaken by a heavy blast. That would send the fifty tons of bullion cascading into the hold, and recovery might then be completely impossible.

After each plate was torn free by the carefully placed blast, the grabs would seize upon the torn plates to tear them free. The result would be a tug of war in which the salvage ship, the new *Artiglio*, would lean far over. It was slow, painful work, and the summer went by and the time of storms came. The men defied weather to stay on the job as they tore their way down through the promenade deck and the upper deck. Already they had torn and blasted away five hundred tons of steel, and still the heavy main deck lay between them and the treasure. They had to move more carefully than ever now. Working so close to the bullion room, any heavy blast might send the bullion plunging into the hold. By December 1, working in the dim wintry light of the short days, the divers had torn off one of the plates above the bullion room. Now the storms came with such fury that it was impossible to work any longer that year. Reluctantly they gave up and sailed away. Three years of hard labor and half a million dollars spent had not yielded a single bar of the precious gold.

Discouraging as the work had been, the summer of 1932 found the men back at the lonely spot on the sea beneath which lay the fabulous treasure. The winter had not been wasted, for during it Quaglia and his men had devised a special kind of hoist designed to raise the gold itself. The claws of the clutching hoist could be opened to a width of three feet. When closed, they formed a tight ball. To make doubly sure that nothing slipped through it, a second set of jaws was designed to close around the first. When at last they actually tore off the last plate, and the grab dropped into the bullion room, every man on the salvage ship stood with bated breath. In tense silence they watched the grab swing up over the deck. Eagerly they waited for the golden shower as the jaws opened. Yellow metal came showering down on the deck, and with wild shouts the men rushed forward. Then their cries of joy turned to expressions of shocked dismay. The yellow metal was not gold. Instead, it was a useless pile of brass cartridges. In numbed silence they stared at one another. What had gone wrong? Had they blasted their way into the wrong room? Had the bullion been stored somewhere else on the ship?

Quaglia said grimly, "We'll go on digging."

The grab soon brought up great quantities of Indian paper money from the State of Hyderabad. Well, perhaps that was worth something. For a while they felt better, until the radio message came back from London which told them that the money was worthless, having long since been canceled by the State of Hyderabad. Weeks went by, and the grabs brought up only a miscellaneous collection of soggy debris. The crew was completely discouraged, but Quaglia insisted that they keep on. Then one day a seaman discovered two gold coins in the rubbish that was being dumped on board. There was excitement again as the grab went down; this time it came up filled with gold. At last some of the ingots actually lay on the deck of the *Artiglio*. In three days they had a million dollars worth of it aboard. Throughout the rest of 1932 they continued to bring up gold. Again storms drove them away until the summer of 1933, and even that year was not enough; so they came back for still more work in 1934. The great undertaking ended that year, with the last of the five million dollars aboard. The faith and courage of Quaglia and his men had accomplished the impossible, and made the saving of the *Egypt's* treasure one of the great epics of modern salvage.

CHAPTER 15

# ADVENTURES ON INLAND SEAS

*Plying between Detroit and Buffalo this passenger side-wheeler makes surprising speed.*

THE BOY walking along the wild shores of Thunder Bay Island looked out across the crimson waters of Lake Huron with eager eyes. In the rays of the setting sun he could see that just a mile off shore two ships were about to pass each other. One of them he knew was the *Pewabic,* one of the finest ships of her day. The ship she was passing was the *Meteor,* an older ship but still a sturdy one.

The boy, John D. Persons, listened to the throb of the engines and wished, as he had wished a thousand times before, that he could be aboard one of these vessels. As he watched, the *Meteor* swerved suddenly. There was a tremendous booming crash as her sharp prow tore deep into the side of the big *Pewabic,* cutting her almost in half. Almost instantly the crippled ship went down, carrying with her 125 people, 300 tons of copper, and a fortune in currency.

Years later John Persons had his wish. He became one of the greatest of the Great Lakes sea captains. Yet in all the years he traveled the

*Freeing a light buoy from the icy grip of winter on the Great Lakes.*

lakes he never forgot the strange and terrifying sight he saw on the red-streaked waters of Lake Huron that evening in 1865. It taught him that disasters on the Great Lakes can come as easily to ships within sight of shore as to ships far out on a storm-tossed ocean.

What John Persons had seen was just one of the episodes that make up the colorful history of the Great Lakes. Some of the great adventures of the sea have taken place not on the oceans but on the cold waters of America's mighty inland seas. The saga of Great Lakes shipping is a story of a growing America that needed iron to make the steel to build her railroads, her bridges, and her huge buildings. That iron came from the great Mesabi range of Minnesota, and ships carried it east to be smelted. It is a story of a hungry world, fed by the great wheat-raising regions of the United States and Canada. Ships carried the wheat down the lakes on its way to world markets. It is a story of great human ingenuity, courage, and skill, of mighty battles with sea and storm, with hurricanes, ice, and snow, of races with time and the elements. Although they sail on fresh water and are seldom out of sight of shore, the sailors of the Great Lakes are a hardy breed of seafaring men.

The story of the big storm of 1913 shows what can happen to Great Lakes shipping.

On November 8, 1913 the weather forecast was: "Snow or rain and colder, Saturday, with west to southwest winds. Sunday, unsettled." There was little hint that a terrible storm was taking shape, a storm that would sweep down with such fury that in three days forty vessels would be wrecked and 235 lives lost. In that storm, gigantic waves thirty-five feet high raced across the lakes. Winds reached eighty miles an hour and stayed at points above sixty miles an hour for sixteen hours at a stretch. Lake Superior, Lake Michigan, and Lake Huron were the hardest hit. Shore installations were battered and even ships that were anchored in harbors were lost.

Out in the open lake, ships fought a losing battle against the fury of the storm. One of them was the *L. C. Waldo,* far out on Lake Superior when the storm struck. Almost at once the sea spray froze on her, coating every inch of the deck and pilot house with a heavy load of ice. The blizzard made it impossible for Captain Duddleson to see anything in the blinding swirl of snow, so he laid a compass course for Manitou Island, where he hoped to find refuge. They had not gone far when a tremendous wave struck the vessel. It swept away the pilot house completely, but Duddleson and the wheelsman managed to cling to a stanchion. As the pilot house went overboard, it smashed the ship's compass and damaged the steering gear so the ship could no longer keep a course against the wind.

"We'll get there somehow," Duddleson said grimly, and sent the wheelsman on the perilous journey forward to get a compass from one of the lifeboats. After that Duddleson and the wheelsman took turns steering their foundering craft with the hand compass. The captain's calculations and steering were remarkably accurate, for they came within half a mile of reaching their destination. Only a man of rare courage would have undertaken the passage between Gull Rock and Keweenaw Point, but the captain was confident that he could do it. He might have, if a hidden reef had not gored the *Waldo.* With his craft aground, Captain Duddleson knew that it was just a question of time before she would be battered completely to pieces, yet in the storm there was no way to launch lifeboats.

The captain ordered his men to take refuge in the after deckhouse,

*Ore boats on the Great Lakes following a lane left by an ice breaker in the early spring.*

*A mate makes use of a FM radio-telephone installed aboard a Great Lakes steamer.*

where they burned the furniture to keep from freezing. The storm continued to tear away portions of the ship, and the men feared that at any moment the lashing water would carry away the deckhouse. For three days they huddled there together, until at last the storm abated and they were rescued by Coast Guardsmen.

Another great story of the same storm is the account of the crew of the *Turret Chief*, a wooden ship that likewise was thrown ashore on the ragged coast of the Keweenaw Peninsula. Her crew rushed onto her deck, where they saw that she would be battered to pieces in a few minutes. Throwing lines over the side, they scrambled down, struggling over jagged rocks toward the shore. Half frozen, they managed to build a rude shelter out of driftwood, and all eighteen men crowded into it to escape some of the fury of the wind. They had no food or fire, and their situation looked hopeless as, hour after hour, day after day, the storm continued. Heavy snow fell, blanketing their shelter and the forest around them. After three days, they looked out from their crude shelter and saw something that brought shouts from their hungry throats.

A file of Indians came marching through the drifts! The Indians provided the shipwrecked men with food and led them to safety.

Among the stories of famous Great Lakes ship disasters is the fate of the *Mataafa*. On November 28, 1905 she set out from Duluth for her last trip of the season. It was already late, and the treacherous storms of winter would not leave the lake free of ice much longer. Behind the *Mataafa* was towed the barge *Nasmuth*, loaded with ore. Hardly had the two ships passed out of the harbor than a tremendous blast of wind came hurtling out of the northeast. The *Mataafa's* captain promptly ordered her back to port. To get into the closed harbor, where there would be safety from the storm, it was necessary to go through a narrow, pier-lined canal. The barge was cast adrift, because it was apparent that there would be no chance of guiding her through the canal. At first it seemed that the *Mataafa* would get into the canal safely. Half her length had passed into it when a great rolling wave picked her up and hurled her against a pier. For a moment she struggled there, her engines hammering furiously as she shuddered from stem to stern. Slowly she swung, as if to head out to sea, then again the great rolling seas seized her and battered her against her pier head, ripping off the entire rudder. Now the crew was helpless to avert catastrophe, for there was no way to steer the ship. She was driven against the rocky shores, where in a short time her hull was broken in two.

Meanwhile, the news of the *Mataafa's* struggle had spread, and a crowd of forty thousand people gathered on the shores to watch this tragedy. Probably never before or since have so many people watched a shipwreck taking place. On board the battered remains of the ship, the crew was in a terrifying position. Part of the men were in one part of the ship, part in the other. The heavy seas rolled up, completely covering the ship. There was no possible way to launch boats to get ashore, even though shore was just a few yards

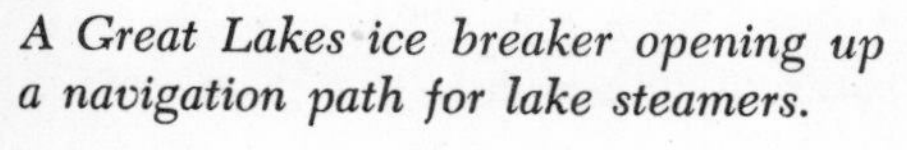

*A Great Lakes ice breaker opening up a navigation path for lake steamers.*

away, for no boat could survive in such a surf. Rescue efforts were made from land; life-saving crews shot rockets aboard the *Mataafa.* The line carried by the rockets froze into a rope of ice and broke before they succeeded in hauling out a heavier hawser. Members of the crew tried to get hawsers to float ashore by fastening them to boxes, but they were quickly battered to pieces on the rocks. All through the night they struggled while the crowd of spectators on the shore built huge bonfires to tell the doomed men that they had not been forgotten. In the morning the seas subsided, and rescue crews managed to get aboard what was left of the *Mataafa*. They found the men in the forward cabin still alive, but all those in the aft cabin were frozen to death. It is the strange fate of the fresh-water sailors that death and destruction can come a few yards from shore.

Storms are not the only enemies of the Great Lakes seamen. Winter is a worse one, because it completely stops shipping as a solid ice floe locks the lakes. As winter approaches, there is an air of grim expectancy among all the men who risk their lives on the lakes. They are getting ready for the last run, the final desperate venture down the lakes before the ice closes in for good. Everyone on the lakes remembers the winter of 1926. At four o'clock on the afternoon of November 30, twenty-two freighters loaded with five and a half million bushels of wheat set out from Port Arthur and Fort William, to try to make their final run in the face of lowering clouds and a warning snowstorm that had already delayed their departure by many hours. They managed to get across Lake Superior and went through Sault Sainte Marie heavily coated with ice, for the temperature had fallen to twelve degrees below zero. They were the last ships to try to make the run that year, and when they reached the Soo they found ahead of them nearly 250 vessels, already frozen in the ice. This frozen fleet was one

*Assisted by a tug, a lake steamer prepares to unload under a giant crane.*

of the oddest spectacles ever seen, for, with its forest of stacks, all belching black smoke, and its lights casting a strange glow upon the sky at night, it looked like some curious city that had sprung up on the ice. They waited there just ten days and then, miraculously, there was a flaw. Ice breakers battered at the ice and finally broke a passage. The armada of ships began to move. With whistles bellowing, they plunged through the floating ice fields and on out into the clear waters of the lower lakes.

*Iron ore boats passing through the canal locks at Sault Ste. Marie, Michigan.*

There were many disasters in the early days of steam travel on the lakes, but none more terrible than the fiery end of the *Phoenix*. The stout new *Phoenix* sailed up Lake Huron one day in November, 1847, carrying as passengers more than two hundred settlers who were traveling toward the shores of Lake Michigan. The sharp clanging of firebells brought the passengers struggling from their berths at four o'clock in the morning. They found huge clouds of smoke swirling up from below, and then sharp tongues of flame started showing through the smoke. After a time the pumps failed, and the passengers formed a bucket brigade. The water poured into the flames in the engine room had no effect. They only roared higher, and it was soon apparent that the fire was completely out of control. There were only two small lifeboats aboard. When they were filled and were rowed away, the two hundred people aboard were left without even a chance to escape. Just five miles away lay the Wisconsin shore, and the lights of Sheboygan were plainly visible, but those five miles were filled with the icy water of Lake Michigan. By the time rescue boats put out from Sheboygan in the morning, the *Phoenix* had burned to the water line, and there were only three survivors. The forty-three persons who had left the *Phoenix* in the lifeboats had some narrow escapes too, as they fought heavy seas and were forced to bail water with their wooden shoes.

*Loading coal at Toledo, Ohio, for the great steel industry of America.*

The lakes provide another hazard to shipping in the form of the thick gray fog that frequently blankets the water. Fog is an enemy of ships of all the seven seas, but it is a greater enemy of Great Lakes craft. In waters so filled with ships and so confined, there have been many collisions. Strangely enough, many of them have been caused by a system of whistle signals. Lake ships use a whistle talk that consists of many different signals. By this means they talk back and forth with each other and the shore, identifying themselves, giving orders and telling what their next move will be. This whistle language has been developed in the course of the last one hundred years to meet the special needs of lake shipping. Because these signals are entirely different from those used by salt-water ships, there have been some confusing situations when sailors new to the lakes failed to realize the difference.

The International Code of salt-water signals has a fog signal consisting of one blast, which means that the vessel giving it is underway. On the lakes it means, "I want to pass you on the right." The experience of the *Thomas Lynch* on May 28, 1935 is a good example of what can happen because of this difference in signals. She was bound out of Gary, for Two Harbors. As she passed the light of Manitou Shoal, the weather suddenly closed in solid. Promptly her captain put into operation the Great Lakes fog signal of three blasts at one minute intervals.

Suddenly, a one-blast whistle sounded close ahead and to the right. The skipper of the *Lynch,* a lake sailor of long experience, checked to slow speed and ordered hard right rudder. Bearing straight down on him out of the white gloom was a steamer. The ships missed each other by inches. It was learned that the steamer in the fog was the Norwegian *Ba,* whose skipper had been giving salt-water signals.

The skipper of another Norwegian craft brought his ship to disaster by the same error that same season. His ship, the *Viator,* was plowing through pea-soup fog in Lake Huron ten miles south of Thunder Bay Island Light. Suddenly, the captain saw a large craft, the *Ormidale,* bearing down. Quickly the *Viator's* captain gave three sharp blasts, the International Code signal for "full speed astern." To the *Ormidale* this was merely a fog signal. She struck the *Viator* with full force amidships, driving her prow through the stranger's side. With keen presence of mind, the officers of the *Ormidale* kept the *Viator* impaled there until her crew had been brought aboard. Then the captain backed the *Ormidale* off, and the ship she had struck went down almost instantly.

The task of moving iron ore alone is tremendous. Every year some three hundred ore boats undertake to carry something over ninety million long tons of iron ore from remote mines in northern Michigan, Wisconsin, and Minnesota to the great steel centers of the nation. There, in such places as Pittsburgh, Chicago, Cleveland, and Buffalo,

*Great Lakes steamers carry a huge supply of raw materials to Detroit docks.*

it is made into the steel that finds countless uses in our machine civilization. The ore adds up to twice as much freight as passes through the Panama and Suez Canals combined in any peace-time year. If you stand at the foot of Woodward Avenue in Detroit in the summer, you will see the ore boats passing at an average of one every fifteen minutes. They may be gliding swiftly downstream with ten to seventeen thousand tons of ore in their hold, or they may be heading upstream laden with a return cargo of coal.

The Great Lakes ore and wheat boats are marvels of efficiency. They are really giant floating bins that can haul cargoes of over twelve thousand tons. An important part of their efficiency is the amazing speed with which they can be loaded. Looming along the docks in Duluth are great ore bins, into which railroad cars have dumped their cargoes. When an ore boat comes in for lading, it slides in under these bins or pockets, each one of which is perfectly aligned with a corresponding pocket in the boat. Electrical controls permit operators to open the hinged bottoms of the pockets, which then drop their ore directly into the boat. It takes, at the most, only a few hours to get the boat's entire cargo aboard. Wheat is loaded aboard special wheat boats by somewhat similar methods. There are some startling records for quick loading. The *D. G. Kerr* loaded 12,508 tons of iron ore in 16½ minutes on September 7, 1921. The record for loading grain is held by the *G. A.*

*Equipped with a long boom amidships, the* Diamond Alkali *can unload itself without dock machinery.*

*Tomlinson,* which took aboard 157,565 bushels of wheat in one hour on July 7, 1932. Even these records could probably be exceeded if the operators made an effort to do so.

Unloading, too, is amazingly fast, thanks to a device known as the Hewlett Unloader. These unloaders are singularly like giant crabs, with great claws. The operator sits in an enclosed cab just above the tremendous claws. The unloader moves along rails above the vessel being unloaded, and the operator can make it do anything that can be done with a shovel. By pulling levers, he makes it go down into the hold of the ship, where its claws seize a fifteen-ton load at one bite. An arm swings the filled claw over a car that climbs up an incline to dump its load on the big stock piles. Even after the loading of vessels had been greatly speeded up, unloading was a bottleneck until the coming of the Hewlett Unloader. It can unload 7,000 tons of ore in 4 to 6 hours, instead of the several days required by old hand methods.

*Giant bucket legs unload the chambers of an ore boat.*

This swift process of loading and unloading makes possible some truly astonishing results. Ore that is just part of the reddish mass in the pits of the Mesabi on a Monday morning may be rolling out of the steel mills of Gary as finished steel by Thursday. Ore dug from the Michigan mines on Monday may end up in a finished automobile before the week is over! Nowhere in the world has sea shipping achieved such standards of speed as those of the Great Lakes freighters.

The ore ships themselves are perhaps the most distinctive type of cargo vessel in service in the world today. They are very long, many of them well over 600 feet. An ore boat may be likened to a gigantic steel box, 500 feet long, 65 feet wide, and 30 feet deep. Added to the box is a bow and a stern to permit the box to be sailed. In the bow are located the bridge and deck crews' house. Amidships, in the part represented by the steel box, are the cargo holds, compartments covered with removable hatches. When the ships are loaded, they ride very low in the water, so low that anyone accustomed to deep-sea vessels is a little alarmed when he first sees a lake boat. Their cigar-shaped hulls are far from beautiful, but they are perfect for the job they have to do.

These remarkable ships can be traced back to one of the grand old men of the lakes, Captain Alexander McDougall. When he was a small boy, McDougall's parents left their home on the island of Islay off the coast of Scotland and settled in a little community on the southern end of Georgian Bay. Here young Alexander watched the ships moving up and down Lake Huron. He wanted to be a sailor, but his practical parents felt that he would make a better blacksmith. He kept at the task as a blacksmith's apprentice until he was sixteen; then he gave it up and ran away to get a job as a deck hand. As soon as he set foot on the throbbing deck of a lake steamer, he knew that this was his work. He loved the ships and the blue waters of the lakes. In two years he had become a second mate; by the time he was twenty-five he was master of the *Thomas A. Scott*. During the years he captained various ships that plied the lakes he dreamed of a different kind of ship.

*Carrying wheat in her hold, a Great Lakes freighter approaches a Buffalo grain elevator.*

*These Great Lakes steamers are specially built to carry iron ore and coal.*

"It will be built for the lakes, built for the cargo she'll carry," he would point out. "All the ships on the lakes now are just ocean-going types."

He got his chance at last, in 1889. In the shipyards at West Superior, he built a strange-looking craft that was quickly called "McDougall's Dream." To seafaring men of her day she looked strange indeed. McDougall called her a "whaleback," although she bore little resemblance to any natural or man-made creature of the sea. She was long, with a pilot house on her bow and engines on her stern, with nothing but cargo holds in between. Whatever sailors said about the whalebacks, McDougall built more than fifty of them, some of which are still in existence, still plowing through the waters of the lakes McDougall loved.

Among the strange ships that ply the Great Lakes are those which carry the seagoing railroad across Lake Michigan. Three railroads, the Ann Arbor, the Père Marquette, and the Grand Trunk line, use the lake as a short cut on the long haul from East Coast to West and help to relieve the complicated rail traffic tangle in Chicago.

The story of these floating train yards that carry whole trains across stormy Lake Michigan began more than fifty years ago when Harry Ashley, an enterprising manager of the Ann Arbor Railroad, proposed a bold scheme.

"The Chicago yards are getting too crowded," he reported. "Something has to be done. I propose a new Northwest Passage—a new coast-to-coast route across Lake Michigan."

The stockholders were astonished. "Bridge Lake Michigan?" they asked.

"Who said anything about a bridge?" Ashley retorted. "We'll use boats. Give me two seaworthy craft, we'll lay tracks on the decks, and there's our bridge."

Ashley's idea for speeding up traffic to the Pacific Northwest got off to a bad start. His first car ferry, the *Ann Arbor No. 1,* was a rather ungainly craft that promptly developed a heavy list when she was loaded with twenty cars of coal. Ashley ordered them unloaded, and set to work to redesign his boat. A second trip worked out successfully, but the third one found the *Ann Arbor No. 1* held fast on a sandbar off Ahnapee, Wisconsin. The heavy load pushed the hull deep into the sand, and it looked as if she would stay there, a symbol of Ashley's ignominious defeat. Finally five tugs got her loose after working for two days. A few more trips went successfully, then bad luck struck again in the form of a gale. The water raced through the ferry, tearing at the cars. Four of them went overboard, and the rest were in danger as the craft listed heavily. She managed to limp into port hours later.

*Iron ore pouring through these spouts flows directly into the hold of the ship.*

Her misfortunes were not over, because in the winter, the *Ann Arbor No. 1* got herself locked securely in the ice off shore. An enterprising young passenger agent set a gang of workers to blasting a path through the windrows of ice. Teams hauled out sacks of coal that were taken aboard to give the craft fuel for an attempt to break free at the first sign of weakening in the ice.

*A Great Lakes coal and iron ore steamer approaching the docks of Toledo.*

These adventures of the *Ann Arbor No. 1* were foretastes of events to come, but they did not deter the building of more box-car ferries. Ashley's idea was a good one, and the vast saving in time and money was worth some chance-taking.

Today the big freight-car ferries that ply the troubled waters of Lake Michigan between Chicago and Ludington, Michigan, Manitowoc, Wisconsin, and Frankfort, Michigan, and other routes, are marvels of maritime engineering. The big *City of Midland,* the last craft turned out before World War II, is the world's first streamlined car ferry. It took six million pounds of steel to build her, and cost the Père Marquette close to three million dollars. When her big steel seagate comes down, her four hundred and six feet can easily swallow a thirty-four-car freight train.

Like all other ships of this seagoing railroad, the *City of Midland* has her own crew on each shore. These men, an engineer and fireman, a foreman and two helpers, know every trick of loading. By long experience they have learned that rolling a freight car onto a ship is a delicate matter. There are cases on record of rough handling that sent heavy box cars crashing through a bulkhead.

There are four loading tracks on every deck. Load the wrong tracks first, and the ship will list, so the railroaders have worked out the correct way of doing it. First they roll two cars onto the left center rails, then two on the track farthest right, then two more on the farthest left track, then two into the empty right center. This process goes on in precisely this order until the ferry is loaded. Once aboard, jacks and chains lift the box cars from their springing and fasten them so securely that for all practical purposes they become part of the ship itself. They must be fastened tightly, or there will be plenty of trouble when waves lash the lake. The floating freight yards with their burden of trains keep railroading schedule, rain or shine, twenty-four hours a day, 365 days a year, so they must be equipped for any kind of weather.

*The City of Flint* probably rolled up an all-time record for water craft when she recently made one thousand trips between Ludington and Milwaukee on 363 consecutive days. That added up to more than one hundred thousand miles. In all those trips the ship's time in port averaged only two hours—a good example of how fast the expert car loaders can get the trains aboard and secured.

The loss of the Père Marquette Number 18 is one of the classic disasters that can overtake the car ferries. She started out in weather that was calm enough, with twenty-six freight cars aboard. Although she put out at night, there was no word of impending disaster until 5:30 the next morning, when the air waves suddenly crackled with "C. D. Q. Car Ferry Number 18 sinking. For God's sake send help!" Number 17 rushed to the scene and picked up the half-hysterical survivors who could tell what had happened, but not why. That was to remain one of the many mysteries of the Great Lakes. The craft had started to leak as soon as she left port, but powerful steam pumps soon emptied her of water, and she continued on her way. Then suddenly there was a terrific explosion that literally tore the ship apart. Captain Kilty was thrown hundreds of feet through the air, and many of the crew were drowned.

Whatever kind of craft they may sail in, the fresh-water sailors of the Great Lakes have jobs that are no less exciting than those of the men who sail the salt seas. Certainly, their jobs are no less important, for the Great Lakes carry the very lifeblood of American industry.

CHAPTER 16

# HARBORS AND HARBOR MEN

*A small but powerful workboat chugs into Mariner's Harbor, Staten Island, New York.*

IT WAS a hot sultry afternoon in August, 1941, and the New York Harbor seemed peaceful, though as busy as usual. Millions of dollars worth of precious Lend-Lease supplies were being loaded on ships tied up at the Brooklyn piers. The loading went on night and day at top speed, for the supplies were desperately needed in England.

Suddenly, there was an explosion and a spurt of smoke and flame from pier 26 in Brooklyn! Every seaman in the vicinity turned quickly in the direction of the explosion, horror-stricken. A fire along the crowded waterfront was a bad thing under any circumstance. But fire on board a ship loaded with ammunition! And there were more than one hundred storage buildings right along that waterfront crammed with equipment that must get overseas without fail!

Within a moment or two, the awesome wailing of the fire siren could be heard all over the harbor. The speedboats of the harbor police raced across the bay. The harbor fire boats churned up the water speeding to the scene. Overhead a United States Coast Guard flying boat winged its way in the direction of the Brooklyn pier. Soon there were speedy Coast Guard cutters on their way to the spot, directed by means of a

*The helmsman takes over after the harbor pilot leaves the ship.*

two-way radio by the pilot of the plane.

It was soon found that the burning craft was the *Panuco,* a freighter tied up at a pier close by an ammunition ship. Flames leaped from her hold, indicating that her cargo was on fire. In a few minutes the pier would catch fire and then the ships in the adjoining slips, and the whole waterfront would be in peril.

The captain of a little Dalzell tug close by sized up the situation quickly. He called out to the skipper of a sister tug.

"Think we can get her out?"

"Guess we'd better."

The two gallant little tugs swung into action and nosed their way right up to the burning ship. Deck hands swung heavy line over the stern of the *Panuco.* The grateful crew hauled up the towing lines of the tugs and secured them quickly. The injured men aboard the *Panuco* were transferred to the tugs and soon the flaming ship was being eased away from the pier and towed to open water where the fire boats went to work on it, sending huge sprays of chemical fluids into the burning hold. There was an ever-present danger of new explosions, but the two little tugs stayed with the stricken ship and towed her to the flats, where she sank harmlessly. A terrible catastrophe had been averted. The waterfront and its ships, piers, and warehouses had been spared. The Lend-Lease ships had been saved. All because two fearless men of the harbor saw their duty and performed it without delay.

Every harbor in the world has such men, who spend all their days in their harbor, know every corner of it, are fiercely proud of it, and respond to fire or disaster on its waters the way they would aid a neighbor whose house caught fire. The harbor is their home. The ocean-going ships that come to the port are welcome or unwelcome visitors, depending on their manners. Harbor men like to get news of other harbors, but they have only a passing interest in the open sea. Let a seaman from a big ship talk about hundred-foot waves and hurricanes and the harbor man will only nod and then tell him about treacherous tides, cross currents, or ice floes that can smash a ship in a twinkling in early spring, and the creeping terror of fog in the harbor. A harbor man doesn't really believe that much of interest can happen outside the harbor. Whether he works on a tug, a pilot ship, a dredger, a lightship, or a ferry boat, he is one hundred per cent sold on the harbor. How could a man of sense want to be anywhere else?

The great harbors of the world are busy places. Ships must unload their passengers and cargo, allow time for maintenance and repairs, take on fuel and new cargoes, and at regular intervals go to dry dock for a major overhauling. A great variety of services must be maintained to take care of arriving and departing ships. Every port has its quarantine department and health officers who must go aboard ships before they enter the harbor and make sure that there is no one aboard who has contracted a contagious disease that might plague the country, and that no plants or animals are on board that might bring pests or disease to the country's agriculture and livestock. There are custom officials who must make sure that duty is paid on articles subject to a

*French fishing boats make a forest of masts in a French port.*

*An aërial view of Singapore, Britain's great seaport in Asia.*

tariff. There are immigration officials who must make sure that everyone coming ashore has a right to enter the country.

Pilot ships must go to the entrance of the harbor and send a pilot to the incoming ship so that he may pilot her safely to her berth. If some disaster should overtake a ship at the entrance of the harbor, it might delay all incoming and outgoing ships, and, in the case of harbors with narrow channels, even close the harbor for several days. A fleet of tugs must be in readiness within the harbor to maneuver each ship into her berth, and thus prevent damage to the ships and the piers. A gang of longshoremen must be on hand at the pier to unload her cargo. A fleet of trucks must be waiting to take the cargo to its destination. Guards and plain clothes detectives must keep a sharp watch on the pier while the ship is being unloaded. The harbor police, in powerful speed boats, must patrol the waters on the lookout for thieves and smugglers. The harbor fire boats must be always on the alert when a ship is being loaded or unloaded.

The harbor itself needs a lot of care. Its channels must be dredged and kept free of debris, silt, and wrecks. The buoy markers along the channels must be cleaned, repaired, and painted at regular intervals. Buoys marking shoals, rocks, and other underwater obstructions in the harbor must be serviced and a sharp eye kept on them, especially after storms, to make sure that they have not shifted from their proper places or been washed away. In midwinter the ice breakers are kept busy clearing passageways for incoming and departing ships and for local traffic on the harbor, such as ferries.

Every harbor man considers his own port the finest one on earth, and you would have a hard time arguing with him about it, for every harbor has special features of its own. Liverpool, which has the second largest foreign commerce of any city in the world, is located at the Mersey River estuary, and by a system of locks the water level of the inner harbor is made independent of the tides. Its docks cover an area of 660 acres, and there are about 40 miles of quays. But a London Harbor man would laugh at a Liverpool man, for the London docks cover an area of more than 800 acres, and each dock is an interior basin accessible by means of a lock! An Antwerp Harbor man in Belgium would sniff at both of them, for Antwerp is located on the Scheldt River, about 50 miles inland from the North Sea, and the river is 2,200 feet wide at this point. A Lisbon man would say "Shucks" to this, for Lisbon is beautifully situated at the head of the Tagus estuary only seven miles from its mouth at the Atlantic Ocean, and the Lisbon Harbor is one of the finest in the world. But then, the harbor men of San Francisco, Baltimore, Marseilles, LeHavre, Algiers, Alexandria, Singapore, Kobe, and Sydney would have something to say about that!

*Stevedores unload the* William H. Kendrick *at New Orleans.*

But deep in their hearts, all harbor men know that the greatest one of them all is the New York Harbor. It was considered the finest harbor in the world more than three hundred years ago—long before there were any skyscrapers on Manhattan Island, long before there were any piers, warehouses, or any harbor facilities to greet an incoming ship. It is a natural harbor, magnificently protected from the gales and storms of the Atlantic, with an inland water area of more than 1,500 square miles! It has 8 sheltered bays, 4 rivers, 650 miles of waterfront, and, owing to the fact that Manhattan Island is a rocky shelf, there is deep water right up to the shore. Most important, the tides change the water level only three or four feet as a general thing. Along the Irish coast, for example, the tides change the water level as much as thirty or forty feet! A ship caught at low tide is beached and stranded. The tides along the South American coast at the mouth of the Amazon River are so fierce that they produce tidal waves or "bores," which rush up the river with a loud roar. By comparison, the Hudson River is as gentle as a lamb.

Today the harbor has 1,822 piers, 50 floating docks, and the most modern freight-handling equipment in the world. There are huge fixed cranes, a fleet of derrick lighters, and gigantic floating cranes that can lift 150 tons as easily as you can pick up a match. On the piers you will find tractors, power-driven trucks, and lumber carriers which shuttle back and forth between the ship and the transit sheds and warehouse. Many of them are equipped with prongs, forks, and small hoists. Altogether, more than one billion dollars has been invested in the wharves,

*A United Fruit liner in New York Harbor.*

*A Liberty ship drops her anchor in the harbor of Manila.*

warehouses, dry docks, and other harbor equipment. Besides that, the harbor has forty-seven shipyards! There are more than 40,000 factories along the shores of the harbor, and a great fleet of ships and small vessels are required to serve their needs. The shipyards are always busy.

As you can well imagine, the traffic on the harbor is very heavy and requires a good deal of supervision. New York's harbor police are especially trained and are equipped with powerful speed boats that have two-way radios, machine guns, and immense searchlights that can pierce a mile and a half through the darkness. More than 150 of these harbor policemen patrol the waters twenty-four hours a day. A United States Coast Guard Station, located near Floyd Bennett Field, also maintains a fleet of speed boats and cutters that are held in readiness for any emergency in the harbor. The United States Coast Guard Service provides constant supervision of the six hundred buoy markers used in the harbor. A fleet of War Department dredgers are kept almost continuously at work clearing the harbor's channels, keeping them wide enough and deep enough for giant ships such as the *Queen Mary* and the *Queen Elizabeth* and the *America* to pass safely through when they come to port.

*Liverpool, England's second seaport, has a magnificent water front on the River Mersey.*

Nearly all the ports in the world have a pilot service, but in some harbors this service is optional. In others, it is obligatory. At the port of London it is necessary to take on three different pilots to bring a ship from the sea to the harbor! A sea pilot will take the ship from the Downs to Gravesend. Then a river pilot comes on board to take the ship to the dock entrance. Here, a dock pilot is required to berth her. But in the New York Harbor only one pilot is obligatory, and the second, optional. It works like this:

Let us say that a freighter from Europe is on her way to New York. Three days out her radio man will notify the office of her company of the ship's probable time of arrival at Ambrose Light. The company's dispatcher will then make docking arrangements for the ship in the harbor and inform the dispatcher of the Sandy Hook Pilots' Association of the need of a pilot at that hour. When the day comes, a stoutly built pilot ship, which can take plenty of rough weather, will stop at the Battery and pick up not only the pilot for this freighter but perhaps eight or ten other pilots. More than seventy-five ships a day must be guided in or out of the harbor. The Sandy Hook Pilots' Association dispatcher must plan his schedule so that the pilot ship can cruise around the harbor and drop off pilots where they are needed and take the rest to Ambrose Light, where they will wait for the ships to which they have been assigned to come over the horizon. When the freighter reaches Ambrose Light she will send up the international signal flag for a pilot. Then the pilot ship will come alongside and lower a yawl. The pilot will clamber into the yawl and row to the freighter and go aboard. Then the pilot ship will go back to her station and await new arrivals.

New York Harbor pilots require sixteen years of training before they are permitted to bring a ship into the harbor. During this period they are often employed as apprentice pilots on board pilot ships. Other ports have similar standards. In England a pilot ship stationed in the waters of the Thames estuary will supply pilots not only for ships bound for the port of London, but also for outgoing ships on their way to Rotterdam, Amsterdam, or Hamburg. These master pilots of the European waters are so thoroughly trained that their services are acceptable in many harbors as well as their own. But the channels of the New York Harbor are so tricky and difficult that it is a great accomplishment for a pilot to have a letter-perfect knowledge of this one harbor.

A ship's troubles are not ended by merely taking a harbor pilot aboard. As soon as she draws near her pier she must be docked by tugboats. An ocean-going ship usually has the power and tonnage to cause havoc by merely kissing a pier, in the event that the captain tries nosing her into the pier under her own power. A fleet of about six hundred tugs plays the rôle of coolies in the New York Harbor, towing ships in or out of their piers, towing oil barges, sand and coal scows, or dredgers. All day long you can see them chugging and puffing along, in and out of every corner of the harbor. Some are painted a bright yellow or red, others are brown. About three hundred of them are privately owned

*A cargo of beans in the hold of a freighter.*

*Rotterdam is the Dutch port that most visitors to Holland see first.*

by railroads or by manufacturing concerns and work only for their own line. The rest are owned by various towing companies, the heads of which were nearly all tugboat skippers once themselves.

Tugs are assigned to ships in much the same manner that the harbor pilots are sent on their missions. The company of an incoming ship will notify the tugboat dispatcher, who is also stationed in an office building near the Battery, that she needs a number of tugs at her pier at a certain time. By means of two-way radio between the shore and the tugs in the harbor, the dispatcher will tell certain captains where they are needed next. Or if the tugs happen to be reasonably near the Battery, the dispatcher will use a megaphone and bawl out the orders from a window in his office overlooking the bay. In the old days all tugboat captains received their orders in this way, and some of the dispatchers are old-fashioned men who still prefer a megaphone to the radio. Besides it is cheaper. The two-way radio system is serviced by the New York Telephone Company, which charges fifty cents a minute for these calls. The megaphone involves only lung power.

Before a man can get his papers and become a captain of a tugboat in the New York Harbor, he must work for four years as a deck hand. Then he must take an examination, in which one of the tests required is to draw from memory a map of the 431-square-mile harbor district, all its buoy markers, also, the contours of the harbor floor! He must know every hill and valley of the harbor floor, the water level at each point at high and low tide, and the average speed of the currents at strategic points in the harbor. All these things are terribly important when a tugboat captain must berth a big liner. He is in command of not only the tugs used in the operation but the great ship itself. He never wears a uniform, not even a skipper's cap, and he has no official title. He is addressed as "Joe," or "Barney," whatever his friends call him. But when he goes aboard a big liner to direct his fleet of tugs and berth her, he has more authority than the captain of the liner. He is known as the "mud pilot." His word is law. Some skippers have masters papers that permit them to pilot ships of only five hundred tons or less. Others have masters papers that allow them to pilot unlimited tonnage.

Ten tugs accompany the *Queen Mary* when she sails upriver against a slow ebb tide. Six throw hawsers to her bow, and four fasten their hawsers to her stern bitts. The tug captain directs the ten tugs by means of whistles. He uses the ship's whistle to signal the tugs at her stern,

*Marseilles is the most important Mediterranean port of France.*

*Unloading cargo on lighters and barges in a Philippine port.*

and a police whistle to direct the tugs at her bow. To bring the great 80,000-ton giant into her pier, he brings her abreast of the pier until the pier is about amidships. The tugs at her bow push downstream while those at her stern pull upstream. He works the tugs against the tide and wind just enough to keep her straight and then gently eases her into her berth with the aid of her own engines. It may seem simple, but it is always a great feat. Should the captain misjudge the current, the giant ship might smash the pier like a match box, causing thousands of dollars worth of damage, or worse, his tugs might be trapped between the giant and the pier and crushed beyond recognition. Big Diesel-powered tugs that cost $600,000 apiece are used in berthing the two Queen ships. Each tug has a crew of seven men aboard who would probably be killed.

Now and then the impossible happens in the harbor. It was in October, 1938, that an event took place that still makes tugboat men look at each other in wonderment when they talk about it. There was a strike of all the tugs in the harbor that month. The *Queen Mary* arrived in port as per schedule and there were no tugs on hand to berth her. She had several thousand passengers on board including 1,100 officers and crew. It was clear that if she anchored in the harbor and waited for the strike to end, that the passengers would eat her out of house and home. Furthermore, there were a good many important business men on board who had to get to their offices without delay. Captain R. B. Irving studied the situation from the bridge and noticed that in a few minutes there would be a slack tide. "Slack water" is the five-minute lull between tides. Sometimes slack water is deceptive, for only the surface may be quiet, with a swift current running far below! Captain Irving, an officer of great coolness and daring, had more courage than an ordinary man. He nosed the *Queen Mary* gently upstream until she was abreast her pier and swung her slowly around. His timing was perfect. The ship was ready to move into her pier just as the slack tide began. He berthed her with only a slight bump against the pier. It was an unparalleled example of superb seamanship.

Not all tugs remain in the harbor. In 1907 the *Catherine Moran* made tugboat history by steaming all the way around Cape Horn to La Boca, Panama, to help build the Panama Canal! During World War II when so many ships were torpedoed in the Northern Atlantic waters right off our coast, the seagoing tugs sped out across the sea to bring crippled ships back to port. Many of the tugs were attacked by submarines before they reached the harbor, their crews injured or killed.

In times of peace the big seaworthy tugs are used in salvage operations. Some of these ships are nearly 200 feet long with a 5,000 horse power on a single screw, actually enough power to drive a cargo ship 400 feet long with a carrying capacity of 10,000 tons at over 14 knots. These tugs have powerful wireless sets, radio-direction finders, echo sounders, and all other modern aids to navigation. A salvage tug must be able to deal with fire and has powerful centrifugal pumps that are driven by electricity, which is supplied by

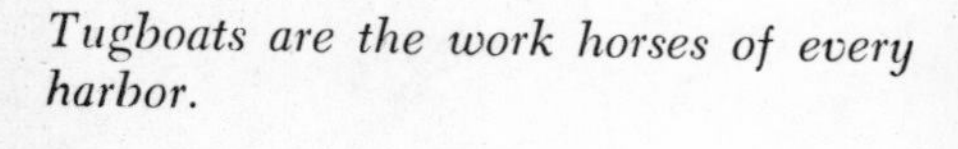
*Tugboats are the work horses of every harbor.*

auxiliary generators on board. Above all things, the salvage tug must have speed. If she is to reach a rich salvage prize before other ships do, she must be able to get under way in a hurry as soon as she is notified of a sea prize. Incidentally, because fire at sea is a commonplace hazard, she must carry a crew of "runners," men who are extremely skilled at boarding a ship on fire and remaining on board the hulk to be towed to look after the mooring ropes and to supervise navigation as far as possible. In European waters such salvage tugs sometimes remain for weeks at strategic areas, waiting for a call from a crippled ship. The Dutch build more of these big expensive tugs than do other nations and have practically a monopoly on this kind of work.

Big tugs of this type are also used in the New York Harbor for ice-breaking work. Smaller ones often ply the New York State Barge Canal and the Great Lakes in summer time, leaving the harbor in the spring and returning in the fall. But most of the harbor tugs are home-bodies and are busy all day long hauling car floats, flat oblong shaped vessels which convey railroad cars from the terminals on the New Jersey shore to the piers on Manhattan, or towing sand scows, coal barges, oil barges, or docking ships. In the harbors of South Africa, larger and more

*Cherbourg is usually the port of entry of transatlantic visitors to France.*

powerful twin-screw tugs are used, most of them being built in British shipyards. In the harbor of Southampton twin-screw tugs are preferred to the single-screw type. But on the Thames much smaller tugs of the single-screw type are more useful. Like our own tugs, they average 85 feet in length with a gross displacement of about 140 tons, and seen from a distance look like so many energetic, purposeful ducks.

*Rhodesian copper unloaded into a barge on the Thames, England.*

But it would be a mistake to suppose that the little ships that ply back and forth in the harbor all of their days lead an uneventful existence. Even the placid, spacious New York Harbor has its Hell's Gate Channel with swift, unpredictable currents and jagged rocks on both sides. Picture a little tug, with a string of barges in tow, making her way down the East River. Then, just as she reaches the entrance of Hell's Gate Channel, a large freighter comes into view, traveling north. There is mist on the river, and it thickens, blotting the freighter from view! The swift current sweeps the tug along. She is in danger of being rammed by the freighter at any moment, and she can't stop, pull out of the channel, or turn around. The captain and the seven men on board must take their chances. By using the tug's whistle at forty-five second intervals, they can judge by the echo their distance from shore and position in the channel. They can only stick to their side of the channel and hope that the freighter has a sound "Gate" man at the helm.

The ebb tide on the Hudson River gives the tug men plenty of anxious times, too. The current during the ebb tide reaches three or four knots an hour, and in spring when the river is swollen with ice and snow, as much as five or six knots an hour. It isn't always possible for tug men to wait for a slack tide to berth a ship. The traffic in the harbor is very heavy. In fact, 14,000 ships a year enter the harbor and

*Nicknamed "Tiddlers" because of their small size, these tugs serve the port of London.*

must be berthed. That means that 28,000 times a year the tugs must be on the job. They are busy all day long. Ships must be eased in or out of their berths, slack tide or no slack tide. There is always the chance that the swift current will get the upper hand and that the little tug will be crushed like a beetle between the heavy ship she is berthing and its pier.

In midwinter, death is always lurking in the harbor, hidden in the winter mists and fogs. Floating ice cakes impede navigation, are responsible for smashed propellers and rudders, and play hob with every skipper's "timing." Because the traffic is heavy, with big ships entering and leaving the harbor, ferries shuttling up and down and back and forth in a crazy quilt pattern, long processions of barges crisscrossing each other in the harbor, and tugs nosing their way in and out, it is imperative that every skipper handle his craft with perfect timing. In fact, timing is everything in the harbor. When the currents are swift and winter fog swallows up everything in sight, timing becomes impossible, and every skipper inches his ship along with death at his elbow. The icy waters of the harbor numb a man to death or unconsciousness within three and a half to four minutes after he strikes the water. His heart may stop beating at once from the shock of the icy water, or he may lose consciousness and disappear from sight. So a collision in a fog in midwinter is a frightful thing. A harbor man would be a thousand times safer in the open sea where there is plenty of elbow room.

Perhaps the most nerve-racking job in the harbor is that of piloting a passenger ferry to and fro all day long in midwinter. Ferryboat captains are a stalwart race of men, but the very monotony of this work is its greatest danger. Fifty, a hundred, perhaps a thousand trips are made without incident. The captain is lulled into a false sense of confidence and security. Ferries are almost unsinkable anyway, a fact that is conducive to this state of mind. Then comes a trip with a little ragged mist on the water, a big slow-moving vessel proceeding right across the path of the ferry, a fast cutter swerving in between, and a long procession of barges on the other side, and all at once the mist blots out the scene and the ferry captain is shocked from his reverie. A very slight error in judgment may mean a collision, and every once in a while ferries *do* sink. Usually the mist clears in the nick of time. But the ferryboat captain is not the same man for a long time afterwards.

The most courageous men in the harbor might well be the pilots

*London's port on the River Thames has room for twelve miles of shipping.*

who go out to Ambrose Light to meet incoming ships and go aboard to take them through the channels. In summer time this chore is pleasant and unexciting. In midwinter it is perilous beyond belief. Picture yourself climbing down the pilot ship's swaying ladder to a tiny yawl that is sucked down ten or fifteen feet by great rollers and brought swiftly up to the crest of a wave. In the moment that the yawl comes to the wave's crest, you jump aboard and clamber to the center seat and grab the oars. As you do so, the yawl slips down into the trough in a slithering motion, and you look up to see a wall of water above you. An icy wind stuns your face and makes your eyes smart. You start rowing toward the ship you will board. The yawl is like a peanut shell slipping and slithering around, now on the crest and now in the trough of giant waves. The pilot ship eases up close by, and the crew are ready to throw you a line if you need one. But if you capsize, it will probably be just too bad. You can last four minutes in the water. The crew of the pilot ship will act fast, but the wind and the big waves may prevent them from acting fast enough. A man is quickly lost from sight in a heavy winter sea.

Yet, pilots take this risk day after day, summer and winter alike. It is all part of their job. Life in the harbor is a special way of life, with special thrills and satisfactions that the seagoing man never knows. Harbor men are harbor men to the end of their days, scorning a job on the high seas.

CHAPTER 17

# HOW SHIPS NAVIGATE

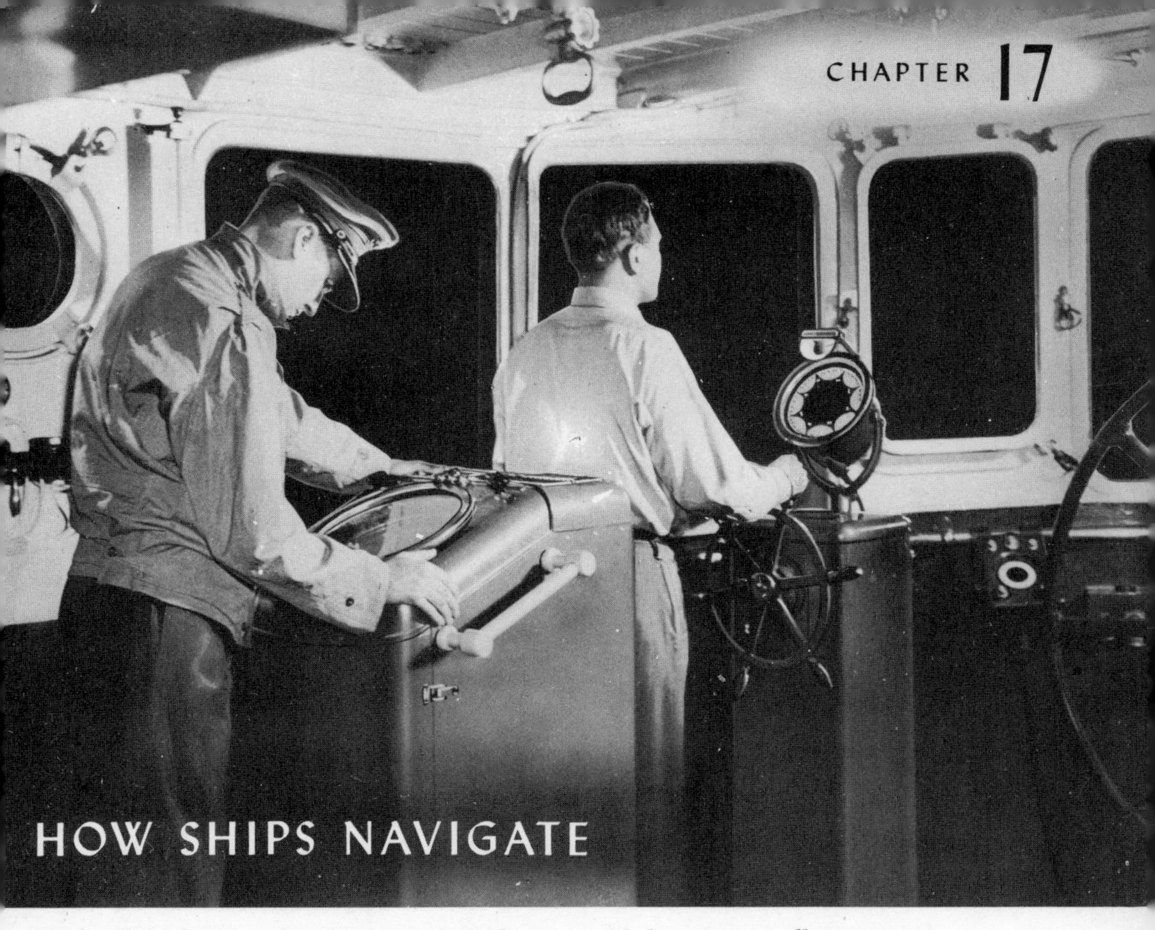

*Radar* (left) *locates other ships at night and in fog and helps prevent collisions at sea.*

IT WAS a strange, eerie scene. There were miles of angry waters on every side, tossing, breaking, and ridged with great waves running toward the west. The wind had blown the sky clear, and the translucent moon was sinking in the west, casting a cold, serene light on the roaring sea. Dipping and sliding up and down the giant waves was a small open boat about twenty-three feet long and so heavily laden that she was in constant danger of foundering. Aboard were nineteen castaways, their ragged clothing soaked through by the salt spray. Every bone in their emaciated bodies ached with the cold. They were hungry and tired. But hour after hour they bailed water from the boat, fighting to keep their shallow craft afloat. At the tiller was a stalwart man dressed in rags and an odd-looking turban fashioned from an old pair of trousers. There was a two weeks' growth of beard on his gaunt face. He sat motionless, as if carved in stone. His name was Captain Bligh, and he had been sitting there for thirty-six hours. It was the year 1789, and

*A second officer guides the helmsman as the two stand watch on the navigating bridge during the night.*

on April 28, near the island of Tofoa in the South Pacific, his crew had mutinied and cast him, with his loyal officers and men, into the small launch—to what they believed to be certain death. Beautiful islands abounded through this region, but they were inhabited by some of the most bloodthirsty savages to be found anywhere in the world. The castaways were unarmed.

To sail into any one of the placid, lovely harbors in this area was to court almost immediate annihilation. The savages were waiting on the shore, hiding in the undergrowth. Several times the castaways did attempt it, only to lose a man. The rest barely escaped with their lives. The nearest white man's settlement was at Timor in the Dutch East Indies, 3,600 miles away. A vast uncharted ocean lay in between.

As a gesture of civility, the mutineers had given the castaways a little food and water, enough to last about a week, and had permitted Captain Bligh to keep his compass, a sextant, and his journal. These rude, clumsily made instruments were to make possible one of the greatest feats of navigation in the annals of the sea.

It so happened that Captain Bligh had served as master on board the *Resolution* when Captain Cook had made his third voyage of exploration of the South Pacific, and Captain Cook had once described to him, in much detail, an earlier voyage he had made through these very waters. Captain Bligh now made a rough chart from memory, based on what Captain Cook had told him of this region. Then he planned a course for his small boat, using the sextant to establish his exact position at sea and the compass as an aid in steering in the right direction. Through devastating tropical cloudbursts in which rain came down in solid sheets obscuring visibility for more than a few feet, through raging gales and the blackest of nights when not a star was to be seen, Captain Bligh kept his little craft on her course, following almost a straight line from the Friendly Islands on past the Fiji Islands, the New Hebrides and on to the Great Barrier Reef at the tip of Australia, and then through the Endeavor Straits on to Timor. Once he sat at the tiller for seventy-two hours without rest. Unlike navigators of his day, he did not hug the shore lines of the islands en route, but struck boldly out to sea, trusting his sextant and his compass to see him

*A ship's officer "shoots the sun" with a sextant at noon to check the ship's position.*

*Radio is the voice and ears of a ship at sea.*

through. It was a supreme test of the wit of a man against the treacheries of the vast Pacific.

The earliest navigators crept carefully along the shores of the lands they wished to visit, never daring to trust themselves out of sight of land. Even when the use of the compass became fairly well known to all seamen, few navigators would cut across open seas out of sight of land. The first European explorers hugged the shores of Africa when making their initial visits to that continent. The early explorers found the compass unreliable, though at that time they did not know the reason why.

Actually, the needle of a compass does not point to the true geographical north, but to the magnetic north. Also, this variation between the true north and the magnetic north changes from place to place on the globe. In the region of Queenstown, a seaport in South Ireland, the needle points to the left of the true north. Hence, the westerly course of a ship by compass is really many degrees south of west. Out in the Atlantic Ocean the variation of the compass increases. There, a western course by the compass would take the ship still farther southward, far from the ship's destination.

Today, a complete magnetic survey of the earth has made possible a chart that shows the variation of the needle at different places. Consequently, the modern seaman can use the compass with confidence. However, new surveys have to be made every few years because the magnetic poles, to which the compass needle will point, change their position from place to place on the earth's surface every now and then.

Another great handicap that confronted the early navigator was the fact that swift currents at sea often carried ships way off their courses. Today nearly all these currents have been charted, the speed at which they move has been recorded, and the modern seaman can make allowances for them in his calculations. Yet Captain Bligh, without any of these important aids to navigation, managed to keep his small craft on the course he had set for her! Actually, it was his sextant that enabled him to do this, for this made it possible for him to find his exact position at sea at regular intervals.

To find the position of a ship at sea you must determine the latitude and longitude. By latitude is meant the angular distance north of the equator. Latitude on earth is measured north and south of the equator, along the meridians of longitude. It is easier to think of the globe as marked off with imaginary streets or avenues, with one set running north and south from the north pole to the south pole, and the other set running east and west parallel with the equator in the center. The lines that run from pole to pole are meridians of longitude. The east and west lines running parallel with the equator are called parallels of latitude. The prime meridian, or main street on the globe, is the meridian which passes through Greenwich, England. Hence, to locate a ship's ex-

*A Merchant Marine cadet learns how to use the sextant while standing watch at night.*

*Loran now permits officers to determine ship's position without navigation instruments.*

act position at sea means to find its position north or south of the equator, and east or west of Greenwich, or the prime meridian.

The north and south poles are each 90° from the equator. This is the limit of latitude that we can reach on earth. The greatest longitude we can attain, east and west, is 180°, at the meridian directly opposite the prime meridian. Because of the spherical shape of the earth, latitude and longitude are measured in degrees, minutes, and seconds. All points on the same meridian of longitude are the same number of *degrees* from the prime meridian. These points are not, however, the same number of *miles* from the prime meridian. A degree of longitude at the equator measures sixty nautical miles; north and south of the equator it becomes less and less. At the poles where all the meridians come together, it decreases to nothing. A degree of longitude always has the same length, except near the poles where, because of a slight flattening of the earth, it becomes somewhat longer.

It is not very difficult to find the latitude of a ship at sea. If the sun is directly overhead at the equator, then all that is necessary is to measure the angle between lines drawn from the vessel to the sun and to the horizon. This angle should then be subtracted from 90°, and the result is latitude. However, the sun is directly overhead at the equator only twice a year. At all other times it is either north or south of the equator. The angle between its actual position and its position when it is overhead at the equator must be added to or subtracted from the latitude found, as described above. This angle has been carefully calculated for every day in the year and is recorded in the *Nautical Almanac* which navigators usually carry aboard.

The angle that a line to the sun makes with one to the horizon must be measured at noon when the sun is at the highest point of its course across the sky. Therefore, a few minutes before noon on a clear day,

Captain Bligh would get out his sextant, and holding it in his right hand, look with one eye through a small telescope, and move the instrument about until he saw the horizon in the center of the field of view. Then he pushed forward a mechanical arm carrying a mirror, which reflected light from above to a second mirror, which directed it into his telescope along a course parallel to that taken by the rays of light from the distant horizon. The second mirror was in the path of the rays from the horizon, and one-half of it was left unsilvered in order to allow these rays free passage.

The sextant must be pointed in the direction of the sun, of course, and Captain Bligh would move the arm of his instrument until the image of the sun, reflected by the mirrors, appeared in the field of view of the telescope, with the lower limb touching the horizon, which was simultaneously viewed. Along the arc of the instrument, the angular elevation of the sun could then be read.

A moment or two later, a second observation would be made. This would be found to be a slightly greater angle than before. Several additional observations would be made, and each time the angle would be

*Protected from the weather by the glassed-in wheelhouse, the helmsman keeps the ship on its course.*

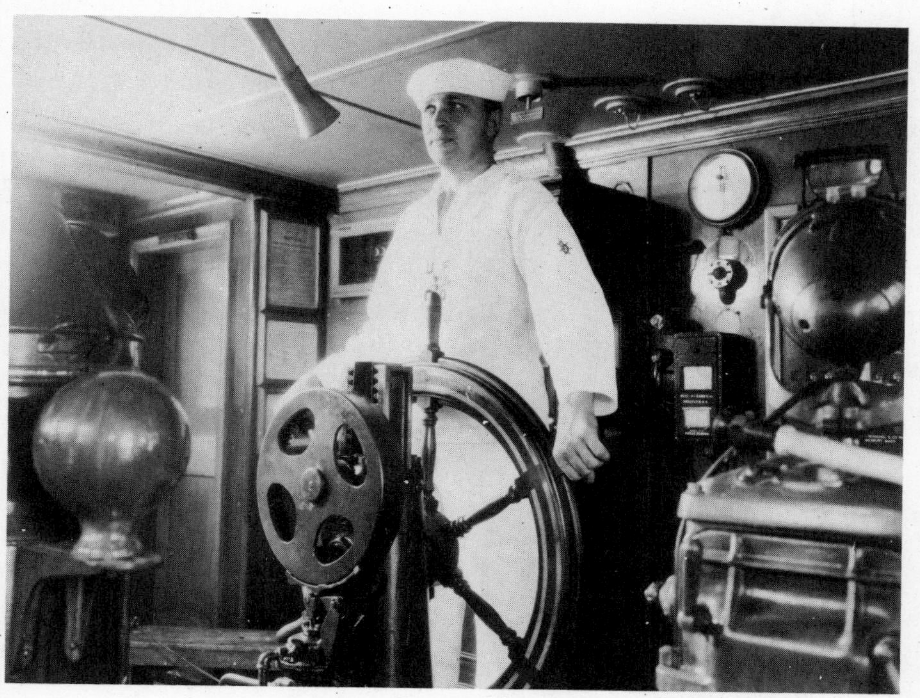

greater than the last one, until presently, the sun would begin to dip once more. High noon would be over. Then the angles would become smaller and smaller. The greatest angle measured would be the angle of elevation at noon. Then all that would remain to find latitude would be to apply the correction that makes allowance for the change of position of the sun with the seasons. The *Nautical Almanac* would supply this information. Fortunately, Captain Bligh was permitted to bring his journal along.

Longitude may be found by means of a clock. The clocks used at sea for this purpose are extremely accurate and are called chronometers. They always register the time at Greenwich, which is different from the actual time at any point on any other meridian. Suppose we take the meridian of 180° west of Greenwich. The sun makes its daily journey around the earth in twenty-four hours, and at points on this meridian it will reach its greatest altitude twelve hours after noon at Greenwich. Thus, when it is twelve o'clock midday on the meridian of 180° W., it is twelve o'clock midnight at Greenwich. At points in between these meridians the local noon will occur at other times. On longitude 90° W. for example, it will occur at 6:00 P.M. Greenwich time.

So you can see that the difference between local time and Greenwich time depends on the longitude. Therefore, on a ship at sea, if the navigator knows at any point the difference between local time and Greenwich time, he can find the longitude of that point. A difference of one hour between the two times corresponds to a difference in longitude of 15°. This will be west

*Officers using the pelorus, an instrument for making land observations.*

longitude when the local time is behind Greenwich time, and east longitude when the local time is ahead.

Among the men who came aboard the small boat with Captain Bligh was Peckover, the gunner, who brought with him a big silver watch which enabled Captain Bligh to estimate the ship's longitude every day. On cloudy or stormy days when the sun was not visible, and on dark nights when no star shone, Captain Bligh relied on "dead reckoning." This means that he formed an estimate of his craft's position from the distance she had traveled and the direction taken since the last observation had been made. To do this he had the men make a chip log.

A chip log consists of a flat, triangular piece of wood, rounded on one side, and weighted so that it will float point upward in the water. It is attached to a line wound upon a freely moving reel. The line is marked every 47 feet 4 inches, each division being called a knot. The log is cast overboard and allowed to run out for twenty-eight seconds after the first knot has left the reel, the time being measured by a twenty-eight-second sand glass, made just like an hourglass or a three-minute egg glass. The speed of the vessel in nautical miles per hour is equal to the number of knots which the log line runs out in twenty-eight seconds. You will see that this is so if you recall that a nautical mile is 6,080 feet long and that an hour has 3,600 seconds.

Captain Bligh's men did not have a sand glass with them, so with the aid of Peckover's watch they practiced counting the seconds aloud until they could do this without the watch. Once every hour Captain Bligh ordered the chip log heaved overboard and the seconds counted aloud as the line with its knots passed over the stern. The men used a handkerchief torn into small bits of rag, and used each of these bits to tie a knot in the line at carefully measured intervals. When the boat was traveling very fast the line would pay out quickly. When there wasn't much wind for the boat's sail and the boat traveled slowly, the knotted bits of rag on the line would move slowly. In this way, Captain Bligh could tell how many knots—or how fast—his craft was moving.

By changing the miles his boat had traveled into degrees of latitude and longitude, Captain Bligh could determine his position at sea, at least approximately, and aided by his compass, revise this calculation until nearly correct. And, no doubt, his experienced eye judged the tides and currents en route and made allowances for them too. Then, on the first clear day or night, he could use the sextant and find out how accurate his calculations had been.

Incidentally, the term "knots," denoting speed at sea, was derived by sea captains of the old sailing vessels from the use of a chip log with a knotted line.

Modern ships use a patent log. This device consists of a propeller, which makes a revolution when pulled a certain distance through the water. Its revolutions are counted by an instrument something like a speedometer, which is fixed at the stern of the ship. A dial reveals the distance traveled. By using the patent log in conjunction with a watch, the speed of a vessel can be quickly determined. The ship's position can then be judged by the distance and the direction she has traveled since the last check was made.

Another important way that a ship's position can be found, especially if she is near shore, is by finding the depth of the water beneath the ship and examining the character of the ocean floor. Good sailing charts give accurate information about the sea floor. The best way of doing this is with a lead line. There are three kinds of leads, the hand lead weighing 7 to 14 pounds, the coasting lead weighing 25 to 50 pounds,

*Reporting the ship's course to the captain according to the reading on the gyrocompass.*

and the deep-sea lead weighing 80 to 150 pounds. The leads are hollowed out at the bottom, and when the hollow is filled with tallow, it will bring up a specimen from the ocean bottom.

*An assistant engineer watches the dials that tell how the ship's engines are behaving.*

The heavy deep-sea lead is seldom used any more. Instead, ships have a sounding device consisting of a spool or drum on which is wound a long steel wire bearing a heavy lead weight at its outer end. Just above the lead is an instrument which records the depth of the sea. It is a brass tube with holes in the bottom. Before the lead is cast, a glass tube, sealed at one end and coated on its inner surface with chromate of silver, a chemical which sea water will discolor, is placed in the brass tube. As the glass tube goes down toward the bottom, the sea water enters it. The height to which the sea water will force its way in the tube depends upon the pressure of the water, which in turn depends upon the water's depth. When the lead line is pulled in, the depth of the water is indicated by the length of the discolored portion of the glass tube.

Modern ships also use a sonic depth finder. This is more complex. An electric oscillating device at the bottom of the ship sends vibrations or sound waves toward the sea bottom. When they reach the floor of the ocean they are reflected back, just like an echo from the side of a mountain. A microphone on the ship, placed at a known distance from the oscillator, catches the echo, and the depth of the water is indicated by the time it takes the vibrations to reach the sea bottom and return.

Captain Bligh did not have any elaborate device of this kind to aid him. Nor did he have a chart of the ocean floor of the region he was traveling. But he frequently took a sounding, using a stout fishing line rigged up with weights in the place of a lead line. Judging by the depth of the water under his craft, he would estimate the position from

*Members of the engine room crew check the main engine of a merchant ship.*

the nearest shore. This helped him considerably in keeping his little craft on her course.

One of the most remarkable devices used today in helping ships safely from one place to the other is the gyrocompass. The gyroscope itself is the oldest mechanism in the universe. It existed before any living thing could be found on the earth's surface, simply because the world itself is a gyroscope. Though toy gyroscopes had been known for centuries, it remained for Dr. Elmer Sperry to put the gyroscope to work. Dr. Sperry knew that the magnetic compass with which all ships were equipped in the early years of the century was vastly less trustworthy in a steel hull than it had been in wooden ships. The needle had a tendency to be affected by the metal in the vessel. In battleships, it even had a tendency to swing when a gun turret was turned. Changes in the temperature in the smokestack might cause as much as a degree of deviation. When the new American dreadnought, the *Delaware*, was launched in 1911, she was equipped with the first of Sperry's famous gyrocompasses. In it Sperry had found a way to utilize the combined effects of the earth's rotation and the force of gravity in order to keep the gyro axle in line with the earth's meridian and thus provide mariners with a true north indication.

Improvements were made in this gyrocompass through the years, but one of the greatest changes came when the type known as Mark 18 was developed during World War II. There were many dramatic instances during this war when the gyrocompass helped to save ships.

On one occasion, a long line of ships homeward bound from England groped their way slowly through a blinding fog off the Grand Banks, creeping uncertainly toward Cape Cod. From vessel to vessel ran the commodore's signal:

"Urgent—ship needed with gyrocompass."

Contact was quickly made with the skipper of a vessel so equipped, and he was instructed:

"Come to the head of the line . . . lead us through the fog."

And so the gyrocompass, being nonmagnetic, free from all variation and deviation, provided a fixed steering reference that guided the convoy through Massachusetts Bay to the eastern entrance of the Cape Cod Canal.

The skipper reported later: "I navigated entirely by the gyrocompass. After three hours I looked up from my charts to tell my Chief Officer that according to my reckoning the convoy was at the canal entrance . . . and just then the fog lifted and we had our objective dead ahead, with all the convoy assembled behind!"

Closely related to the gyrocompass is the device known to mariners and airplane pilots alike as "Iron Mike," or "Metal Mike," colorful terms for the gyropilot, a complicated mechanism which can actually steer a ship. Connected to the steering apparatus, it translates the compass readings into action, steering the ship with more skill than human hands. It was aboard an oil tanker, the *J. A. Moffett*, that the gyropilot was first tried, in 1923. The experiment was a success, although like any green quartermaster, "Mike" applied too much helm at first. When adjustments were made, however, the ship held straight to her course. Even heavy storms and an enormous waterspout fully fifty feet in diameter, which passed close by, failed to keep the mechanical pilot from its work. After this experiment, the gyropilot was installed on the *Mungaro*, which became the first passenger ship to use automatic steering. Today the equipment is utilized by ships of all kinds the world over.

No device has contributed as much as radio to making the ocean highways of today safe for travel. It is used by giant liners and ships no bigger than Captain Bligh's open boat. On August 21, 1946, a little sloop only thirty-eight feet long brought eighteen refugees from Europe to America, among them six young women and a little girl of five. They started from Sweden on May 30, made one stop in England and were at sea almost continuously for two and a half months. All were in good health and the best of spirits when they arrived in Miami on August 21. It had taken the little sloop just thirty days to cover the distance between the Madeira Islands in the Atlantic, west of Morocco, their last stop, and Miami, Florida. The ease with which this voyage was made was due to the invention of radio and the many

*The main switch panel of the* S.S. America *showing its complex electrical installation.*

navigational aids that are available today. Many lighthouses and lightships are equipped to send out radio signals, each station having a distinctive signal. Such radio beacons, as they are called, have been established at more than sixty-five places on the Pacific, the Atlantic, and the Great Lake shores of the United States. Radio signals from such beacons are received on a vessel by radio compass, a remarkable aid to navigators. This device consists of a round metal column that is usually installed on the roof of the chart room of a ship and that receives radio signals from other ships or from the shore. The radio impulses from any sending station within a certain radius are captured by a metal loop enclosed in the column on the roof, and these impulses become fainter or stronger depending on the angle from which the loop takes them from the air. The operator of the radio compass turns the loop to the position at which the signals come strongest through his earphones. From the compass before him, he can tell from which direction they are coming.

By obtaining the bearing of two or more stations of known location, and plotting the path of their waves on a navigating chart, a navigator can determine his position at sea when cloudy weather makes it impossible for him to find his position by observing the sun or stars. In this way a ship surrounded by the densest fog can move steadily on her course. Ships of nearly all sizes carry on board a radio compass, for it has become an almost indispensable navigating aid.

Once when Admiral Byrd was on his way home from Little America, he found it necessary to try to reach a whaling ship he knew to be located at her station in the Antarctic Ocean. Day after day his ship sailed under cloudy skies. But by getting the direction of the whaling ship's position through his radio compass, he was able to steer directly toward the ship without delay. Without this instrument he would have been sailing all over the vast stretches of the Antarctic on an all but hopeless quest, for this region is plagued with fogs, mists, and interminable periods of overcast weather.

It would surprise you to know how long it took ship owners to adopt radio, or wireless telegraphy as it was formerly called, for the safety of their crews and ships. Many seafaring men were inclined to regard it suspiciously too. The first ship to be equipped with wireless apparatus was the East Goodwin Lightship, which marked the hazardous Goodwin Sands off the southeastern coast of England. Four months later, on March 3, 1899, the lightship was rammed at four in the morning by the S.S. *R. F. Matthews.* The first distress call ever sent from a ship at sea now went over the air waves to South Foreland. Tugs were sent at once, and the lightship was towed out of danger.

A few European steamship lines added wireless equipment to their big fancy passenger ships chiefly as an advertising attraction. Some warships, yachts, and other craft carried sets for experimental purposes. But during the next three or four years, wireless remained something of a novelty on ships. In 1903 an International Conference was held in

*A fireman adjusts one of the oil burners in the boiler room of a ship at sea.*

Berlin, and among other issues discussed was the question of signals for distress calls. Since all the wireless operators of ships at this time had received their training in railroad stations or post offices, they brought with them not only their Morse code, but also many of their telegraphic abbreviations. One of them was the general call C Q which had been used to attract attention of all operators along a wire. At sea C Q became a general call to all ships. During the conference it was decided that C D Q should be used as a distress signal. The Germans, however, had been using S O E as a general attention-getter on their lines, and they urged S O E as a distress signal. The objection to this was the fact that the letter "E" is only a dot in Morse code, and it was agreed that the dot would be too easily swallowed by atmospheric disturbances, especially during storms at sea. Therefore the distress signal was changed to S O S—three dots, three dashes, and three dots. This, it was agreed, could not be mistaken for anything else and was therefore more useful as a distress signal. But for a long time afterward, British operators were still using C D Q for distress calls.

Modern navigators are using radar, a form of radio which is enabling them to guide their ships more skilfully. The basic principle of radar, the name of which is derived from RAdio Detection And Ranging, is not a difficult one. In 1886 it was proved that radio waves are reflected from solid objects. In 1904 a German engineer was granted a patent in several countries on a proposed way of using this property as an obstacle detector and a navigational aid for ships. A discovery which led to the actual development of radar was made in 1922 by two scientists working at the Naval Aircraft Radio Laboratory, Anacostia, Maryland. In testing plane-to-ground communications, they noticed that ships moving in the Potomac River distorted the pattern of radio waves, causing a fluctuating signal. From this discovery, development was pursued almost continually after that until 1935, when Congress appropriated a sum of money for more extensive research. A rather crude radar device was tested successfully in 1937 aboard the *Leary*, and a greatly improved one was given sea trials on the *New York* in 1939. World War II brought radar into wide usage on military ships and airplanes of all kinds.

During World War II the Coast Guard made a study of radar to determine its possibilities in peace-time navigation. The cutter *Mackinaw* was radar-equipped for trials on the Great Lakes. Other cutters tried it out on the Grand Banks during 1945. These tests led to the conclusion that radar had so many uses that it should certainly be adopted by all merchant vessels. Radar seems to solve many problems, for it succeeds under the difficult conditions where other navigational methods fail. It is the best anticollision device yet perfected. With its ability to present a chartlike picture of surroundings, it literally gives the seaman a means of seeing through fog.

While radar is most useful to navigators of ships close to moving or solid objects, another radio system is useful for long range navigation. This system is known as Loran. The name Loran stands for the words LOng RAnge Navigation, since the outstanding characteristic of the system is its ability to furnish positions to navigators at greater distances from the transmitting stations than can be achieved through other methods of radio navigation. Loran permits the accurate determination of position at distances from the transmitting stations as great as 1,400 nautical miles by night and 750 nautical miles during the day. Under almost any kind of weather conditions the navigator can determine his position by Loran with an accuracy as great as may be normally expected from good celestial observations. Even though such precision is possible, the determination of position by Loran requires only two or three minutes time! Loran signals are on the air and available to navigators throughout a large part of the major shipping lanes of the world for twenty-four hours a day. This world-wide system came into being during World War II and promises to be one of the great technical contributions of this dreadful armed conflict.

The fundamental principle of Loran lies in the reception by a navigator at sea of two radio signals, each of which is sent out by a different transmitting station of known position. By means of special Loran equipment, the navigator measures the amount of time which elapses between the arrival of the first and the

*Frequent lifeboat drills train seamen for quick action in emergencies.*

second signals. Since radio signals travel at a constant speed, the direct relationship between time of travel and distance traveled makes the measurement of time the equivalent of measurement of distance. The radio signals which are transmitted by Loran stations are not continuous transmissions such as those of everyday commercial broadcasting, but are "pulse signals," or short bursts of radio energy transmitted at regular intervals.

The compass, the sextant, and the old silver watch used by Captain Bligh on his historic voyage are still familiar devices to the modern navigator. But in today's world of radio, ships sail with a speed and safety never dreamed of by navigators who had only these ancient instruments to guide them.

CHAPTER 18

# ALL KINDS OF SHIPS

*The stern-wheeler* Sprague *serves as a towboat on the Mississippi.*

On a clear, sparkling autumn day in September, 1907, a great swarming crowd of people gathered along the waterfront in Liverpool, England. They had come to see a new wonder of the age—the S.S. *Lusitania*, the largest ship afloat. It was a triumphant hour for the British people. For nine years the German ships had held the blue ribbon of the Atlantic. Then the Cunard Steamship Line promised to build a liner that would be bigger and faster than any ship the Germans had launched up to that time. Now, here she was, ready for her maiden voyage! The crowd pressed closer to see the graceful white giant. She was 760 feet long, 87½ feet in breadth, and her gross tonnage was about 31,000. She was a beautiful ship. From all parts of England people came to Liverpool to get a glimpse of her. Soon there were more than 200,000 people milling and shoving along the waterfront, pressing closer to her pier. When the whistle blew, signaling her departure, a mighty shout went up, and men threw their hats into the air. It was a great day. She would surely win the blue ribbon of the Atlantic back from the Germans!

And so she did! Although she encountered fog on this voyage, she averaged more than twenty-three knots—a record in 1907. On her twelfth trip she averaged twenty-five knots. Later, she made the journey from Daunts Rock, near the mouth of Cork Harbor, to Sandy Hook in four days, eleven hours, and forty-two minutes. But she did not hold the blue ribbon very long, for her sister ship, the S.S. *Mauretania,* proved to be much faster.

Many giant liners have been built since that time. But the two Cunard ships set the pace for all that followed. The *Mauretania* held the blue ribbon of the Atlantic for twenty-two years. Then in 1929 the Germans won it back again with the S.S. *Bremen,* a still bigger, faster ship. She was 933 feet long, with a gross tonnage of 46,000. She was especially designed for speed and averaged 27.9 knots. A year later, however, she yielded the trophy to her sister ship, the S.S. *Europa.* Three years later the Italian ship *Rex* won the ribbon from the *Europa.* Then in 1935 came the great French liner, the *Normandie,* with an overall length of 1,029 feet and a gross tonnage of 79,283 and an average speed of 29.98 knots. But the ill-fated *Normandie* was to hold her laurels for only a year. It was in 1936 that the *Queen Mary* won the blue ribbon once again for the British. Then the *Queen Elizabeth* followed.

*Britain's* Mauretania *is well known to travelers on the North Atlantic run.*

*Britain's* Queen Mary *is one of the largest and fastest liners afloat.*

Of all the ships on the ocean highways today, the giant liners are the most thrilling. The *Queen Mary,* for example, has accommodations for 3,240 persons. Her hull comprises twelve decks. There is a main lounge, a ballroom, a smoking room, library, writing room, children's playroom, a magnificent swimming pool, Turkish baths, a fully equipped gymnasium and squash court. There is a vast dining room which can accommodate nearly eight hundred people at one sitting. Nearly every stateroom has a private bath and telephone and its own air conditioning unit. The ship is truly a floating palace.

But there is a limit to the size to which it is sensible to build these giants. It would be possible to build a liner 2,500 feet in length and of great tonnage. But how would such a mammoth ship get through the shallow channels of even the largest ports in the world? How could she be serviced at the existing dock facilities? Actually, modern liners must compete not in size but in speed, in greater comfort and luxury for the passengers, and in lower operating costs. The global air liner is the real rival of the modern passenger ship. In fact, the very appearance of ships has been gradually changed from the outlines of the old sailing vessel to the contours of the modern streamlined airplane.

Every ship in the world has a special job to do and was especially designed for that job. The giant liners, for example, carry passengers and tons of mail across the ocean highways in the shortest possible time with the greatest safety. Then there are big ships, not such huge giants as the *Queen Mary* and the *Queen Elizabeth,* but which are nevertheless magnificent in proportions and carry passengers and cargo at very much lower rates. The Canadian Pacific "Duchess" class liners, the Swedish American liner S.S. *Stockholm,* and the British *Empress of Britain* are good illustrations. These ships are large, but can go through the Suez and Panama Canals and enter many smaller ports to which the giants are barred because of their size. These medium-sized ships are obviously more useful.

Then there are still smaller and much less expensive liners that are used on routes to the Far East and to South Africa carrying passengers, cargo, and mail. They are quite fast. Their passenger accommodations are excellent. Their fares are low. Many of them have refrigerated

*Oil tankers carry most of the oil used in our mechanized civilization.*

cargo space and carry fruit, meat or other perishables from the far corners of the earth to Europe or America. No other type of ship could do their job as efficiently.

Most interesting of all are the tramp ships which carry bulk cargoes. A "bulk" cargo is one that cannot be handled piece by piece, such as coal, salt, grain, and ore. A tramp ship is designed with cargo space that is as flexible as possible. On a trip, let us say, from England to Argentina she may carry coal one way and grain on the return voyage. A "tramp" must be prepared to go anywhere and carry almost anything. Unlike the liner which is owned and operated by one company, a "tramp" is chartered by any company that happens to need her temporarily. Every big seaport has a great number of ship brokers. These men arrange to rent or charter ships to companies, or to individual business men who do not have ships of their own or who may require the services of extra ships. Suppose a coffee planter in South America wanted to send his coffee to Spain and did not have a ship of his own?

He would go to a ship broker in the nearest port and arrange to have his coffee taken by a tramp ship to Spain. He would pay a certain fee for this service. When the tramp ship had completed her job for him, she would, through a ship broker in the Spanish port, pick up a new cargo for another client and go to some other port with it, perhaps all the way across the world.

Suppose the coffee planter wanted to send his coffee to quite a number of ports abroad several times a year. He would then charter a tramp ship and arrange to have her follow a regular schedule for him. She would stop at the South American port and take on the coffee at certain dates and deliver it to the European ports on schedule. If he developed a successful export business, he might charter the tramp for a period of three, five, or even ten years and have her follow this schedule every year for him. Many tramp ships are chartered for a period of years. Others are rented only for a few months. Some operate just like taxis, picking up cargoes wherever they can.

A great variety of freighters are used in different parts of the world. Each type has a special job to do. Some of the freighters used on the Great Lakes, as we have already read, are more than six hundred feet long and can handle 355,000 bushels of wheat in five hours. But they are really little more than monster barges. The machinery is in the stern, and about seventy-five per cent of the total length of the ship is the tremendous hold. They carry grain, iron ore, or coal. There are fast three-decker freighters used on runs between Argentina and Europe, especially designed to carry livestock. There are little "Canal-

*Specially designed for the South American trade, the* Del Brasil *is a United States passenger and cargo ship.*

*Fast cargo ships such as this carry American products across the seas.*

lers," which travel from Oslo, Norway, to Chicago on the Great Lakes and which were especially planned to go through the locks of the Welland Canal system that links the Great Lakes with the St. Lawrence River. These Canallers are less than three hundred feet in length and have a cargo capacity of only a little more than two thousand tons, but they are adaptable; small enough to go through the Welland locks and sturdy enough to face the North Atlantic storms en route to Europe.

There are hard-working little colliers that average three hundred feet in length and carry around forty-five hundred tons of coal to and fro along the Baltic seaports. There are also "flat iron" colliers that carry coal along the Thames River and that have an unusually low superstructure so that they may pass under the Thames bridges. There are great powerful freighters of the shallow draught type that carry passengers and bulk cargo up and down the River Plata in South America. Most important are the little coasters, which must be stout enough to face heavy seas, yet shallow enough to visit the smaller ports to which the big ships are barred because of their size. They aren't very exciting, but they are indispensable. Some of them have low superstructures and masts on hinges so that they may travel up rivers and pass under bridges. There are even some with a removable bridge structure. They ferret their way in and out of harbors with narrow, shallow channels, up dangerous rivers with swiftly moving currents and out to sea again, carrying with them a precious cargo that might otherwise have had to travel expensively by rail or truck. Most of the coasters ply their trade in the North Sea, the Irish Sea, the Baltic, and in small seas in the South Pacific. There are also handsome "coasters," which are capable of handling five hundred to a thousand tons of cargo, with de luxe quarters for twelve passengers.

Unique among all cargo ships are the "Bel" ships that are especially built to handle cargo of exceptional weight—locomotives, tugboats, lightships. Each has special weight-lifting equipment and a tremendously strong hull. Some idea of just how resourceful these ships are may be gathered from the cargo that the *Beljeanne* carried on one voyage: twenty main-line locomotives, twenty-four electric subways cars, two small river tugs, a motor tank barge weighing more than one hundred tons and over ninety feet long! Once the *Belpamela* carried a complete lightship weighing more than 130 tons. Incidentally, the *Belpamela's* lifting gear hoisted the lightship right out of the water on to the deck in one operation!

In and out of every busy port in the world you will see the low-lying oil tankers nosing their way along. Some are little more than shells and are used on inland waters or small seas. Others are good-sized ships capable of holding their own in an Atlantic or Pacific gale. Years ago oil was carried in tanks built inside the ship's main structure. Today, tankers are designed so that oil may be carried right next to the ship's skin. The cargo space is divided into separate tanks by means of steel partitions. In order to allow for the expansion and contraction of this liquid cargo in transit, and to prevent an undesirable movement of the oil when the ship is rolling and pitching in a seaway, which would endanger the stability of the ship, a long expansion tank running down the center and connecting with each individual tank along the way takes care of the excess oil. In some tankers, this expansion trunk may extend along the ship's sides. In this case the center space is used for auxiliary tanks. Large tankers can carry about 15,000 tons and travel at twelve knots or better when fully loaded. But the small coastal tankers may carry only five hundred tons and move along at a steady leisurely speed of five knots or less. The size of a tanker depends upon the duties it must perform.

But not all tankers carry oil! Some are loaded with chemicals or gases such as Butane. Gas is the trickiest cargo of all, for unless the captain checks his tanks for leaks while en route, he may arrive at his destination to discover that his cargo has vanished! Protane, Butane, and other gases

*A Diesel-driven barge used by the United States Navy to carry gasoline.*

are by-products of crude oil refinery, and the oil companies sometimes use their tankers to transport these valuable products.

One of the most beautiful ships you may have the luck to see in a busy harbor is a cable ship. You would never guess that she was a hard-working ship with important duties. She looks like a yacht. She has a white hull with a graceful clipper stem and often a stern with an old-time counter shape. But she is a stouter ship than she seems. The laying and repairing of cables can be done only in fair weather, but she must be prepared to ride out storms at sea. In fact, she is often at sea for weeks and even months without touching port. In her hull she has powerful machinery, usually twin screws that will give her a speed of fourteen to sixteen knots and more, for when she has a job to do, she is in a hurry. A great deal depends upon the work of the cable ship. She must lay, repair, and service the submarine telephone cables that link continent with continent and provide the chief communication service for the commercial enterprises of the world.

Some cables—for example, those around the British Isles—are in shallow waters and are often damaged by the tides or by ships' anchors or even fishermen's trawls. Occasionally, wrecks will settle on cables laid in deep water at sea and cause them to break. Now and then some great deep-sea monster is responsible for the damage to a cable. Then the cable ship is notified of the break in the line and all hands go to their stations with the alacrity of firemen getting ready to go to a fire, and the ship sets forth, full speed ahead. Electrical-detecting machines locate the exact spot at which the trouble is to be found. An anchor with a marker buoy is dropped over the side to mark the spot. The ship steams for a couple of miles until she is clear of the cable. Then a grapnel is lowered to the sea bed, and the ship sweeps back across the line of the cable in an attempt to pick it up. The grapnel rope is passed over a dynamometer that indicates the strain on the rope. The cable is then carefully hauled up, and the strain, as indicated by the dynamometer, is closely watched to prevent serious damage to the cable. When the cable is severed, a search must be made for the broken ends, and they must be hauled up and mended by the insertion of a new length of cable.

This work must be done as quickly as possible. A terrible loss in revenue takes place when a cable is not in use. When a flaw or break occurs far out at sea and takes days or weeks to repair, the loss may run into thousands of dollars. This work can only be done when the sea is calm. Otherwise the tossing and pitching of the ship would strain the section of the cable that had been hauled on board, and new breaks would occur. Sometimes a high wind or storm will come up while the crew is mending the cable, and the captain will be obliged to halt the work at once. He may have to wait for ten days or more before the

*This Mississippi tugboat also serves as a passenger ferry.*

work can be resumed. The laying or repairing of a cable in oceanic waters calls for superb seamanship and the finest and most seaworthy ship that naval architects can design.

Nearly every country in the world with a coastal strip has its fishing fleets. Most of them are made up of trawlers, drifters, draggers, and smaller boats. The British are fond of a seventy- to one-hundred-foot type of trawler for fishing in the North and Irish seas. Some are steam-driven and others use oil. Scandinavian fishermen prefer steam trawlers

*A fast refrigerator ship designed for the Central American fruit trade.*

for fishing in Arctic waters. The New England fishermen now use Diesel motors in their draggers. Across the world the Chinese rely on junks with a lug sail. In fact, nearly every type of boat you can imagine is used by different countries for fishing. But there is one thing these ships all have in common: they are very ruggedly built and can take bad weather in their stride. Some of the trawlers used for fishing in Arctic waters are 180 feet long and often undertake voyages that are 5,000 miles long.

Whaling is a brand of fishing in a class by itself. It should be called hunting at sea. Fast killer ships, or catchers, as they are known, hunt down the whale, kill it, and get it ready for the final stage of its journey. Then the mother ship, a huge 20,000-ton vessel that is really a floating factory, hauls the whale aboard. The carcass is cut into pieces on the deck, the oil from the blubber is pumped into large tanks in the hold, the meat is cut up and passed through a number of small hatches on deck to steam boilers below, and the bones are sawed into pieces by steam-driven saws. Every part of the whale is used in this factory between decks. Then the whale mother ship proceeds to her port to discharge her cargo. The fleet of trawlers remain at their stations in the Northern waters, or in the Antarctic seas, as the case may be, and the whale mother ship soon joins them to process another whale.

So you can see that every ship in the world has a special job to do and is particularly well chosen to do it.

Just as interesting as the different kinds of work that ships do are the different types of engines that enable ships to carry out their duties. Consider the needs of a great transatlantic liner such as the *Queen Mary*. Her engines must not only supply her with power that will speed her over the ocean highways but also with power to light several thousand electric light bulbs, the giant searchlight, and hundreds of electrical devices required for the passengers' comfort, in addition to hundreds of other mechanical devices needed to operate the ship's equipment: navigation aids, communication facilities, sewage disposal, fire apparatus, cooking and cleaning aids, and hundreds of pumps for a dozen or more duties, electric baggage conveyors for loading and unloading the passengers' luggage, about eight winches with a lifting capacity of five tons, and about the same number of derricks, also with a lifting capacity of five tons, for servicing the ship's cargo. Power is needed to operate the machinery for at least four refrigerated rooms in the hold

*A Diesel-engined tugboat towing log rafts down the Willamette River in Oregon.*

*California fishermen leaving Monterey on their way to fishing grounds.*

where perishable foodstuffs are kept. Power is required to operate the laundry machines. Actually, the *Queen Mary* needs enough power to service a small city!

Deep in her hull is an immense turbine plant that develops 200,000 horse power and requires twenty-four boilers delivering steam at four hundred pounds per square inch to operate it. She has seven great generators that generate as much as 9,100 kilowatts. Two mammoth switchboards, one of them thirty-seven feet long and another forty-six feet long, are needed for the switches required to operate the ship's "hotel" side and the equipment of the ship itself.

Contrast that picture with the needs of an oil tanker that merely needs enough power to pump oil in and out of her tanks, to maintain her navigation equipment, the modest kitchen and comfort facilities required for a crew of about forty officers and men, and enough propulsion power to enable her to travel to and from her loading and unloading stations! You can see that many kinds of marine engines are needed to serve the different kinds of ships afloat.

Robert Fulton's 1803 steamboat with its paddle wheels was the granddaddy of all steam engines for ships. But not until the screw propeller was developed for the *Archimedes* in 1839 was the steam engine really on its way. In fact, all marine engines got their start with the invention of the screw propeller. Paddle wheels are bulky and suitable only for gentle lake or river waters. An ocean-going ship needs a propeller below the water line where it can grip the water and turn it around and make the ship move swiftly. Once the screw propeller was invented, the whole question of a marine motor boiled down to building an engine that would turn the propeller. The steam engine was the first to be used. It was very simple. By heating water in a boiler, steam was generated from the water in the boiler and led, under pressure in pipes, to an engine which would convert the heat and pressure energy into rotational energy and turn the screw of the propeller. There are two ways of getting rotational energy. You can use a machine that is rotary, known as a turbine, or you can use an engine that changes the up and down motion of a piston, by means of a piston rod guide and connecting rod, into a rotary motion on a shaft known as a crankshaft, which turns the propeller. This is called a reciprocating engine, and it is the oldest marine engine, having been used for over one hundred years.

*When the fleet is at anchor, this strange-looking barge supplies it with fresh water.*

But an ordinary steam reciprocating engine will run at about 400 revolutions a minute, whereas a turbine usually averages several thousand revolutions a minute. A turbine consists of two parts, a stator or static part, and the rotary part. Steam comes in from the boiler through a valve, hits the blading on the stator and bounces off on to the blades of the rotary part, thus causing the rotor to turn. After leaving the last stage of the turbine expansion, the steam is condensed back into water again and goes to the hot well and then back into the boiler. The water can be heated with oil, but throughout the Scandinavian and English waters most small vessels use coal instead of oil because it is cheaper.

You can also turn the propeller of a ship with a Diesel motor. In fact, the pistons of a Diesel motor may be connected directly to the propeller shaft. Think of the tremendous saving in space this means! No boilers needed to provide steam. No condensers required to change the steam to water. Furthermore, it uses far less fuel than the reciprocating or turbine engines. Only 0.36 pounds of oil per horse power are required as against 1 to 1¼ pounds of coal for the reciprocating steam engine. This also means more space. Incidentally, there is a big saving in labor,

*With her tanks empty, this oil tanker rides high as a tug prepares to turn her around.*

for fewer men are required to take care of the Diesel. All these advantages are important on cargo ships, and more and more freighters are changing from steam reciprocating engines to Diesel oil motors.

The Diesel motor uses fuel oil in its cylinders much in the same way that an automobile uses gasoline, except that in the Diesel there is no electric spark and the oil is exploded by high compression. It merely burns, and the hot gas from the combustion drives the motor. There are two main kinds of Diesel engines in general use today—the two-cycle and the four-cycle. There is also a third type gaining popularity—the opposed-piston engine type.

There is still another way of getting rotational energy with which to turn the propeller of a ship. The Diesel engine can be coupled to an electric generator which will transmit energy to the motors at the stern of the ship. There are also ships that are completely electric, with electric motors driving the screw or screws. Some form of energy, either a steam reciprocating engine or a steam turbine, is coupled to an ordinary generator set which in turn supplies the current by means of cables to the propelling motor.

The largest electric ship in the world was the *Normandie,* which had 160,000 horse power on four screws. Two huge aircraft carriers, the *Lexington* and the *Saratoga,* were also fitted with an electric drive. The *Lexington* developed 210,000 horse power on the propeller shafts and attained a speed of 34.68 knots. Both ships had four large generating plants, and each one was capable of delivering more than 50,000 horse power to one propeller shaft. Both carriers had four propellers. But the most familiar electric ship in America is the river ferryboat. Control of the ship's speed is at the bridge, and the ferryboat can be moved forward and backward by the captain just as a motorman would move a trolley car.

Each type of engine for ships has virtues of its own. The reciprocating steam engine is cheaper to run than oil burning engines unless space is vitally important. The steam turbine is preferred to the reciprocating engine for passenger ships because vibration is reduced to a minimum. The Diesel is preferable for ships with certain kinds of work to do because it takes less space, fuel, and man power. The electric ship that is operated by turbo-generators is in many ways preferable to all of them, but the initial cost of this equipment is very high. Then there are variations on each one of these types that have superior qualities of their own. But it is the nature of the work that a ship does for her living that determines the best type of engines for her. The shape, size, and construction of her hull also determines what kind of engines she may have. A ship cannot be turned into a floating power plant unless she has a hull of the right design and sturdiness necessary to support such equipment. As we saw earlier, every ship in the world has a special job to do and her engines are chosen accordingly.

# CHAPTER 19

# LANGUAGE OF THE SEA

*Handsome is the word for the United States Coast and Geodetic Survey ship* Explorer.

MANY and varied are the terms used by men of the sea, and the language they use is strange and colorful. Here is a list of nautical terms most generally heard; among them are some that are as old as the custom of going to the sea in ships.

A: An Anglo-Saxon prefix for "on" or "in." It is in constant use at sea, as in *aback, aboard, astern,* etc.

ABACK: Spoken of square sails blown back against a mast by a sudden change of wind, or in some instances, put in that position purposely for some special purpose.

ABAFT: Behind or toward the stern of a vessel. Thus, *abaft* the bridge will mean toward the stern from the bridge.

ABEAM: On the side of a vessel, amidships. Thus, an object *abeam,* or *on the beam,* is an object at right angles to the vessel amidships.

ABOARD, OR ON BOARD: On, or in, a vessel.

ABOUT: A turning round. To go *about:* To turn a vessel round, in sailing, so that the wind comes over the other side. See *tack.*

ADRIFT: Anything that floats unfastened, as a boat or a spar, which may have broken away, or a ship that has parted from her anchor. Seamen also refer to articles carelessly lying around a ship as *adrift.*

AFT: Behind; toward the after or stern part of a vessel. Thus, the poop deck is *aft.*

ALEE: Toward the lee side; opposite of *aweather.*

ALOFT: Up in the tops; overhead. In the upper rigging, or on the yards, etc.

ALONGSIDE: By the side of.

AMIDSHIPS: Generally speaking, the middle portion of a vessel.

ANCHOR: A metal hook specially designed to take hold of the bottom in comparatively shallow water. A cable connecting the anchor and the ship makes it possible for a ship to maintain her position against wind or tide or current. Anchors are of many shapes and vary in size from a few pounds to a number of tons.

ANCHORAGE: A section of a harbor or a roadstead where ships may anchor.

ANEROID: A barometer operated by the pressure of the atmosphere on a metal disc covering a partial vacuum. The varying pressure operates the hand on a dial, which is graduated to the same scale as a mercurial barometer.

ARTEMON: A sail used on Roman ships. It was square and was mounted at the bow on a kind of mast that leaned over the bow. Later its place was taken by the spritsail.

ASTERN: Behind. In the after part of the vessel; behind the vessel; in her wake.

ASTROLABE: An instrument of the late Middle Ages with which mariners attempted to learn their latitude. The instrument was very imperfect in its working.

ASTRONOMICAL RING: An instrument that was meant to improve on the astrolabe, but which was just as inaccurate.

ATHWART, ATHWARTSHIPS: Across. Hence the rowers' seats in an open boat are called thwarts because they lie *athwart,* or across, the boat. To drop *athwart* anything—To come across it; to find it.

AUXILIARY: A sailing ship equipped with an engine for use in emergency or in crowded waters is said to be an auxiliary. Sometimes sails are carried on power-driven vessels for use in case it is desirable not to use the engine or in case of breakdown. In this case also the ship is an auxiliary.

AVAST: The order to stop or pause in any exercise; as, "*Avast* heaving."

AWEATHER: Toward the weather side, i.e., the side upon which the wind blows.

AWEIGH: Spoken of an anchor when it has been lifted from the bottom.

AYE (adverb, source uncertain): Yes; always used in lieu thereof at sea, with a repetition, "*Aye, aye,* sir," meaning, "I understand, and will execute the order."

BACK: With sailing ships, to *back* a square sail is to haul it over to windward so that the wind blows it against the mast. With steam vessels: *back* her is an order to reverse engines, so that the ship may be suddenly stopped or made to go astern.

BACKSTAYS: Ropes stretched from a mast to the side of a vessel, some way aft of the mast, to give extra support to the masts against falling forward.

BAIL, BAILER: To *bail* or *bail out* is to remove water from a boat by means of a *bailer,* which may be any small container that is capable of holding water.

BALANCE LUG: See *lug.*

BALLAST: Weight deposited in a ship's hold when she has no cargo, or too little to bring her sufficiently low in the water. It is used to counterbalance the effect of the wind on the masts and give the ship a proper stability, that she may be enabled to carry sail without danger of upsetting and is sometimes used in steam vessels to increase their stability or to correct their "trim," that is, in order that neither bow nor stern will float too high.

BALLOON CANVAS: Any sail (or canvas) that pockets the wind like a parachute, or balloons out.

BANK (of oars): A tier of oars all on one level. In ancient oar-driven ships there were often several *banks.* All the oarlocks that were at the same distance above the water level mounted oars said to be in the same *bank.*

BARBETTE: The heavy armored foundation on which the turret of a modern battleship is mounted.

**Barge**: A general name given to most flat-bottomed craft. In ancient and medieval times the name was given also to large boats of state or pleasure, and in later days to one of the small boats of a man-of-war. The *barges* of today are of various descriptions, being either seagoing, river, or canal.

**Bark**: A three-masted sailing vessel, square rigged on the fore- and mainmasts, and fore and aft rigged on the mizzen.

**Barometer**: An instrument for measuring the weight or pressure of the atmosphere. A careful study of its changing record makes it possible to foretell many of the changes in the weather.

**Batten**: A long strip of wood. *Battens* are used for many purposes, such as covering seams inside the hull. To *batten* down: To cover up tightly; usually spoken of hatches when they are closed tightly.

**Battle Cruiser**: A large and very powerful fighting ship, of high speed, and with an armament equal or superior to that of a battleship, but very lightly armored.

**Beam**: The width of a vessel at her widest part.

**Bearing**: The direction, or angular distance from a meridian, in which an object lies.

**Beat**: To *beat* windward is to make progress in a sailing vessel in the direction from which the wind is blowing by means of alternate tacks.

**Belay**: To make fast; as, to *belay* a rope, by winding around a pin.

**Belaying Pin**: A movable pin or bolt of wood or metal to which lines are belayed.

**Below**: To *go below* is equivalent, on shipboard, to going downstairs.

**Berth**: A bed or bunk on board ship; a place for a ship to tie up or anchor is sometimes called a *berth*.

**Between Decks or 'Tween Decks**: Any spaces below the main deck of a vessel but above the lower hold.

**Bilge**: That part of the hull of a ship where the bottom joins the sides.

**Bilge Keel**: Fins of wood or steel approximately paralleling the keel but built into and projecting from the ship at about where the bottom and the sides might be said to join. They are intended to minimize the rolling of the ship.

**Bilge Water**: Water that collects in the bottom of the ship. As this is always at the lowest part of the hull, oil and other impurities are always a part of the bilge water, with the result that its odor is generally offensive and it is very dirty.

**Binnacle**: The fixed case and stand in which the steering compass of a vessel is mounted.

**Bireme**: An ancient ship, driven by two banks of oars.

**Bitts**: Posts of metal or timber projecting from the deck, to which lines may be made fast.

**Blackwall Hitch**: A knot.

**Block**: A pulley used on board ship.

**Boat**: A small vessel. It is improper to refer to large ships as boats.

**Bob Stay**: A stay or rope made fast to the stempost of a ship at the cutwater and leading to the end of the bowsprit.

**Bolt-Ropes**: The ropes along the borders or edges of a sail for the purpose of strengthening those parts.

**Bonnet**: A narrow strip of canvas laced to the foot of sails on small vessels to increase their area in light winds. Common in medieval times.

**Boom**: The spar at the foot of a fore and aft sail. There are other *booms* for other uses, such as a *boat boom*, a spar projecting from the side of a ship and to which small boats floating in the water are made fast when the ship is at anchor.

Bow: The front end of a vessel. The *port bow* is the left side of the front end, and the *starboard bow* is the right side.

Bowline: A knot.

Bowsprit: The spar projecting from the bow of a ship and to which the fore stays are led from the foremast. It is a highly important part of a sailing ship's rigging, but when used on power-driven ships, as it often is on steam yachts, it is more decorative than necessary.

Boxing the Compass: Repeating the points of the compass in order, starting from any point.

Brace: Ropes on a square-rigged ship leading to the ends of the yards and used for the purpose of setting the yard at the proper angle to the mast are called *braces*.

Breaker: A small water barrel.

Breakers: Waves that curl over and break because of shallow water.

Breakwater: An artificial bank or wall of any material built to break the violence of the sea and create a sheltered spot.

Bridles: Several lines leading from a larger line to distribute the strain on an object to which they are attached.

Brig: A vessel with two masts (fore and main), both square-rigged.

Brigantine: Same as a brig, except that it has a fore and aft mainsail.

Broadside: The firing of all the cannon on one side of a warship at the same moment.

Bulkhead: A partition of almost any material. Today steel bulkheads are most common. Their purpose is to divide the ship, generally laterally, into separate compartments that, in the highest designs, are water-tight.

Bulwarks: A parapet around the deck of a vessel, serving to guard passengers, crew, and cargo from the possibility of being swept overboard.

Bumboat: A small harbor boat allowed to visit ships in port and supply the sailors with various articles.

Buoy: A floating marker intended as a guide or warning. Buoys have been more or less standardized, but in many different parts of the world similar shapes and colors still stand for different things.

Cabin: A habitable apartment on shipboard.

Cable: The rope or chain by which a ship's anchor is held.

Calking: Stuffing the seams of wooden ships with oakum. Also the making tight of seams of a steel vessel by the use of a cold chisel.

Can Buoy: A buoy that shows above water the form of a cylinder.

Canoe: A light boat propelled by paddles. Sometimes sails are also used.

Capstan: A kind of windlass sometimes found on ships; used principally for raising the anchor. It operates on a vertical shaft.

Caravel: A ship commonly in use in the "age of discovery," that is, during the fifteenth century. Columbus' *Santa Maria* was one of these.

Careen: The operation of tilting a ship over to one side or the other by means of tackle led from her masts to points at some distance from her side.

Cargo Liner: A freight ship that sails on schedule dates over a given route, as passenger liners do.

Carrick Bend: A knot.

Carvel: A method of small boat-building in which the board coverings present a smooth surface.

Catamaran: A boat made up of two parallel and equal hulls held together by a framework.

Catboat: A small sailing boat with one mast and a single sail, which is generally similar in shape to the mainsail of a sloop.

Centerboard: A movable sheet of metal or wood sometimes used by small sailboats. It extends through the keel and presents a large surface to the water and tends to eliminate lateral motion while the boat is under sail. A kind of folding keel.

CHART: A map of the sea and coast projections for use by navigators. Features of the bottom are also shown for shallow water.

CHRONOMETER: An accurate timepiece generally registering the time at Greenwich, England. Navigators require this instrument in working out their longitude.

CLINKER: A method of small boat-building in which the covering planks overlap as weatherboards do on the side of a house.

CLIPPER: A fast sailing ship suddenly developed in the first half of the nineteenth century. Generally, but not necessarily, the clippers were full-rigged ships. They were popular for about fifty years.

COCKPIT: See *well.*

COLLIER: A vessel employed in the coal trade.

COMPANIONWAY: The entrance to a ladder or flight of stairs leading from one deck to the one below.

COMPASS: A magnetized instrument that points approximately in the direction of the magnetic pole and from which directions can be learned.

CORVETTE: A small warship of the late eighteenth and early nineteenth centuries.

CROSSJACK (pronounced "krō′jĕk"): The square sail sometimes hung from the lowest yard on the mizzenmast of a full-rigged ship. It is not commonly used.

CROSSTREES: The arms extending laterally near the head of a mast at right angles to the length of the vessel and to the extremities of which the topmast shrouds are stretched for the purpose of giving support to the topmast.

CRUISER: A large, fast, and lightly armored ship of war. The expression is also used in yachting, meaning a boat meant for cruising.

CUTTER: A sailing boat with one mast carrying staysail, jib, fore and aft mainsail, and sometimes a topsail. Other sails are also sometimes added. In various navies the expression is used to denote a large heavy rowboat propelled by as many as ten oars.

CUTWATER: That portion of the stem of a vessel that cleaves the water as she moves ahead.

DAVIT: A light crane mounted on a ship's side and used for hoisting and lowering boats. Ordinarily two davits are used to each boat. The projecting beam over which the anchor is sometimes hoisted is also sometimes called a davit.

DECK: The covering of the interior of a ship, either carried completely over her or over only a portion. Decks correspond to the floors and roof of a flat-topped building.

DERELICT: A ship adrift at sea without her crew.

DESTROYER: Formerly called "torpedo-boat destroyer." These ships are enlargements of torpedo boats and were originally designed to destroy those small, fast warships. They have proved very useful for many naval duties and are now an important part of every large navy's forces.

DHOW: A small sailing vessel common in Egyptian and Arabian waters, with one or two lateen sails.

DINGHY: A small open boat used as a tender for a yacht.

DOCK: An artificially constructed basin for the reception of vessels. It may be a wet dock, where ships lie while loading and unloading, or a dry dock, in which they are repaired after the water is pumped out.

**Dock Yard**: An enclosed area in which the work connected with the building, fitting out, or repair of ships is carried on.

**Drabbler**: An additional strip of canvas, sometimes laced to the bottom of the "bonnet" on a square sail when the wind is light. Rarely seen nowadays, but common in the Middle Ages.

**Draft**: The depth beneath the surface of the water of the lowest point of a ship's keel.

**Dreadnought**: A modern battleship carrying heavy armor and a main battery of guns all of a very large and uniform caliber.

**Driver**: The fore-and-aft sail on the mizzenmast of a square-rigged ship. It is sometimes called the *spanker*.

**Dry Dock**: An artificial basin that can be flooded in order to permit the entry of ships and then pumped dry in order that their hulls may be examined, painted, and repaired.

**Dugout**: A canoe or boat made from a log hollowed out and cut down until it has become a vessel capable of carrying one or more passengers.

**Ensign**: The flag carried by a ship as the insignia of her nationality. Also, the lowest commissioned officer of the United States Navy.

**Fathom**: A nautical measure, equal to six feet.

**Fid**: A bolt of wood or metal that holds the heel of a topmast.

**Fife Rail**: A plank or rail in which a group of belaying pins is kept.

**Figure of Eight**: A knot.

**Flagship**: That ship of a fleet or squadron which flies the flag of the admiral in command.

**Fore and Aft**: An expression signifying those sails which, when at rest, lie in a line running from bow to stern of a vessel. The sails of a schooner are fore and aft.

**Forecastle**: Formerly a raised "castle" built at the bows of ancient and medieval ships from which the decks of enemy ships could be attacked. Nowadays the quarters of the crew on board ship, generally in the bows of ships.

**Foremast**: The mast nearest the bow of a vessel having more than one mast, except on yawls, ketches, and other sailboats where the mast nearest the bow is larger than the mast farther astern.

**Foresail**: On a square-rigged ship, the lowest square sail on the foremast. On a schooner, the sail stretched between the boom and the gaff on the foremast.

**Forward**: The forward part or the forepart; that is, the vicinity of the bow of a vessel. To go *forward* is to go toward the bow.

**Freeboard**: The distance between the main deck and the water.

**Freighter**: A ship engaged in carrying freight.

**Frigate**: A warship of the last days of the sail. It was full-rigged and had two decks on which guns were mounted. The *Constitution* was a frigate.

**Full-Rigged Ship**: A ship carrying three masts, each mounting square sails.

**Funnel**: The smokestack or chimney connected with the boilers of a ship.

**Furl**: To roll a sail and confine it to its yard or boom.

**Gaff**: The spar at the top of some fore and aft sails, such as the mainsail or foresail of a schooner.

**Galleon**: A heavy vessel of the time of Spain's nautical supremacy.

**Galley**: (1) In ancient and medieval times a ship of war propelled by oars and sails. (2) The kitchen of a ship.

**Gangplank**: A movable runway used to bridge over the gap from a ship to a pier.

GANGWAY: A narrow platform or bridge, below decks as well as above them.

GEAR: Any part of the working apparatus of a vessel, as the gear of the helm, which consists of the tiller, the chains, the blocks, and all other necessary parts.

GIG: A small boat formerly often carried on shipboard and meant for use when in port.

GIMBALS: The brass rings in which a compass is mounted and which permit it to remain horizontal despite the motions of the ship.

GONDOLA: A Venetian boat, used in the canals more or less as taxicabs are used in streets. It is propelled by one or two oarsmen, each with a single oar.

GRANNY: A knot.

GROUND: To run a ship into water so shallow that she rests on the bottom.

GROUND TACKLE: The gear connected with and including the anchors of a ship.

GUNBOAT: A small warship used for minor naval duties.

GUNWALE: The top of any solid rail along the outside of a vessel is generally called a *gunwale*.

GUY: A steadying rope, as the *guy* of a spinnaker, which serves to keep that sail forward.

GYBE: The swinging over of a fore and aft sail when the wind, accidentally or intentionally, has been brought from one side of it to the other around its free edge. This is sometimes a foolish and dangerous maneuver.

HALYARD: A rope (sometimes a chain) by which a sail, flag, or yard is hoisted.

HANDSOMELY: A term that means the opposite of hastily. It is often used with reference to ropes or halyards, as, "Lower away *handsomely*," which means lower away gradually.

HATCHWAY: An opening in the deck of a vessel through which persons or cargo may descend or ascend.

HAWSEPIPES: Short tubes through which the anchor cable passes from the forward deck to the outside of the bow.

HAWSER: A cable or heavy rope for towing and for making fast to moorings.

HEAD SAILS: All the sails set between the foremast and the bow and bowsprit of a sailing ship. These are the fore staysail and the inner, outer, and flying jibs.

HELM: Used interchangeably with the word "tiller." Theoretically, every rudder is equipped with a helm or tiller, although actually tillers are seldom used except on small boats. To port your *helm* (tiller) means to push the handle of the tiller to the port side. This steers the vessel to starboard. Therefore, when the order to port the *helm* is given on board any ship, it is intended that the steering apparatus be so operated that were there a tiller on the rudder it would be moved to port. By international agreement dating from 1931, all steering orders are given in the direct sense, using the words "right" or "left" to indicate the direction in which the wheel, the rudder, and the ship's head move.

HERMAPHRODITE BRIG: A two-masted sailing ship with square sails on the foremast and fore-and-aft sails only on the main. This type is often incorrectly called a brigantine.

HOLD: The inner space in a vessel, below decks, in which the cargo is stowed.

HOLYSTONE: A soft, porous stone used for scouring the decks. Its name comes from its shape, which fancy has suggested is that of a Bible. Where holystones are used today, they are fitted on handles.

HULL: The body of a vessel, exclusive of rigging or equipment.

JACOB'S LADDER: A collapsible ladder made of wooden steps strung between two ropes. It is used over the sides of a ship when the ship is at sea, as, for instance, when a pilot comes aboard or departs.

JAWS: The horns at the end of a boom or gaff, which keep it in its position against the mast.

JIB: One of the triangular headsails of a sailing vessel. There are several, as follows: balloon jib, flying jib, inner jib, jib of jibs (only on large ships), jib topsail, middle jib, spitfire, standing jib, storm jib.

JIB BOOM: A spar running out beyond the bowsprit for the purpose of carrying other jibs. *Flying jib boom*—a boom extending beyond the *jib boom* for the purpose of carrying the *flying jib*.

JIGGER: The fourth mast from the bow in a ship carrying four or more masts. The second from the bow in a yawl or a ketch.

JOLLY BOAT: A dinghy.

JUNK: A ship common in China and Japan. It is ungainly in shape, but is often remarkably seaworthy. It is driven by sails that are often made of matting.

KAYAK: A small canoe used by the Eskimos. It is made by covering a light framework with skins, and is decked. Generally there is but one hatch, just large enough for a single occupant to sit in. Occasionally there are two of these openings. It is propelled by paddles.

KEDGE: A small anchor carried by large vessels for use in shallow water or for use in keeping the main anchor clear.

KEEL: The backbone of a ship. It is a strong member extending the entire length of the center of the bottom, and from it the ribs are built at right angles. *Fin Keel:* A thin and deep projection below the keel of some sailing ships, principally yachts, designed so as to prevent the ship from being blown sideways by the wind, and generally weighted at the bottom by an addition of lead or iron to insure stability to the vessel.

KEELSON: An addition to the keel inside the boat. It rests upon the keel and strengthens it.

KETCH: A sailing vessel with two masts and with fore-and-aft sails. The mast nearer the bow is the larger of the two and is called the main. The one toward the stern is, in America, generally called the jigger; in England, the mizzen. It is placed just forward of the wheel or tiller. It is in this particular that it differs from a yawl.

KNOT: (1) A unit of velocity equal to one nautical mile per hour. It is often incorrectly used as a synonym for a nautical mile. (2) The fastening of a rope.

LANDLUBBER: An uncomplimentary term used by sailors in reference to anyone who has not had experience with ships and the sea.

LARBOARD: The old term for port, or the left-hand side of a vessel. No longer in use because of its close resemblance to starboard, which is the term meaning the right-hand side.

LATEEN: A triangular sail of large size hung from a very long yard. It is common in Egyptian waters and is to be seen occasionally around the Mediterranean and in the East. The yard is often of immense length, sometimes twice as long as the boat itself.

LAUNCH: A small vessel propelled by some kind of motor, and generally used for pleasure. To *launch:* To put a new vessel into the water. This is ordinarily a function of more or less formality.

LEAD: A leaden weight attached to the

end of a line used to measure the depth of the water.

Lee: The lee side of a vessel is the side opposite that against which the wind blows. A lee shore is a shore on the lee side of a ship, and is therefore to be feared, for the force of the wind tends to blow the ship ashore. "Under the *lee* of a shore," however, is an expression meaning in the shelter of a shore line from which the wind is blowing.

Leech (meaning Lee Edge): The aftermost, backmost, or lee margin of a sail. It also applies to each of the side edges of a square sail.

Leeward: On the lee side. An object to *leeward* is on lee side. Pronounced "lē'wẽrd" or "lū'ẽrd."

Leg-of-Mutton: A triangular sail sometimes used on small sailboats.

Lifeboat: A boat carried for the purpose of saving lives in case the ship which carries it is wrecked. Strict laws force all ships to carry these small boats, and the ships must carry life preservers in addition. Lifeboats are also maintained ashore in order to assist the crews of wrecked ships.

Lighter: A barge intended for use in port or on rivers and meant to carry freight. The name comes from the fact that these barges "lighten" or unload ships. Ships also are often loaded from them.

Lighthouse: A structure erected ashore or in shallow water and equipped with a powerful light, visible for miles at night. This acts as a warning and shows the position of the danger to navigation which it is erected to mark.

Lightship: A floating lighthouse, securely moored where it may mark a danger, such as a reef, or a shoal, or at the entrance to a harbor in order to show the safe way in.

Line: A small rope. *The line:* A nautical expression for the equator.

Line-of-Battle Ship: The most powerful naval vessels at the end of the days of sailing navies.

Liner: A term that has come to mean a large passenger ship operated by a steamship line. The expression seems to include only salt-water ships. For instance, a river steamer, even though operated on a regular schedule by a steamship line, would not be called a liner.

Log: (1) An instrument that measures the distance a ship travels through the water. (2) The journal in which all the events of importance and interest on board ship are written.

Lubber: An awkward fellow.

Lubber's Line: A line marked on the inside of a mariner's compass case, showing the exact fore and aft direction of the ship. The moving compass card revolves so that the points or degrees with which it is marked pass close to this line; thus the man who is steering the ship can always tell the exact direction in which the ship is headed.

Luff (of a sail): The weather edge, that is, the edge toward the wind. To *luff*, in sailing, is to bring a vessel's bow more toward the wind.

Lug: A type of sail of which there are three principal kinds: dipping lug, balance lug, and standing lug. A lug sail is four-sided and is hung from a yard that is mounted on a mast in a fore and aft position.

Lugger: A boat using a lug sail.

Main: In all rigs of vessels the word "main" applies alike to the principal mast and the principal sail it carries. Generally in ships equipped with two or more masts the second from the bow is the mainmast, although in some rigs, such as ketches and yawls, the mast nearest the bow is the main.

Marine: A man in the naval service serving something like a soldier on board a warship. Nowadays the duties of marines often take them ashore where their services are identical with those of soldiers.

MARINER: Anciently a first-class or able-bodied seaman.

MARTINGALE: The rope extending downward from the jib boom to the dolphin striker. Its duties are those of a stay or brace.

MAST: A long piece or system of pieces of timber or metal placed nearly perpendicularly to the keel of a vessel to support rigging, wireless antennæ, halyards, etc.

MASTER: The captain of a merchant vessel.

MATE: Literally, the master's assistant. There may be as many as four or five mates on a ship, rated first, second, third, etc. They are officers next in rank to the master.

MESS: At sea a company of men or officers who eat or live together.

'MIDSHIPS: See *amidships*.

MILE: A nautical mile equals one-sixtieth of a degree of latitude, and is invariably taken as 6,080 feet.

MIZZEN: Generally the third mast from the bow of a ship carrying three or more masts is called the mizzenmast. The sails set from this mast have the word "mizzen" prefixed to their names, as *mizzen* topsail, *mizzen* topgallant sail, etc. Also parts of the mast prefix the word, as *mizzen* topmast.

MOONRAKER (or MOONSAIL): In square-rigged ships the sail set above the skysail. (Very rare.)

MOOR: To moor is to make a ship fast to a mooring that is a kind of permanent anchor to which a buoy is attached.

MOTHER CAREY'S CHICKEN: A small sea bird; the stormy petrel.

NAUTICAL MILE: See *mile*.

NAVAL ARCHITECTURE: The science of designing vessels.

NAVIGATION: The science that enables seamen to determine their positions at sea and to lay down courses to be followed.

NUN BUOY: A buoy that shows above water in the shape of a cone.

OAKUM: A substance to which old ropes are reduced when picked to pieces. It is used in calking the seams of boats and in stopping leaks.

OAR: An instrument used in propelling boats by hand. It may be of any length over four or five feet, although, as it is meant to be operated by man power, it must be limited in size so as not to constitute too great a weight. It is made up of a handle, a shaft, and a flat section meant to come in contact with the water. At about one-third of the distance from the handle to the end of the blade it rests in a special fitting called an oarlock or a rowlock. By submerging the blade in the water and pulling the handle in a direction at right angles to the length of the oar it tends to propel the boat. It differs from a paddle in that a paddle does not rest in a lock. A *sweep* is a very large oar, generally operated by several men.

OILSKINS: Waterproof coats and trousers worn over other clothing at sea.

ON SOUNDINGS: When a ship is in water shallow enough to permit the depth to be easily ascertained by means of the lead she is said to be *on soundings*. At sea the expression *to sound* means to learn the depth of the water by means of the lead.

OUTBOARD: Board means the side of a vessel; therefore *outboard* means outside her or beyond the gunwale.

OUTRIGGER: A type of small boat common in the East Indies. It is made up of a narrow hull kept from overturning by a small timber floating in the water parallel to the hull and made fast to the hull by means of crossbars. This type is known as an *outrigger canoe*. The outrigger is the small float that keeps the canoe from capsizing.

OVERBOARD: Over the side of a ship.

PACKET: A small passenger or mail boat, sailing between two or more ports at regular intervals.

PADDLE: A kind of oar. In use, however, a paddle uses no leverage except what is offered by the hands of the operator.

PADDLE WHEEL: A large wheel sometimes used by steamboats and on which flat boards are so arranged that when the wheel turns the boards come in contact with the water, thus propelling the boat.

PAINTER: A rope attached to the bow of an open boat, by which the boat may be tied.

PEAK: The upper end of a gaff. Also, the uppermost corner of a sail carried by a gaff.

PEAK HALYARDS: The halyards or ropes by which the peak is elevated.

PIER: A long narrow structure of wood, steel, or masonry, built from the shore out into the water, and generally used for the transfer of passengers and goods to and from ships.

PILOT: A man qualified and licensed to direct ships in or out of a harbor or channel. He boards the outgoing ship as she sails and is taken off by a pilot boat when the ship is outside the restricted waters that he is licensed to take her through. Incoming ships take pilots from the pilot boat as they approach the restricted waters where pilots are needed.

PLIMSOLL MARK: Generally called the load line mark. It is a mark placed on ships to show how deeply they may be laden. This is done under governmental supervision, usually by a classification society. As a cargo comes aboard, a ship sinks in the water. If a vessel submerges its load line mark, it is subject to detention by governmental authorities.

POINT: The card of a mariner's compass is generally divided into thirty-two parts. These are the points of the compass. Nowadays compasses are more and more being divided into degrees, but still the points are generally shown as well. *Reef points:* Short ropes hanging in rows across sails to make it possible to tie a part of the sail into a restricted space so as to present less surface to the wind.

POOP: Properly, an extra deck on the after part of a vessel.

PORT: The left-hand side of a vessel when one is facing the bow.

PORTHOLE: An opening in the side of a vessel. Generally refers to the round windows common on most ships.

PORT TACK: A sailing vessel is on the *port tack* when under way with the wind blowing against her port side.

PROPELLER: A heavy apparatus somewhat similar to an electric fan in appearance, which, when mounted on the end of a shaft outside the stern of a vessel, below the water line, and set to turning by the engines, moves the ship through the water.

PROW: The cutwater of a ship.

PUNT: A small flat-bottomed boat, generally square ended, usually propelled with a pole.

QUARTER: That section of a ship's side slightly forward of the stern. The port quarter is on the left side and the starboard quarter is on the right to the observer facing forward.

QUARTERMASTER: A petty officer on board ship, whose duties have to do primarily with steering the ship and other tasks about the bridge.

QUAY: An artificial landing place, generally of greater area than a pier.

QUINQUIREME: An ancient ship propelled by five banks of oars.

Raft: A group of any timbers bound together to form a float.

Ratlines: Small lines crossing the shrouds of a ship and forming the steps of a ladder by means of which sailors may mount the masts. (Pronounced "răt'lĭns.")

Reef: (1) A low ridge of rock usually just below the surface of the water. (2) To *reef* a sail is to reduce the area spread to the wind by tying part of it into a restricted space.

Revenue Cutter: A ship operated by a government to prevent smuggling and otherwise to enforce the law.

Ribs: The members which, with the keel, form the skeleton of a vessel.

Riding Lights: The lights that a ship is required by law to carry at night while anchored.

Rig: The manner in which the masts and sails of a vessel are fitted and arranged in connection with the hull.

Rigging: The system of ropes on a vessel by which her masts and sails are held up and operated.

Roadstead: A place of anchorage at a distance from the shore.

Row: To propel a boat by means of oars.

Royal: In the built-up mast of a square-rigged ship the fourth section above the deck is the *royal mast*. Its complete name prefixes the name of the mast above which it rises, as *fore royal mast*. The sail on the *royal mast* is named accordingly, as *fore royal*. The royal yard is the yard from which the royal sail is spread.

Rudder: A flat, hinged apparatus hung at the stern of a ship, by the movement of which the ship is steered.

Running Lights: The lights that a ship is required by law to carry at night while under way.

Sail: A sheet of canvas or other material which, when spread to the wind, makes possible the movement of a vessel.

Schooner: A fore-and-aft rigged vessel with two or more masts, the foremost of which is the foremast.

Scout Cruiser: A very fast and lightly armored modern warship smaller than a battle cruiser but larger than a destroyer, used for scouting.

Scow: A large flat-bottomed boat without power and of many uses.

Screw Propeller: See *propeller*.

Scuppers: Openings in the bulwarks of a ship to carry off any water that may get on the deck.

Seam: The space between two planks in the covering of a vessel. It is in the *seam* that the calking is placed.

Seamanship: The art of handling ships.

Sextant: The instrument in almost universal use at sea for measuring the altitude of the sun and other celestial bodies. From this the latitude and longitude may be worked out.

Sheepshank: A knot.

Sheer: The straight or curved line that the deck line of a vessel makes when viewed from the side.

Sheet: The rope attached to a sail so that it may be let out or hauled in as occasion may require.

Ship: A term applied indiscriminately to any large vessel, but among seamen it means a sailing vessel with three masts, on all of which square sails are set.

Shoal: A shallow place in a body of water.

Shoot the Sun: A bit of nautical slang, meaning to determine the altitude of the sun with a sextant.

Shrouds: Strong ropes forming the lateral supports of a mast. Nowadays they are usually wire rope.

Skiff: A small open boat. In different localities it is of different design. Occasionally fairly good-sized sailing vessels are called skiffs.

Skipper: The master of a merchant vessel, called captain, by courtesy, ashore and always so at sea.

**Skysail**: The square sail sometimes set above the royal. It carries also the name of the mast on which it is set, as *main skysail.*

**Sloop**: Sailing vessel with one mast, carrying a fore-and-aft mainsail and one or more jibs.

**Smack**: The name given indiscriminately to any sort of fishing vessel using sails.

**Snow**: A vessel formerly common. It differs slightly from a barque. It has two masts similar to the main and foremasts of a ship, and close behind the mainmast is a trysail mast. This vessel is nearly extinct.

**Sounding**: Determining the depth of water and the kind of bottom with the lead and line.

**Southwester**: (pronounced sou'-west'er)—A waterproof hat with the widest part of the brim at the back.

**Spanker**: The fore-and-aft sail set on the mizzenmast of a square-rigged ship; sometimes called the *driver*.

**Spar**: A spar is any one of the timber members of a vessel's gear.

**Spinnaker**: A racing sail of immense spread, reaching from the topmast head to the end of a spinnaker boom, which is a spar set out to take it. Sometimes it is possible for the same sail to be made to perform the services of a balloon jib, by carrying the spinnaker boom out until the end to which the sail is made fast is beside the end of the bowsprit.

**Splice**: (Verb) To join rope by interweaving the strands. (Noun) The joint made in rope by interweaving the strands.

**Spritsail**: A sail common before the introduction of the jib. It is a small square sail set on a yard hung below and at right angles to the bowsprit. Sometimes, formerly, a short vertical mast was erected at the end of the bowsprit, and from this was set the sprit topsail.

**Squadron**: Part of a fleet of naval ships under a flag officer.

**Squall**: A sudden and very strenuous gust of wind or a sudden increase in its force. Small storms that come up quickly are often called *squalls.*

**Square-Rigged**: That method of disposing of sails in which they hang across the ship and in which they are approximately rectangular in shape.

**Starboard**: The right-hand side of a vessel to a person facing the bow.

**Stays**: Supports made of hemp or wire rope supporting spars, or, more especially, masts.

**Staysails**: Sails set on the stays between the masts of a ship or as headsails.

**Stem**: The foremost member of a vessel's hull to which the sides are attached.

**Stern**: The rear end of a vessel.

**Stern Castle**: In ancient times an erection built at the stern of a ship to assist in its defense.

**Stevedore**: A man whose task it is to stow the cargoes of ships and to unload cargoes.

**Stoke Hold**: That compartment in a steamship from which the fires under the boilers are stoked or tended.

**Stoker**: A man who stokes or feeds the fires beneath the boilers of a ship.

**Stow**: To stow a cargo is to pack it into a ship so that it will not shift as the vessel pitches and rolls.

**Studding Sails**: On square-rigged ships narrow supplementary sails set on small booms at the sides of the principal square sails.

**Submarine**: A ship so designed as to be able to dive beneath the surface.

**Supercargo**: A member of a ship's crew whose duties have to do only with superintending transactions relating to the vessel's cargo.

**Superdreadnought**: A battleship of considerably greater strength than the original British battleship *Dreadnought,* which gave its name to a class of ships.

SWAMP: To be swamped is to have one's boat filled with water, but not necessarily to sink.

SWEEPS: Very large and clumsy oars, sometimes used on sailing ships to move them in calms or in narrow places where it is impracticable to use the sails. They are also sometimes used on barges and rafts.

SWELL: An undulating motion of the water, always felt at sea after a gale.

TACK: To tack in sailing is to change the course of a vessel from one direction or *tack* to another by bringing her head to the wind and letting the wind fill her sails on the other side, the object being to progress against the wind.

TAFFRAIL: The sternmost rail of a vessel, that is, the rail around the stern.

TARPAULIN: A waterproofed canvas. Formerly it was waterproofed by the application of tar.

TELLTALE: An inverted compass, generally mounted on the ceiling of the captain's cabin. Thus, without going on deck, or even without lifting his head from his pillow, the captain can check on the course the helmsman is steering.

TENDER: A small vessel employed to attend a larger one.

THOLES or THOLE PINS: Pegs fitted into holes in a boat's gunwale and between which oars are placed when rowing.

THROAT: That part of a gaff that is next to the mast, and the adjoining corner of the sail.

THROAT HALYARD: The rope that elevates the throat.

THWART: Athwart means across. In a boat the seats are called the *thwarts,* because they are placed athwart or across the boat.

TILLER: The handle or beam at the top of the shaft to which the rudder is attached, and by which the rudder is turned. It is in use only on comparatively small vessels.

TONNAGE: The measure of a ship's internal dimensions as the basis for a standard for dues, etc., this is register tonnage. There is also dead-weight tonnage, or pay load capacity, and (with respect to naval vessels) displacement tonnage or gross weight.

TOP: In square-rigged ships the platform built on the masts just below the topsails, and to which the sailors climb by means of the ratlines. The name of the mast on which the top is located is prefixed, as, *main top, mizzen top,* etc.

TOPGALLANT MAST: In a mast built up in sections the *topgallant mast* is the third section above the deck.

TOPGALLANT SAIL: The third sail from the deck on any mast of a square-rigged ship, except when the ship is equipped with lower and upper topsails, in which case the *topgallant sail* is the growth.

TOPMAST: In a mast built up of two or more parts the *topmast* is the second from the deck.

TOPSAIL: The second sail from the deck on any mast of a square-rigged ship. Sometimes ships have lower and upper topsails, but in this case each of these is narrower than the ordinary topsail. The name of the mast on which the topsail is set is prefixed, as *fore topsail, main topsail,* etc. On fore-and-aft rigged vessels the topsail is a triangular sail set between the gaff and the topmast.

TOPSAIL SCHOONER: A schooner which, on the foremast, spreads a square topsail.

TORPEDO BOAT: A small, fast ship of war built to use torpedoes as its major weapons. This type was common during and after the Spanish-American War, but became extinct, or practically so, after the introduction of the torpedo-boat destroyer.

TRAMP: The name usually given to merchant freighters that have no regular routes. They carry almost any cargoes that offer, and may carry them to almost any port.

TRAWLER: A vessel usually driven by power and used in fishing. It tows a heavy net called a trawl.

TRICK: At sea, the time allotted to a man to be at the wheel or on any other duty.

TRIREME: In ancient times, a ship propelled by three banks of oars.

TRYSAIL MAST: In old ships a mast for hoisting a trysail. (Seldom seen.)

TRYSAILS: Small sails used in bad weather when no others can be carried, or, occasionally, for rough work.

TUG: A small, powerful vessel usually propelled by steam and used to assist larger ships about protected waterways. Tugs are also used to tow barges or almost anything that can float. In the narrow waters of harbors and particularly in going alongside piers and quays, large ships need the assistance that these small vessels give them. There are also larger tugs for use in towing barges or other vessels at sea. These are known as seagoing tugs.

TURRET: An armored turntable in which the larger guns of warships are mounted.

TURRET STEAMER: A steamer which, below the water line, is similar to other ships, but which above the water line has its sides turned abruptly in, so that its main deck is greatly narrower than its water-line beam.

TWIN SCREW: A ship equipped with two propellers is a *twin screw* ship.

UMIAK: An open boat used by the Eskimos and some Northern Indians. It is made up of a frame covered with skins. Its size varies, but an average size would probably be in the neighborhood of twenty feet in length.

VESSEL: From the French *vaissel.* A general term for all craft larger than a rowboat.

VINTA: A Philippine name for one type of outrigger canoe.

WAIST: Actually that part of a vessel between the beam and the quarter. In old ships with sterns highly raised it was that portion forward of this raised section—that is, the section of the deck that was lower than the rest.

WAKE: The track a vessel leaves behind her on the surface of the water.

WATCH: To stand a watch on board ship is to be on duty for a given time, usually, but not always, for four hours.

WATER SAIL: A small sail sometimes set beneath the foot of a lower studding sail. (Rare.)

WAYS: An incline built for a working foundation on which to erect the hulls of ships. When the ship is ready to be floated, it is slid, generally stern first, from the *ways* into the water.

WEATHER: As a nautical expression this term is applied to any object to windward of any given spot; hence, the *weather* side of a vessel is the side upon which the wind blows. A vessel is said to have *weathered* a gale when she has lived safely through it.

WEIGH: To lift anchor from the bottom is to *weigh* anchor.

WELL: (1) A depression sometimes built in the decks of yachts or sailboats that is not covered over by a deck. It is often called a cockpit and is for the convenience and protection of passengers and crew. (2) An opening leading to the lowest part of the bilge, in which the depth of bilge water may be measured.

WHALEBACK: A type of steamer once common on the American Great Lakes, used for transporting grain, ore, etc.

WHALEBOAT: A boat that is sharp at both ends and is propelled by oars. This type was used by whalers, and is now common on ships of war, because of its seaworthiness, ease of handling, and sturdiness.

WHALER: A ship used in the whaling industry.

WHARF: A loading place for vessels.

WHEEL: When used in its nautical sense, this expression refers to the *wheel* by which a ship is steered. *Wheel* also refers to the ship's propeller.

WHERRY: In different localities *wherries* are of different sizes and designs. They are light, shallow boats, generally driven by oars.

WINDJAMMER: A slang expression for a person who prefers sails to engines. Also derisively used for a sailing vessel.

WIND SAIL: A tube of canvas, with wings of canvas at the top so arranged as to direct fresh air below decks. It is a kind of temporary ventilator.

WINDWARD: That side of a vessel or any other object upon which the wind is blowing is the *windward side*. An object which is to *windward* is in the direction from which the wind is blowing.

WING AND WING: In a fore-and-aft vessel it is possible, when running directly before the wind, to haul the sails on one mast out to starboard and those of another mast out to port. This is said to be sailing *wing and wing*.

WRECK: A wreck is the destruction of a ship. The ship herself or the remnants of her after the catastrophe.

WRECKAGE: Good parts of a ship cast up by the sea after a shipwreck.

XEBEC (pronounced "zē'bĕk"): A small three-masted vessel, lateen rigged, and often with an overhanging bow. Common in the Mediterranean.

YACHT: A pleasure boat. The term is indefinite in application, and generally means only the more elaborate pleasure craft owned by the wealthy.

YARD: A spar suspended from a mast for the purpose of spreading a sail.

YAW: To *yaw* in a sailing vessel is to deviate from the true course. It is often the result of having an inexperienced man at the wheel.

YAWL: A sailing vessel equipped with two masts, the main and the jigger. (In England the jigger is often called the mizzen.) The mainmast is the larger of the two and supports one or more jibs, a fore-and-aft mainsail, and sometimes a topsail. The jiggermast carries a small fore-and-aft sail, and the mast is set astern of the tiller or wheel.

ZENITH: The point directly overhead.

# INDEX